WORLD FOOD SUMMIT

13-17 November 1996
Rome, Italy

Volume 1

Technical background
documents 1-5

FOOD AND AGRICULTURE ORGANIZATION OF THE UNITED NATIONS

The assistance of the World Bank
in publishing the final version of this series of documents
is gratefully acknowledged.

M-90
ISBN 92-5-103878-3

1
Food, agriculture and food security: developments since the World Food Conference and prospects

Contents

Acknowledgements

The preparation of the World Food Summit technical background documents has mobilized, in addition to FAO's own staff contributions, a considerable amount of expertise in the international scientific community, drawn from partner international institutions and governmental or non-governmental circles. The process has been monitored at FAO by an internal Reading Committee, composed of staff selected ad personam, *and established to ensure that the whole collection meets appropriate quality and consistency criteria.*

The present document has been prepared by Nikos Alexandratos, with contributions from Jelle Bruinsma, both of the Global Perspective Studies Unit of FAO. After initial review within FAO by all technical departments, invited colleagues and the Reading Committee, and by selected external reviewers, a first version was published and circulated for comments to governments, intergovernmental organizations (IGOs) and non-governmental organizations (NGOs), as well as further peer reviewers. Much appreciated comments and advice have been received from Messrs Don Winkelman, Chair, Technical Advisory Committee to the CGIAR; Martin Piñeiro, Inter-American Institute for Cooperation on Agriculture (IICA); Klaus Leisinger, on behalf of the Government of Switzerland; Kirit Parikh, Indira Gandhi Institute of Development Research, India; Michiel Keyzer, Centre for World Food Studies, the Netherlands; Alex Duncan, Food Studies Group, Oxford University; Prof. M. Kassas, Cairo University; Bob Livernash, World Resources Institute and International Food Policy Research Institute, Washington, DC; USAID, United States; Piet Bukman, on behalf of the Government of the Netherlands; the Government of the United Kingdom; and the World Trade Organization.

While grateful for the contributions received from all reviewers, the FAO Secretariat bears the responsibility for the content of the document.

Executive summary

This technical paper is a brief review of developments in world food and agriculture and food security from the early 1960s to the present, with particular reference to developments since the World Food Conference of 1974. It also presents the possible evolution over the period to 2010, as depicted in the 1995 FAO study *World agriculture: towards 2010 (WAT2010)*.

The main, generally available indicator for monitoring developments in world food security is per caput food consumption, measured at the national level by the average dietary energy supply (DES) in Calories on the basis of national food balance sheets (FBS) and population data. This makes it possible to follow, through space and time, the evolution of food supplies as national averages. On that basis, the evolution of world food security in the period beginning after the World Food Conference up to the study's projections to 2010 can be envisaged as shown in Summary Table 1.

There are no internationally comparable comprehensive data for tracking the evolution of access to food for individuals or population groups within countries. Remaining at the level of national averages, the population of developing countries can be regrouped as shown in Summary Table 2.

To interpret these data, the following concepts are useful to derive inferences on the extent of undernutrition within countries. A threshold is defined as corresponding to the average (given gender, age distribution and average body weights) DES that represents a minimum level of energy requirements for individuals, allowing for only light activity. This level ranges from 1 720 to 1 960 Calories/day/person, depending on the country. Indirect evidence from household food consumption or expenditure surveys is used to estimate the extent of inequality of distribution of available food supplies within countries. This makes it possible to draw inferences about the approximate proportions of the population with access to food below the given nutritional threshold. It results that, for countries where the average DES is close to the threshold, the majority of individuals are undernourished, while experience shows that for countries with DES about a level of, say, 2 700 Calories, the proportion of undernourished individuals becomes small, except under extreme inequalities. Accordingly, and this is the information closest to the concept of access to food, the population in developing countries below the respective threshold has been estimated as shown in Summary Table 3.

For several developing countries, the 1970s was a decade of improvement faster than that of the 1960s. Rapid progress continued up to about the mid-1980s, and at a slower pace afterwards. But several countries and whole regions failed to make progress and experienced outright reversals, foremost among them many African countries, while South Asia made only meagre progress in the 1970s but more substantial gains in the 1980s.

The dependence of the developing countries on food imports from the developed countries grew strongly in the 1970s and their self-sufficiency fell. This trend was much attenuated in the subsequent decade. Together, the developed Organisation for Economic Co-operation and Development (OECD) countries readily increased cereals production to supply the growing import

Summary Table 1
AVERAGE PER CAPUT DIETARY ENERGY SUPPLY (DES)

Countries	1969-1971	1990-1992	2010
	(Calories/caput/day)		
World	2 440	2 720	2 900
Developed countries	3 190	3 350	3 390
Developing countries	2 140	2 520	2 770

Summary Table 2
POPULATION IN COUNTRIES GROUPED BY AVERAGE PER CAPUT DES

Country group (average DES/caput)	1969-1971	1990-1992	2010
	(million)		
< 2 100 Calories	1 747	411	286
2 100 to 2 500	644	1 537	736
2 500 to 2 700	76	338	1 933
> 2 700 Calories	145	1 821	2 738

Summary Table 3
UNDERNOURISHED POPULATION

Population with access below the nutrition threshold	1969-1971	1990-1992	2010
Number *(million)*	920	840	680
Percentage of total	35	20	12

demand of the developing countries as well as that of the former centrally planned economies (CPEs) of Central and Eastern Europe and the former Union of Soviet Socialist Republics (USSR). However, world production of cereals levelled off in the first half of the 1990s, the demand-supply balance in world markets became tighter, prices rose and stocks diminished. These recent developments reflected the temporary declines in the former CPEs during the economic transition, weather shocks and policy reforms in the main developed exporting countries towards a reduction of structural surpluses and publicly held stocks.

World agricultural growth is likely to be slower in the future compared with that of earlier decades, although not as slow as that observed in the first half of the 1990s. This slow-down is imputable to a slower world food demand growth, which reflects both positive and negative developments in the world food and agriculture scene. The positive ones include the slow-down in world population growth and the fact that, in many countries with fairly high levels of per caput food consumption, the scope for further increases in this variable is smaller than in the past. Negative developments include the totally inadequate growth in per caput incomes and the continued prevalence of severe poverty in many countries with very low levels of nutrition.

The implication is that, in many developing countries, per caput food supplies may remain stubbornly inadequate to allow for significant nutritional progress, even though for these countries as a whole the average may increase further to nearly 2 800 Calories per day by the year 2010. Under the circumstances, and given population growth, the numbers of undernourished in these conditions may decline only insufficiently from the current 840 million to possibly 680 million, although this would represent a significant decline in the share of the total population.

The dependence of the developing countries on food imports will most likely continue to increase with net imports of cereals growing to over 160 million tonnes by 2010. The main developed exporting countries will probably not face major constraints in generating this level of net exports. A contribution to this possible outcome may be forthcoming from the former CPEs, initially by their transition to being much smaller net importers and eventually to their emergence as net exporters. But while the global capacity to increase food production to match the growth of effective demand may not give cause for excessive concern, production growth constraints facing individual countries will continue to be a major factor conditioning the prospects for progress in food security. This is particularly the case of low-income countries heavily dependent on their own agriculture for food supplies, income and employment and with limited potential to import food. And, of course, the well-known constraints to increasing output of capture fisheries is another example of how the prospects for improved food security could be affected by limitations on the side of production.

In considering the role of production prospects as a key factor in the food security problem, the issue of sustainability assumes particular importance. The historical experience is that the expansion and intensification of agriculture has often been associated with the buildup of pressures that have led to resource degradation and adverse impacts on the wider environment. Such pressures will continue to increase in the future and a major issue will be how to minimize the negative effects on the resources, the environment and the sustainability of agriculture. This is particularly important for those low-income countries where the exploitation of agricultural resources is the mainstay of their economies and the deterioration of their resources threatens both their food security and overall economic well-being. At the same time, it is in these very countries that continued poverty and further increases in the population dependent on agriculture intensify pressures that contribute to degradation and unsustainability.

The overall conclusion is that, without deliberate changes from the normal course of events, many of the food security problems of today will persist and some will become worse. This need not be so, however, if action is taken now to promote poverty-reducing growth and agricultural development as well as to put agriculture on to a more sustainable path.

1. Introduction

1.1 The World Food Conference of 1974 was held in the very year that world market prices of cereals had reached a peak following the hefty increases of the year before. Three years later, world prices had fallen to below the levels of 1970, and indeed they were lower than at any year after 1950.

1.2 The widespread fear expressed at the time, that the world had entered a new era in which the growth of production would find it difficult to keep up with the growth of demand at non-increasing prices, proved to be unfounded. Indeed, the early 1970s ushered in an era of further declines in world food prices. It may be said that the world food problem reverted to being recognized for what it has always been: failure of effective demand on the part of people with inadequate nutrition to grow by as much as is required to raise their consumption to levels compatible with the elimination of food insecurity and undernutrition. In other words, developments in the post-World Food Conference years demonstrated that the world as a whole had the potential, if demand had grown faster, to increase production (at non-increasing prices) even faster than it actually did.

1.3 These developments put to rest, at least temporarily, the neo-Malthusian interpretation that world production could not grow fast enough to meet the effective demand for food of a growing global population. The notion that the world food problem was not one of production but instead one of demand and/or distribution gained currency. However, this notion confounds rather than clarifies and it can lead to error concerning what are appropriate policy responses. This is so because it is based on the paradigm of advanced societies, in which there is a fairly clear separation between demand and supply of food. In these societies, the great bulk of the demand for food is generated by people earning their incomes in activities other than food production. Farmers and their incomes account for only a minuscule proportion of total demand for food and access to imported food is not a problem. In such circumstances, it is proper to think that any existing food security problems have their roots in the inadequate growth of demand and are not problems of production. The situation is different in the majority of the low-income countries, where the bulk of the population depends on agriculture and there is no clear-cut separation between demand and supply of food. In such cases, inadequate growth of demand reflects that of incomes of most of the population whose very incomes depend on the growth of agriculture itself. Given that the food insecurity problem is concentrated in these countries, it is proper to speak of it as being a problem of production, even if world markets fail to express it in the form of rising prices.

1.4 In conclusion, as long as the essence of the world food problem is the high incidence of food insecurity and undernutrition precisely in the countries with low per caput food supplies and high dependence on agriculture, there can be no appropriate policy responses to it that do not include a hefty dose of measures to improve agricultural and rural development in order to increase both demand

and the supply of food in those very countries, at least not at this stage of their development. An idea of the countries that combine these characteristics, i.e. those that have a high share of the rural population in the total population and low levels of per caput food supplies, can be had from the data in Table 4. Countries in this class are generally those in the upper left quadrant of the table.

1.5 This paper, by necessity very brief, concentrates on describing the evolution of the world food security situation in the last three decades (Section 2) and highlights the main factors that explain successes and failures (Section 3). It then goes on to describe what may be the evolution over the period up to 2010 in the minimum amount of detail required to put in evidence the possible trajectories of the key variables (Sections 4 and 5). Finally, selected issues of sustainability and the environment are considered in relation to the quest for sustainable responses to the world food security problem (Section 6).

1.6 This paper is one of a series of technical background documents prepared for the World Food Summit. It is not comprehensive in its coverage of the manifold dimensions of the food security problem nor exhaustive in the treatment of the aspects it covers. A more comprehensive treatment can be found in the 500-page FAO study entitled *World agriculture: towards 2010 (WAT2010)* (FAO, 1995), while discussion and analysis of individual topics are to be found in the other technical background documents.

2. Historical developments and the present situation

TRACKING THE EVOLUTION OF THE FOOD SECURITY SITUATION THROUGH TIME

2.1 There are two interrelated variables that can be used for this purpose:
- The first is the per caput availability of food for direct human consumption (also called per caput food supplies). It is the only variable for which data, admittedly of varying quality, are available for all countries from 1961 to 1992. It can be used to construct the pattern of world distribution (over countries) of food supplies to show what part of the world's population lives in countries with given levels of per caput food supplies for direct food consumption. Such information would make it possible to draw inferences about changes through time. For example, statements such as the following can be made: In the early 1960s, 1.6 billion people (50 percent of the world's population) lived in countries with very low per caput food supplies (under 2 100 Calories per day), while today – that is, in the three-year average from 1990 to 1992 – only 410 million people (8 percent of the world's population) live in countries in this class.
- The second variable concerns the distribution of the food supplies within each country, i.e. given the national average of the preceding variable, what proportion of a country's population has access to any given level of per caput food supplies. One such relevant level for food security analysis is that of per caput food supplies (Calories/day) equal to 1.55 times the basal metabolic rate (BMR). If a person's access to food is below this level, he/she may be classified as chronically undernourished. It results that, from 1969 to 1971, 900 million people in the developing countries (35 percent of their total population) could be so classified. By 1988-1990, the proportion had fallen to 20 percent, but there were still about 800 million undernourished people, given that the population of the developing countries had in the meantime increased from 2.6 to 4.1 billion.

2.2 The time frame used here to present the historical evolution of the food security situation is influenced by two factors:
- The World Food Conference documents (United Nations, 1974) described the aspects of the food security situation related to per caput food supplies up to 1969-1971, because this was the latest three-year average for which relevant data were available. Therefore, in what follows, the starting-point for describing the evolution in the post-World Food Conference period is the three-year average 1969-1971.
- It is also relevant to the issue at hand to describe the evolution in per caput food supplies in the decade of the 1960s, because this was the period that had shaped thinking about the fundamentals of success, failure, persisting problems and required policy responses. This is not to deny that the food shortages and world market upheavals that precipitated the food crisis in

1972-1974 had a profound influence on perceptions of the food security problem. But a brief review of developments during the decade preceding the World Food Conference will help put in perspective differences between the pre- and post-conference periods.

Box 1

PER CAPUT FOOD SUPPLIES FOR DIRECT HUMAN CONSUMPTION: THE VARIABLE FOR DIAGNOSING THE EXTENT OF FOOD INSECURITY

Available food supplies for direct human consumption are estimated in the framework of food balance sheets (FBS) on the basis of countries' reports on food production and trade data, which for several of them inevitably imply that their per caput food supplies are totally inadequate for good nutrition. The parameters for the latter are well known, though not devoid of controversy. In the first place, there is the amount of food or dietary energy supply (DES) that is needed for the human body to function (breathe, pump blood, etc.) even without allowing for movement or activity. This is the basal metabolic rate (BMR). It is in the general range 1 300 to 1 700 Calories per day for adults in different conditions (age, sex, height, body weight). Taking the age/sex structure and body weights of the adult populations of the different developing countries, their national average BMRs are defined. Making an allowance for the growth requirements of children, the amount of energy as a national average per person that must be actually absorbed if all people were in a state of rest, or "in bed" as the nutritionists put it, is estimated.

Adding an allowance for light activity, estimated to be about 55 percent of the BMR, results in a range of between 1 720 and 1 960 Calories per person per day for the different developing countries. It follows that population groups in which an average individual has an intake below this level (the threshold) are undernourished because they do not eat enough to maintain health, body weight and engage in light activity. The result is physical and mental impairment, characteristics that are evidenced in the anthropometric surveys.

Add to this threshold an allowance for moderate activity and the result is an estimate of the national average requirement, which for the different developing countries is situated in the range from 2 000 to 2 310 Calories per person per day. In principle, a country having per caput DES at the national average requirement level would have no undernutrition problem provided the total food supply were accruing to each person exactly according to his/her respective requirements. However, this is never the case; some people consume (or have access to) more food than their respective moderate activity requirements[1] and other people less. Thus, an allowance must be made to generate an estimate of average supplies so that enough food accrues to the persons at the bottom end of the distribution chain since those in the higher ranges will, by definition, consume more than their moderate activity requirements. Empirical evidence suggests that, even at moderate levels of inequality (a coefficient of variation of 0.2, meaning that the average difference of the food intake of individuals from the national average – the standard deviation – is 20 percent of the latter), the national average requirement must be increased by about 28 percent to allow for this factor of unequal access and ensure that practically no one is left with food intake below the threshold level. This brings the thus adjusted average requirement to a range of 2 600

Box 1 *(continued)*

to 2 950 Calories for the different developing countries depending on the threshold level corresponding to the population structures (age/sex/body weight) for 1990-1992.

These numbers, or norms, are, therefore, a first guide to assessing the extent of this key dimension of food insecurity, that is, the adequacy or otherwise of food availabilities. Indeed, the DES is the principal variable used to generate estimates of the incidence of undernutrition as explained elsewhere (FAO, 1996). Numerous countries fall below the norm of the adjusted average requirement, and, in many cases, by considerable margins. Therefore, even if nothing more is known about the incidence of undernutrition, the inevitable conclusion is that such incidence cannot be anything but significant, ranging from moderate to high or very high in the different countries, even when inequality of access to food is moderate. It follows that progress towards reducing or eliminating undernutrition must manifest itself, in the first place, in the form of increased per caput DES. Naturally, this is not equivalent to saying that the DES is itself a policy variable that can be operated upon directly. But changes in this variable do signal the direction and magnitude of movement towards improved or worsened food security status.

In this connection, reference must be made to the often-raised question of just how reliable are the FBS data, which in many cases show very low levels of food availabilities. The answer is: they are as reliable as the primary data on production and trade supplied by the countries. It is these data that are processed in the form of the FBS to derive the indicators of per caput food supplies used here. Given the primary data, the conclusion that many countries are in a difficult food security situation follows logically and inevitably.

---

[1]Including those engaged in heavy work, e.g. a man in this class requires 3 500 Calories per day.

2.3 Finally, it is to be noted that, throughout the period under review, rapid population growth in the developing countries and very slow growth in the developed countries meant that 88 percent of the increase in world population in the last three decades was in the developing countries and that the share of the developing countries in world population increased from 68 percent in 1961-1963 to 77 percent in 1990-1992. What is more important for the evolution of the food security situation are the changes in the numbers of people living in countries with different levels of per caput food supplies. The data in Table 2 present this evolution, while those in Table 3 give estimates of the evolution of the incidence of chronic undernutrition by developing region.

DEVELOPMENTS LEADING UP TO THE WORLD FOOD CONFERENCE
The situation a decade before the World Food Conference

2.4 At the beginning of the 1960s, the world's per caput food supplies for direct food consumption stood at 2 300 Calories per day, very unequally distributed: an average of 3 030 Calories for the developed countries and only 1 960 Calories for the developing nations (Table 1). Most developed countries had per caput food supplies of around 3 000 Calories per day, but with some notable exceptions, e.g. some countries in southern Europe. But only a handful of developing countries had per caput food supplies over 2 500 Calories per day and only about 100 million people (5 percent of the developing countries' population) lived in such countries (Table 2). The bulk of the population of the developing countries (1.6 billion, 75 percent of the total) was in countries with under 2 100 Calories per day and their average was only 1 835 Calories. There were, at the time, only three developing countries with populations of over 100 million (China, India and Indonesia, having together 1.2 billion people) and all three were in the under-2 100 Calories class. The average of 1 835 Calories per day of the 1.6 billion people in these countries is not much above the 1.55 BMR level used for defining chronic undernutrition. Even assuming that the inequality in the distribution of available food supplies in these countries was not very high, it follows that the majority of the population was bound to have had access to food below the threshold of chronic undernutrition. Thus, even without estimates of the incidence of chronic undernutrition at that time, it can be deduced that, in the early 1960s, such incidence must have been rampant, affecting a high proportion of the developing countries' populations, perhaps over 50 percent.

2.5 At the time, the pattern of large imports of cereals from the developed countries had not been established as it is today. The cereals self-sufficiency of the developing countries was high (97 percent) but at the cost of very low consumption. Net imports were 18 million tonnes, about 2 percent of cereals consumption or 8.4 kg per person for a population of 2.1 billion (these numbers today are 89 million tonnes, 9 percent of consumption and 22 kg per caput for a population of 4 billion).

Developments to the early 1970s

2.6 Ten years later, the situation in the developing countries had improved somewhat, but not by much, with average per caput food supplies having risen from 1 965 to 2 135 Calories per day. This was a period when food consumption in the developed countries was also growing fairly rapidly. Indeed their per caput food supplies rose by an increment equal to that of the developing countries, even though they had started from 3 030 Calories in the early 1960s. Thus, the gap of per caput food supplies of the two groups of countries was maintained at about 1 000 Calories per day, which is huge for this variable that would not normally move, for physiological reasons, outside the range of 1 700 to 3 500 Calories for country averages.

2.7 That only marginal progress had been made in the developing countries can also be seen from the fact that the number of people living in countries with under 2 100 Calories per day had risen to 1.75 billion. China, India, Indonesia – still the only three countries with populations of over 100 million – remained in that class. Estimates for the incidence of undernutrition for 1969-1971 on the basis of the 1.55 BMR threshold indicate that 35 percent (900 million people) of the population of the developing countries was classified as chronically undernourished.

Table 1
PER CAPUT FOOD SUPPLIES FOR DIRECT HUMAN CONSUMPTION, HISTORICAL AND PROJECTED

	1961-63	1969-71	1979-81	1990-92	2010[2]
			(Calories/day)		
Developing countries[1]	1 960	2 130	2 320	2 520	2 770
Sub-Saharan Africa	2 100	2 140	2 080	2 040	2 280
Near East & North Africa	2 220	2 380	2 840	2 960	3 010
East Asia	1 750	2 050	2 360	2 670	3 030
South Asia	2 030	2 060	2 070	2 290	2 520
Latin America & the Caribbean	2 360	2 510	2 720	2 740	3 090
Developed countries	3 020	3 190	3 280	3 350	3 390
Former CPEs	3 130	3 330	3 400	3 230	3 380[3]
Others	2 980	3 120	3 220	3 410	3 400
World	2 300	2 440	2 580	2 720	2 900

CPEs = centrally planned economies.

[1] Ninety-three developing countries of the FAO study *World agriculture: towards 2010 (WAT2010)* (FAO, 1995) accounting for 98.5 percent of the total population of the developing countries.

[2] The *WAT2010* projections of aggregate food availabilities for direct human consumption divided by the population projections of the 1992 United Nations population assessment (United Nations, 1993). The latter are for most countries lower than those of the 1990 assessment (United Nations, 1991), which were used in the study's projections of food availabilities.

[3] Average of the pre-reform years 1988-1990 assumed to be re-established by 2010.

Table 2
POPULATION LIVING IN DEVELOPING COUNTRIES WITH GIVEN PER CAPUT FOOD SUPPLIES, 1961-1963 TO 1990-1992

	Per caput food supplies *(Calories/day)*				Population *(millions)*			
	1961-63	1969-71	1979-81	1990-92	1961-63	1969-71	1979-81	1990-92
				(three-year averages)				
Developing countries								
Under 2 100	1 835	2 000	2 025	1 910	1 605[1]	1 747[2]	1 024[3]	411
2 100-2 300	2 200	2 180	2 180	2 185	279	370	405	460
2 300-2 500	2 380	2 415	2 355	2 335	149	274	1 255[4]	1 077[5]
2 500-2 700	2 565	2 580	2 670	2 650	53	76	214	338
2 700-3 000	2 820	2 835	2 800	2 730	32	121	124	1 486[6]
Over 3 000	3 080	3 275	3 170	3 255	21	24	243	335
TOTAL	1 965	2 135	2 330	2 520	2 139	2 612	3 265	4 107
Developed countries	3 025	3 180	3 270	3 330	989	1 075	1 169	1 260
World	2 300	2 440	2 575	2 710	3 128	3 687	4 434	5 368

[1] Includes China (population 668 million) and India (population 463 million).
[2] China (population 816 million) and India (population 555 million).
[3] India (population 689 million).
[4] China (population 979 million).
[5] India (population 863 million).
[6] China (population 1 150 million).

2.8 The potential of the developing countries for importing food from the developed countries had remained extremely limited, with 1969-1971 self-sufficiency in cereals still being 96 percent, net imports only slightly above those of the early 1960s (20 million tonnes) and actually lower in per caput terms (7.7 kg).

DEVELOPMENTS SINCE THE WORLD FOOD CONFERENCE:
DEVELOPING COUNTRIES
The 1970s

2.9 For several developing countries and for three out of the five regions, the 1970s was a decade of improvement faster than that of the 1960s or of the subsequent 1980s (Table 1). Per caput food supplies increased and some developing countries edged upwards towards medium-high levels. The incidence of chronic undernutrition declined from 35 to 27 percent of the population, although it remained stubbornly high in absolute numbers because the total population had increased. Among the countries with a population of over 100 million, only India failed to make much progress in raising per caput food supplies more than marginally. In contrast, both China and Indonesia made significant progress, mainly in the latter part of the 1970s. Brazil, which had also made progress, was added to the group of countries with populations exceeding 100 million by the end of the 1970s.

2.10 But the 1970s was the decade when the differentiation between developing countries and regions, already evident in the 1960s, became more pronounced. Per caput food supplies stagnated at very low levels in South Asia and they actually declined in sub-Saharan Africa, reflecting declines in some major countries of the region that were only partly compensated for by gains in some smaller countries (such as Côte d'Ivoire, Gabon and Mauritius). In contrast, there were significant increases in the averages of the other three regions, the Near East and North Africa, Latin America and the Caribbean and East Asia, though the latter's per caput food supplies were still at the lower-middle level by the end of the 1970s. But there were countries that failed to make progress and remained at very low levels or experienced declines also in these better-performing regions: Afghanistan and Yemen in the Near East and North Africa; Bolivia, Haiti, Honduras and Peru in Latin America and the Caribbean; and Cambodia and Viet Nam in East Asia.

2.11 But perhaps what distinguishes the 1970s from the preceding and subsequent decades is the fact that part of the improvements in per caput food supplies of the developing countries came from the rapid growth of food imports from the developed countries. Net imports of cereals more than tripled between 1969-1971 and 1979-1981 to 67 million tonnes and self-sufficiency fell from 96 to 91 percent. In practice, over 20 percent of the increase in the apparent consumption of cereals in the developing countries came from the growth of net imports.

The 1980s

2.12 Progress in raising per caput food supplies in the developing countries as a whole continued rapidly up to about the mid-1980s and at a slower rate afterwards. Sub-Saharan Africa experienced further declines, there was virtually no further progress in Latin America and the Caribbean and only a modest advancement, by historical standards, in the Near East and North Africa. But progress continued in East Asia and, significantly, in the late 1980s South Asia joined the regions making progress, as both India and Pakistan broke out of the 2 000 to 2 200 Calories range to over 2 300 Calories. Preliminary FBS data for up to 1994 indicate that further gains have been made in these two countries. The progress in Asia, the most populous region with 2.8 billion people (70 percent of the developing-country total), was sufficient to lead to further gains in the indicators used here. The incidence of chronic undernutrition had also declined to 20 percent of the population, but only by a little in absolute numbers (Table 3). The 1970s trend of rapid growth of food imports by the developing countries was not sustained in the 1980s. Their net imports of cereals increased to only 89 million tonnes in 1989-1991 (22 kg/caput) and self-sufficiency remained at 91 percent, the same as ten years earlier.

Table 3
ESTIMATES AND PROJECTIONS OF THE INCIDENCE OF CHRONIC UNDERNUTRITION IN DEVELOPING COUNTRIES[1]

Region	Year (three-year averages)	Total population (millions)	Undernutrition threshold (Calories)	Undernourished[2]	
				Percentage of total population	Persons (millions)
Sub-Saharan Africa	1969-71	268	1 810	38	103
	1979-81	357	1 806	41	148
	1990-92	500	1 802	43	215
	2010	874	1 830	30	264
Near East & North Africa	1969-71	178	1 828	27	48
	1979-81	233	1 836	12	27
	1990-92	317	1 838	12	37
	2010	513	1 872	10	53
East Asia	1969-71	1 147	1 823	41	475
	1979-81	1 393	1 868	27	378
	1990-92	1 665	1 884	16	268
	2010	2 070	1 919	6	123
South Asia	1969-71	711	1 767	33	238
	1979-81	892	1 782	34	303
	1990-92	1 138	1 794	22	255
	2010	1 617	1 833	12	200
Latin America & the Caribbean	1969-71	279	1 834	19	53
	1979-81	354	1 854	14	48
	1990-92	443	1 872	15	64
	2010	593	1 907	7	40
TOTAL	1969-71	2 583	1 808	35	917
	1979-81	3 228	1 834	28	905
	1990-92	4 064	1 844	21	839
	2010	5 668	1 875	12	680

[1] Ninety-three developing countries of the FAO study *World agriculture: towards 2010 (WAT2010)* (FAO,1995), accounting for 98.5 percent of the total population of the developing countries. The estimates presented in *The sixth world food survey* (FAO, 1996) are slightly different because they refer to all developing countries.
[2] The estimates and projections of chronic undernutrition are somewhat different from those reported in the documents of the 1992 International Conference on Nutrition (ICN) (FAO, 1992, p. 7) and *WAT2010* (FAO, 1995, p. 84) for the following reasons: revisions of the historical data and 2010 projections of per caput food supplies (see Table 1, note 2); the total populations (mainly the projections) are different since they are from the 1992 United Nations assessment (5 668 million in 2010), while the earlier data were from the 1990 United Nations assessment (5 758 million in 2010); and, in the present estimates, the undernutrition thresholds shown in this table vary over time to take into account changes in age/sex composition of the population (in the earlier estimates it was the same for all years). These changes mean that the threshold for a typical developing country will be higher in the future because the share of adults, whose minimum energy requirements are higher than those of children, will increase in the total population following the ageing of the population as a result of declining fertility.

2.13 The 1980s were characterized by two significant changes in the growth paths of world food production: after the mid-1980s, aggregate world cereals production grew much more slowly than before and it actually declined in per caput terms from the mid-1980s peak of just over 340 kg; and the world production of fish from capture fisheries (including fish, crustaceans, molluscs, etc.) peaked in 1989 at about 89 million tonnes and by 1993 had declined to 84 to 86 million tonnes, rising again to 90 million tonnes in 1994. While the slow-down in world cereals production reflects some transitory factors (discussed below), the stagnation in the capture fisheries is not temporary, but rather reflects some deep-seated structural characteristics of the resource and the way it is being exploited, the latter having much to do with the open- or semi-open access regimes prevalent in the sector. However, declines in the capture fisheries from their 1989 peak have been made up to a large extent by increases in aquaculture production, which, in the last ten years, added about 1 million tonnes per year to aggregate fish production. In the end, aggregate production from capture fisheries and aquaculture was higher in 1994 (110 million tonnes) than in 1989 (100 million tonnes).

The first half of the 1990s

2.14 At the time of writing (mid-1996), the world food security situation is characterized by a tight demand-supply balance in world cereals markets, reduced stocks, high prices and falling food aid flows. The hardship this causes to the low-income countries that depend on imported food for a significant part of their consumption is obvious, particularly when food aid or other concessional imports play a major role. Current forecasts for 1996 world crop production indicate that it will be sufficient to match the coming year's consumption but not enough to replenish stocks. Thus, the situation will remain sensitive to further shocks, which means that, for the low-income food-importing countries, the risky world market environment will persist.

2.15 However, the developments in recent years, particularly the declines in world per caput production of cereals, need to be interpreted with caution as not all of them are signals of a permanent reversal of trends. This is because they are, to a considerable degree, the result of a confluence of some special circumstances, such as the production declines in the countries of the former Union of Soviet Socialist Republics (USSR) (production in the three-year average 1993-1995 was 151 million tonnes, down from 184 million tonnes in the preceding three-year average 1990-1992), the reforms in major exporting countries away from policies that in the past used to generate quasi-structural surpluses (European Union-15 production was 178 million tonnes in 1993-1995 compared with 188 million tonnes in 1990-1992) and the coincidence of weather-induced production declines (United States' production was 295 million tonnes in 1993-1995, down from 312 million tonnes in 1990-1992, all figures include rice in milled form). Among these factors, the only one that points to a permanent reversal of the historical trends that maintained an easy balance in world cereals markets may be the policy reforms away from the generation of quasi-structural surpluses in major exporting countries. Further discussion of recent developments in a longer-term context is provided in the conclusions at the end of this paper.

STABILITY AND DURABILITY OF GAINS IN FOOD SECURITY

2.16 In addition to the many developing countries that failed to make much progress in raising per caput food supplies above the 1 900 to 2 200 Calorie level or experienced outright declines, there were those that did make significant progress at some stage in their development but then failed to maintain the gains made. Perhaps what distinguishes the developed from the developing countries is the latter's lack of resilience in maintaining past gains in per caput food supplies in the presence of shocks (including war or war-like conditions) or the onset of more deep-seated economic distress. The high share of total income spent on food in these countries means that income declines translate into reductions in the demand for food. It also means that food shortages and rising prices translate into significant declines in incomes, in a vicious-circle pattern.

AN OVERVIEW OF FOOD PRODUCTION GROWTH RATES AND NET CEREAL IMPORTS IN THE DEVELOPING COUNTRIES

2.17 Numerous developing countries failed to make progress in raising per caput food production in the post-World Food Conference period, with the majority of them registering outright declines in the period from 1972 to 1992. The growth rates of per caput food production for this period in the individual countries are shown in parentheses in Table 4. The high frequency of negative growth rates in the countries with a great dependence on agriculture and low per caput food supplies is evident (upper left quadrant of Table 4). At the same time, few of these countries were able to compensate for the production declines through food imports. This is evidenced by the generally low levels of per caput net imports of cereals (including food aid), which are also shown in parentheses in Table 4.

2.18 In the post-World Food Conference period, the growth of yields was the mainstay of production increases for the main food crops, particularly wheat, rice, soybean and, to a lesser extent, maize. But yield growth was very slow in the other main rain-fed coarse grains. Relevant data are shown in Table 9 together with the projections. In addition, the records in raising yields for selected countries are shown in Table 12. The point is made later that the yield differences between countries increased in the post-World Food Conference period, as the countries with better resource endowments made rapid progress while this was rarely the case for those countries that had started the 1970s with very low yields.

THE OVERALL EVOLUTION IN THE DEVELOPED COUNTRIES

2.19 As noted, the developed countries as a whole started the 1960s with food supplies per caput of just over 3 000 Calories per day. At this level, food security problems of the type that plagued the developing countries, that is, those linked to widespread abject poverty and evidenced by the very low per caput food supplies, should not have existed to any considerable extent. In conclusion,

Table 4

CROSS-CLASSIFICATION OF 93 DEVELOPING COUNTRIES BY RURAL POPULATION SHARE AND PER CAPUT FOOD SUPPLIES

Rural population as percentage of total population, 1990	Per caput food supplies (Calories/day), 1990-92					
	Under 2 100	2 100-2 300	2 300-2 500	2 500-2 700	2 700-3 000	Over 3 000
Over 75 percent	Burundi (-0.8; 5) Rwanda (-0.6; 4) Malawi (-3.1; 21) Ethiopia (-1.0; 16) Afghanistan (-1.3; 14) Bangladesh (-0.1; 17) Somalia (-1.8; 31) Kenya (-0.7; 9)	Uganda (-2.5; 0) Nepal (0.5; 2) Cambodia (2.3; 6) Burkina Faso (1.7; 18) Lesotho (-2.2; 122) Laos (2.0; 10) Niger (-1.5; 16) Viet Nam (2.0; -14) Tanzania (-0.1; 4) Sri Lanka (0.3; 57) Sudan (-1.6; 25) Mali (0.2; 14) Madagascar (-1.5; 8)	Botswana (-2.9; 108) Myanmar (0.9; -4) Gambia (-4.4; 114) Thailand (1.4; -104)			
60 to 74 percent	Ghana (-1.6; 22) Cameroon (-1.9; 36) Liberia (-2.2; 52) Sierra Leone (-0.9; 39) Chad (-0.3; 10) Haiti (-1.3; 45) Zimbabwe (-2.9; -6) Angola (-2.3; 35) Zaire (-0.4; 10) Mozambique (-2.6; 44)	Guatemala (-0.4; 33) Nigeria (0.1; 7) Yemen (-0.4; 130) Togo (-1.3; 32) Namibia (-3.4; 75)	Côte d'Ivoire (0.6; 50) Guyana (-0.7; -12) India (1.3; 1) Pakistan (0.5; 4) Senegal (-1.8; 83) Guinea (-0.3; 46)	Indonesia (2.5; 12) Swaziland (-0.5; 146) Benin (0.8; 33)	China (2.7; 6)	
45 to 59 percent	Bolivia (0.7; 34) Central African Republic (-0.7; 14) Zambia (-2.2; 28)	Panama (-0.6; 67) Philippines (-0.1; 32) Congo (-1.0; 54)	Gabon (-1.4; 74) Honduras (-1.0; 34)	Jamaica (-0.2; 162) El Salvador (0.1; 42) Paraguay (2.2; -27) Suriname (2.3; -30) Mauritania (-0.6; 123)	Algeria (0.5; 220) Costa Rica (-1.0; 116) Malaysia (4.6; 159) Mauritius (-0.5; 188)	Syria (0.6; 109) Egypt (0.6; 150) Morocco (1.4; 75)
25 to 44 percent	Peru (-0.9; 74)	Iraq (-0.9; 167) Nicaragua (-3.9; 45) Dominican Republic (-0.6; 103)		Colombia (0.8; 31) Trinidad and Tobago (-2.4; 201) Ecuador (0.0; 43)	Brazil (1.3; 29) Democratic People's Republic of Korea (1.3; 38) Jordan (1.4; 387) Iran (1.0; 88)	Cuba (1.0; 204) Mexico (0.3; 80) Republic of Korea (2.4; 229) Tunisia (0.4; 175) Turkey (0.6; -21)
0 to 24 percent				Chile (1.5; 30) Venezuela (0.4; 117) Uruguay (0.6; -138)	Argentina (0.1; -330) Saudi Arabia (5.7; 279)	Lebanon (4.4; 217) Libya (-0.3; 427)

Notes: (1) Rural population data from *Urban and rural areas by sex and age: the 1992 revision.* 1993. New York, NY, USA, United Nations. (2) Numbers in parentheses: the first number is the growth rate of per caput food production 1972-1992 in percentage of physical area; the second number is the net imports of cereals, five-year average from 1988 to 1992 in kilograms per caput (a minus sign denotes net exports).

these countries as a group had already reached, ten years before the World Food Conference, the stage where aggregate food supplies were sufficient to ensure diets with adequate energy content for all. There was still considerable scope for diversification away from staples and towards the diets characteristic of rich societies. This is indeed the path then followed by the developed countries as a group.

2.20 It must be noted, however, that, notwithstanding the adequacy of per caput food supplies for the developed countries as a whole, pockets of poverty and inadequate food security probably existed then as they do today and some countries classified as developed, mainly in southern Europe, had per caput food supplies still well below 3 000 Calories per day. This latter problem still persists today, or has even become more pronounced, in a number of the economies in transition, particularly some of the Asian states of the Commonwealth of Independent States (CIS). Indeed, the most recent United Nations country classification (in the 1994 demographic assessment) places eight of the republics created from the former USSR in the less-developed regions.

2.21 The shift of the developing countries to become major net importers of cereals, particularly in the 1970s, was mirrored in the increasing export orientation of cereals production in the main exporting developed countries of North America and Oceania. This pattern was accentuated by the emergence of the group of former centrally planned economies (CPEs) as a major net importer, while Japan was also increasing rapidly its net imports. Thus, between 1969-1971 and 1979-1981, the production of cereals in North America and Australia increased by 105 million tonnes (41 percent), of which 95 million tonnes went to increase their net exports. Australia's cereals production grew more than threefold.

2.22 At the same time, Western Europe was following support policies to increase its production and self-sufficiency and substitute for imports. These policies set the stage for Western Europe's emergence as an additional major net exporting region of cereals in the 1980s.[1] These developments demonstrate that these regions were able to create the capacity to increase production quickly, admittedly often with hefty subsidies from their taxpayers and/or consumers, to respond, with only small time-lags, to spurts in world market demand in order to meet consumption growth in the countries where the potential for fast growth in consumption was still considerable and often manifested itself in the form of spurts in effective demand as soon as growth in incomes and import capacity so permitted.[2] This is another way of saying that, in the period up to the early 1990s, food insecurity problems had reflected inadequate growth in demand rather than constraints to increase production. But this statement applies only when the world is considered as one homogeneous area. This is not always the case, however, and, as noted, in many local situations it is production constraints that stand in the way of improving food security.

[1] Cereals production in the European Community-12 rose by 55 million tonnes between the five-year averages 1968-1972 and 1988-1992. In the same period, its net trade position changed from net imports of 21 million tonnes to net exports of 27 million tonnes, that is, 87 percent of the total increment in production was absorbed by changes in the net trade position. This change was less dramatic in practice than it appears at first glance because, at the same time, the region was importing increasing quantities of cereal substitutes for its domestic feed markets. In a certain sense, the European Community increased supplies of cereals to the rest of the world, partly in exchange for increased quantities of cereals substitutes, mainly cassava and oilseeds.
[2] See, however, earlier discussion as well as the concluding section of the paper concerning the changing role of the main developed exporting countries following policy reforms.

3. Main factors in the historical evolution of per caput food supplies

THE CORRELATES OF SUCCESS IN RAISING PER CAPUT FOOD SUPPLIES

3.1 The main characteristics of the historical evolution that probably explain much of the progress made by several countries in raising per caput food supplies may be summarized as follows:

- All of them had above-average economic growth rates, as evidenced by the growth rates in their per caput incomes. This seems to be the most prevalent common characteristic of these countries.

- In most countries, there was a spurt in the growth of food imports, particularly in the period of rapid gains in per caput food supplies, as evidenced by the increases in per caput net imports of cereals. This meant rapid declines in their cereals self-sufficiency, although there were exceptions. In particular, China and Indonesia did not follow this pattern as their own agricultures grew to provide the additional food supplies and, most probably, this was a key factor in raising per caput incomes.

- A contributing factor to the nutritional improvement in this group of countries has been the fact, already noted earlier, that global agriculture provided readily and without much strain the food imports that underpinned the growth of their consumption, mostly in the 1970s.

- Domestic agricultural growth was an essential ingredient in the process of increasing per caput food supplies, by providing supplies, income and employment and by supporting economic growth and the balance of payments. China's experience in the post-reform period after 1978 seems to conform to this pattern. It was less important in countries where agriculture was only a small sector of the economy on which a relatively small share of the population depended for a living and where much of the gains in economic growth and import capacity derived from the non-agricultural sector, particularly from non-agricultural commodity sectors.

- In several countries, much of the quantum improvement in per caput food supplies was achieved in a relatively short period of time, in most cases, approximately ten years. However, as noted, such gains did not always prove durable. There are examples of countries where improvement and retrogression of per caput food supplies follow the commodity boom-and-bust cycles. It is, therefore, possible that the food and nutrition gains will tend to prove more durable in countries where the circumstances that brought them about are part of wider economic and social transformations, such as China and the Republic of Korea. The same probably holds for countries in which the windfalls from commodity booms are put to good use to bring about such transformations.

THE CORRELATES OF FAILURE AND RETROGRESSION

3.2 At the other extreme, the study of the experiences of the many countries that, starting from low initial conditions 30 years ago, failed to make progress or suffered outright declines, should provide some insights into the reasons for failure. The study of the relevant data from a sample of these countries leads to the following conclusions:

- For the great majority of these countries, it could have been predicted that the food situation would be dire even before looking at the data. Many of them are in sub-Saharan Africa, a fact that by itself reveals much, given the overall economic and agricultural stagnation that has been plaguing the region for some time now. Add to this the fact that many of these countries, both in Africa and elsewhere, have suffered or are still going through severe disruptions caused by war and political disturbances, and what results, in a nutshell, is the explanation for failure and retrogression on the food and nutrition front.[3]

- The data do no more than confirm this impressionistic prediction (see Table 4). Indeed, the most common characteristics of these countries are declines in per caput incomes as well as in per caput production. The two are not, of course, independent of each other. Their per caput food imports did increase, often by means of food aid. However, in contrast to the experiences of the countries in the preceding category, their per caput imports of cereals remained at generally modest levels, while the declines in cereals self-sufficiency were accordingly contained, at the cost, of course, of stagnant or declining per caput food supplies.

[3] While it is clear that conflict and political instability are important variables in explaining endemic failures in development and aggravation of food security problems, the more interesting aspect is the existence of causation in the opposite direction, i.e. from development failures to conflict and instability, resulting in the establishment of a vicious circle. If this were the case (as it may well be, though the relevant relationships are likely to be mediated by complex socio-political and institutional variables), policies to improve development prospects, which, in many countries, would mean policies to improve agricultural performance, would be an integral part of the package of measures to prevent emergence of conflict.

4. Prospects to 2010: demand, supply, trade and nutrition

4.1 This section presents in summary form the future prospects for the main food and agriculture variables, with particular reference to the prospects for the developing countries, as derived in the FAO study *World agriculture: towards 2010 (WAT2010)* (FAO, 1995). The study's results for 2010 present the possible future outcomes as they may turn out to be rather than as they ought to be if certain normative objectives are achieved, e.g. the elimination of undernutrition. For example, the conclusion that significant chronic undernutrition is likely to persist results from this positive, rather than normative, approach to looking into the future. Therefore the prospective developments presented here are not goals of an FAO strategy. Instead, they identify areas of progress and failure in the future and can inform the debate about the needed policy interventions that are discussed in the companion papers.

CONTINUING, BUT SLOWER, GROWTH IN WORLD POPULATION

4.2 Over the time horizon of the study, the world's population may grow to 7.2 billion (or to 7.0 billion according to the latest United Nations projections),[4] up from 5.3 billion in 1990 and 3.7 billion only 20 years earlier. Ninety-four percent of the total increment in world population, or 1.8 billion people (1.6 billion in the latest projection), will occur in the developing countries. Moreover, the regional patterns of population growth are very disparate, e.g. 3.2 percent per year in sub-Saharan Africa (reduced to 2.9 percent annually in the latest revision of the demographic projections) and 1.2 percent per year in East Asia. But the growth rate of world population is on the decline. It peaked in 1965-1970 at 2.1 percent annually and declined progressively to 1.6 percent per year, where it now stands. It is projected to decline further, to 1.3 percent by 2005-2010 and then to 1.0 percent by 2020-2025.

4.3 The demographic trends in the developing countries, in combination with their still low levels of per caput food consumption, would require continued strong growth in their food supplies. Not all of these additional needs will be expressed as effective market demand. The aggregate increase in the food supplies of the developing countries is likely to be less than required to raise average per caput supplies to levels compatible with food security for all. This is because the general development scene is likely to leave many developing countries and population groups with neither per caput incomes nor potential for access to food much above present levels.

[4] For 1994, see United Nations (1994).

BETTER PROSPECTS FOR OVERALL ECONOMIC GROWTH IN THE DEVELOPING COUNTRIES BUT WITH SIGNIFICANT EXCEPTIONS

4.4 In the crisis decade of the 1980s, all developing regions experienced declines in per caput incomes, with the important exception of Asia, both East and South. It is likely that these trends will be reversed in the future. The latest World Bank assessment (World Bank, 1996) indicates that Asia should continue to perform at fairly high rates of economic growth while the prospects are for modest recovery in both Latin America and the Caribbean and the Near East and North Africa. Sub-Saharan Africa is also expected to shift to higher economic growth rates compared with the disastrous 1980s, but its per caput income will grow only slightly. These developments in the overall economy already foreshadow the prospect that some regions will continue to make progress towards food security while others may not make much progress.

4.5 The Western developed countries are likely to continue to perform as in the past. The prospects for the former CPEs are mixed. Central and Eastern Europe economies had together in 1994 and 1995 the fastest real GDP growth (above 4 percent) in Europe. The CIS only started to bottom out, from a real GDP level about one-half (53 percent) of its 1989 level. It may take a long time before sustained growth re-establishes per caput incomes at the pre-reform levels for the entire region.

WORLD AGRICULTURAL GROWTH WILL CONTINUE TO SLOW DOWN

4.6 The detailed assessments of production, together with those of demand and trade, indicate that the growth rate of world agricultural production at 1.8 percent per year (and 0.25 percent per year in per caput terms)[5] will be lower in the period up to 2010 compared with that of the past. This slow-down is largely a continuation of long-term historical trends. World production grew at 3.0 percent per annum in the 1960s, 2.3 percent per annum in the 1970s and 2.0 percent per annum from 1980 to 1992. The slow-down is not a negative outcome *per se* to the extent that it reflects some positive developments in the world demographic and development scenes: the decline in the growth rate of world population and the fact that more and more countries have been raising their per caput food consumption to levels beyond which there is limited scope for further increases. Most developed countries (which account for some 50 percent of world consumption of agricultural products) are in this class and they are being gradually joined by some developing countries. To put it in plain language, people who have money to buy more food do not need to do so, although they will probably continue to increase their expenditure on food to pay for the ever-increasing margins of marketing, processing, packaging and the services that go with them.

[5] The growth rate of world per caput consumption is not a very good indicator for judging what happens to food security problems. Even if this growth rate fell to zero or became negative, it could still be compatible with improvements in the per caput food supplies for the countries with low nutritional levels and high population growth rates without compensating declines in the countries with high nutrition (see relevant illustrations in the following section on cereals). It is, therefore, important to realize that the world can still make progress towards food security even with little growth in per caput world production.

4.7 The negative aspect of the slow-down has to do with the fact that it has been happening and will continue to happen while many countries and a significant part of the world population still have totally inadequate consumption levels and access to food, with a consequent persistence of high levels of undernutrition. In short, the slow-down in world agricultural growth is also a result of the fact that people who would consume more do not have sufficient incomes to demand more food and cause it to be produced. World output could expand at higher rates than envisaged in the study if effective demand were to grow faster.

PROGRESS IN FOOD AND NUTRITION, BUT NOT FOR ALL

4.8 The implications of the demographic and overall development prospects, together with the assessments of the study for production, consumption and trade, are that per caput food supplies for direct human consumption in the developing countries as a whole will continue to grow, from the 2 500 Calories of 1990-1992 to nearly 2 800 Calories by the year 2010, also taking into account the fact that the projected population may be lower than that used originally in the FAO study *WAT2010* (Table 1). It is expected that by the year 2010 the Near East and North Africa and Latin America and the Caribbean regions, as well as East Asia (including China), will be at or above the 3 000 Calorie mark, a significant progress particularly for East Asia. Although South Asia may also make significant progress, in 2010 it would still be at a middling position. However, per caput food supplies in sub-Saharan Africa are expected to remain at very low levels.

4.9 Under the circumstances, the incidence of chronic undernutrition could decline to 10 percent or less of the population in the three regions with the better prospects (Table 3). Progress will probably also be made in South Asia, although there could still be some 200 million people undernourished in the region by the year 2010. Chronic undernutrition is likely to remain rampant in sub-Saharan Africa, with 30 percent of the population (265 million) affected. Thus, the scourge of chronic undernutrition in terms of absolute numbers affected will tend to shift from South Asia to sub-Saharan Africa. These estimates are broad orders of magnitude and relative trends rather than precise predictions of what may happen, subject to the necessary caveats. They indicate that it is probable that chronic undernutrition in the developing countries as a whole will persist, perhaps at lower absolute levels: some 680 million people in the year 2010[6] versus about 840 million people today. Therefore, there will be no respite from the need for interventions to cope with the problem nor from the need to seek the eradication of poverty, the root cause of undernutrition.

PROSPECTS FOR MAJOR COMMODITIES
World production of cereals to continue to grow, but not in per caput terms

4.10 An overview of the cereals sector – past history and projections – is given in Table 5. Global per caput production of cereals grew from 303 kg in 1969-1971 to a peak of 342 kg in 1984-1986 but then declined to 327 kg in 1989-1991, virtually the level of ten years earlier. It is probable that the average will not increase further and will still be 327 kg in 2010. This is, however, no cause

[6] See note to Table 3 for an explanation as to why this projected estimate is higher than that of the original study of 1993.

Table 5
ALL CEREALS: ACTUAL PRODUCTION, TOTAL USE AND NET TRADE AND PROJECTIONS TO 2010

	World	Developed countries			All developing countries					
		Ex-CPEs	Other industrialized	Total	Sub-Saharan Africa	Near East & North Africa	South Asia	East Asia & Pacific	Latin America & the Caribbean	Total
	(million tonnes and kg/caput, with rice milled)									
Production										
Actual 1969-71	1 117 (303)	213 (642)	422 (568)	635 (591)	37 (135)	46 (255)	116 (163)	219 (186)	66 (235)	482 (185)
Actual 1979-81	1 444 (325)	227 (628)	566 (700)	793 (678)	41 (114)	58 (246)	148 (165)	317 (223)	87 (245)	651 (199)
Actual 1989-91	1 727 (327)	266 (685)	598 (692)	864 (690)	55 (112)	77 (246)	203 (182)	431 (257)	97 (222)	863 (214)
Actual 1993-95	1 729 (307)	219 (561)	582 (656)	802 (627)	59 (109)	83 (235)	218 (180)	455 (258)	112 (239)	927 (213)
Projected 2010	2 334 (327)	306 (707)	710 (730)	1 016 (723)	110 (125)	119 (230)	292 (181)	638 (301)	159 (267)	1 318 (230)
Total use										
Actual 1969-71	1 115 (302)	216 (652)	400 (537)	615 (573)	39 (143)	53 (293)	120 (169)	225 (192)	63 (225)	500 (191)
Actual 1979-81	1 441 (325)	281 (778)	444 (550)	725 (620)	48 (134)	80 (340)	151 (169)	341 (240)	95 (266)	716 (219)
Actual 1989-91	1 730 (328)	302 (778)	475 (550)	777 (620)	65 (133)	114 (366)	203 (182)	459 (274)	111 (255)	953 (237)
Projected 2010	2 334 (327)	301 (696)	553 (569)	854 (608)	129 (147)	191 (369)	302 (187)	673 (318)	185 (310)	1 480 (258)
Net trade										
Actual 1969-71	2.2	2.3	20.2	22.5	-2.7	-6.5	-5.5	-8.8	3.2	-20.3
Actual 1979-81	2.6	-40.3	109.7	69.4	-8.1	-23.6	-1.8	-24.9	-8.4	-66.8
Actual 1989-91	3.7	-37.2	129.7	92.5	-8.5	-38.4	-3.2	-27.4	-11.3	-88.8
Actual 1992-94	2.8	-24.1	113.2	89.1	-11.2	-35.8	-3.1	-20.1	-15.3	-86.3
Projected 2010	0	5.0	157.0	162.0	-19.0	-72.0	-10.0	-35.0	-26.0	-162.0

CPEs = centrally planned economies.

Notes: (1) Numbers in parentheses are kilograms per caput. (2) Projections are those in the 1994 revision of *World agriculture: towards 2010* (WAT2010) (FAO, 1995) and differ from those in the original 1993 document following the change in reporting the ex-USSR's data in clean weight rather than bunker weight. (3) The projected per caput numbers have been derived by dividing the projected totals by the projected population from the 1992 United Nations assessment. As such they are somewhat different from those reported in the original study (which were based on the projected population of the 1990 United Nations assessment), but the per caput projections are consistent with the most recent historical data. (4) The per caput production data for 1993-1995 have been derived using the latest population data (1994 United Nations assessment) and may not be fully comparable with those for earlier years. (5) The net trade data for 1992-1994 are not fully comparable with those for earlier years.

for general alarm for the reasons discussed earlier in connection with the progressive slow-down in world agricultural growth. In particular, the consumption requirements for all uses in the developed countries (which have total use of cereals per caput of 620 kg and account for 45 percent of world consumption) only grow slowly and may fall in per caput terms. Collectively, these countries produce only as much as is needed for their own consumption and to meet the increase in net exports to the developing countries. They could produce more if more were demanded. These prospects are heavily influenced by possible developments in the former CPEs of Central and Eastern Europe, whose total domestic use of cereals may actually be lower in 2010 than in the pre-reform period. This possible development has its origin in the prospect that per caput consumption of livestock products may not recover fully to the pre-reform levels, that there is significant scope for economies in the use of cereals as feed and that post-harvest losses could be reduced significantly.

4.11 The recent decline in the world per caput production of cereals has been interpreted by some as indicating a structural change for the worse in the world food trends caused by increasingly binding constraints on the side of production. However, the circumstances that have caused the decline since the mid-1980s are, as noted earlier, mostly of a transitory nature. Therefore, the decline may not be interpreted as signalling the onset of constraints on the production side that made it difficult to meet the growth of effective demand. The real problem must be seen in the too-slow growth of effective demand on the part of those countries and population groups with low levels of food consumption.

4.12 The preceding discussion indicates that the world average per caput production has only limited value for measuring trends in world food security. It can also be misleading if it conveys the idea that, with the world average constant, any gains in per caput production of one group of countries must be counterbalanced by declines in another group. This need not be the case. It was not so in the 1980s and it will not likely be so in the future. Per caput production is projected to increase in both the developed and the developing countries while the world average may remain at the 327 kg of 1989-1991 (Table 5). This paradox is a result of the fact that the developing countries start with low per caput production and have high population growth rates while the developed countries are in the opposite situation.

4.13 Indeed, per caput production of cereals in the developing countries is expected to continue to grow, from the 214 kg in 1989-1991 to 230 kg in 2010, 16 kg in two decades. This is a smaller increment than was achieved in the past: about 15 kg per decade in the 1970s and the 1980s. But their per caput consumption for all uses may grow faster than production, from 237 to 258 kg, part of which would be for feed to support the rapidly growing livestock sector. This will require further growth of net imports from the developed countries, which may increase from the 89 million tonnes of 1989-1991 to about 160 million tonnes in 2010. The implied rate of growth of the net import requirements is not particularly high if judged by the historical record. It is more like that of the 1980s rather than the very rapid growth rate of the 1970s. Financing increased food imports may be considered a normal feature of those developing countries in which both incomes and consumption, particularly of livestock products, grow while other sectors generate foreign-exchange earnings. But those developing countries that cannot easily finance increased food imports from scarce foreign-exchange earnings will face hardship. It is, therefore, reasonable to expect a continued role for food aid for a long time to come. If policy reforms towards a more market-oriented international agricultural trade system were to limit the scope for food aid from surpluses, alternative measures would be required to meet the needs. In this respect, the decision included in the Final Act of the Uruguay Round of Multilateral Trade Negotiations concerning measures to attenuate the effects on the food-importing developing countries of an eventual rise in world market prices and the creation of conditions for food security stocks as well as continuation of food aid flows assumes particular importance.

Modest growth in the demand for exports of cereals from the major exporting developed regions

4.14 Although the prospects for further growth of exports of cereals from the major exporting developed countries to the developing countries offer some scope for further growth of production and exports by the former, their net exports to the rest of the world are expected to grow by much less. This is because the group of former CPEs (of Europe) would probably cease to be a large net importer in the future and there is a possibility that it could turn into a modest net exporter of cereals by 2010 (Table 5). Already, the preliminary data and forecasts for the two-year average 1994/95-1995/96 (July/June) indicate that their net imports have collapsed to only 2 million tonnes.

4.15 There might be significant changes in the market shares in these total net exports of the three major exporting OECD areas, Western Europe, North America and Oceania. Current and future policy reforms, particularly in the context of the provisions of the Agreement on Agriculture (AOA) of the Uruguay Round, will probably lead to Western Europe not increasing its net exports from the levels of the late 1980s, with all of the additional combined exports of the three groups, and perhaps more, accruing to North America and Oceania. At least this is what is indicated by the results of most analyses concerning the possible effects of the policy reforms. These findings are, of course, subject to the many caveats attached to the assumptions and models on which these analyses are based.

Continuing strong growth in the livestock sector

4.16 The past trend of the livestock sector in developing countries to grow at a relatively high rate is set to continue, although in attenuated form. Part of the growth in their cereal imports will be for increased production and consumption of livestock products. However, the consumption of livestock products in the developing countries will still be well below that of the developed countries in per caput terms in the year 2010. These averages for the developing countries mask wide regional and country diversities, and in both South Asia and sub-Saharan Africa consumption will generally remain at very low levels.

4.17 The livestock sector of the developed countries may also grow, but at much slower rates compared with the past, with per caput consumption increasing only for poultry meat. This would reflect the prospect that in the former CPEs the production and per caput consumption of livestock products may take a long time to recover to near pre-reform levels after the sharp initial declines and that the other developed countries have generally high levels of per caput consumption.

4.18 With the continued growth of the livestock sector in the developing countries, their use of cereals as feed will continue to grow fast; it may more than double by the year 2010 to some 340 million tonnes, about 23 percent of their total use. This increasing proportion of total cereals supplies used to feed animals in the developing countries may be cause for concern given the persistence of undernutrition. This concern would be well founded if the use of cereals for feed diverted supplies that would be otherwise available for use by the poor as direct food. This could happen, but only in situations where the additional demand for feed would raise prices rather than supplies (whether from domestic production or imports) and price the poor out of the market. There are reasons to believe that this is the exception rather than the rule.

Roots, tubers, plantains: continuing importance in the total food supplies of countries in the humid tropics

4.19 Roots, tubers and plantains account for some 40 percent of total food supplies (in terms of Calories) for about one-half of the population of sub-Saharan Africa, where overall food supplies are at very low levels. Other countries in both Africa and Latin America and the Caribbean also depend significantly on these staples. Production could be increased, and this will be done, to meet future needs. However, the past trends have been for per caput consumption to decline, at least as far as it can be ascertained from the imprecise statistics for this sector. The decline has reflected essentially a trend towards urbanization, where the high perishability and labour-intensive nature of preparation for consumption make these products less-preferred foods. With increasing urbanization, it can be expected that there will be further, although modest, declines in average per caput consumption. But dependence of these countries on these products for their total food supplies will continue to be high. The trend towards decline in per caput consumption may be attenuated if imported cereals become scarcer, which may well be the case if policy reforms in the developed countries raise prices and reduce supplies for concessionary sales and food aid. Likewise, further research into converting starchy roots into less-perishable and more-convenient food products for the urban population could contribute to the attenuation of these trends.

The oil crops sector of the developing countries: continued rapid growth in prospect

4.20 In the last 20 years, the oil crops sector of the developing countries has grown quickly and undergone radical structural change. The oil-palm in East

Asia and soybean in South America have exhibited spectacular growth. The shares of these products and regions in total oil crop production have increased rapidly and those of the other oil crops (coconuts, groundnuts, cottonseed, sesame) of the developing countries and the other regions have declined accordingly.

4.21 The production growth of this sector will continue to be above-average compared with the rest of agriculture. Structural change will also continue, but at a much slower pace than in the past. The expansion of the oil-palm sector will continue to be the most rapid, increasing its share to perhaps 38 percent, up from 32 percent at present and only 16 percent 20 years ago. Soybean production in South America will also continue to grow rapidly, but nothing like the twelvefold increase of the last 20 years, when growth had started from a very low base. The continuation of fairly high growth rates in the oil crops sector reflects the rapid increase in the developing countries' consumption of both vegetable oils for food and oilseed proteins in support of their rapidly growing livestock sectors. They would also increase further their exports of oils and to a lesser extent those of oil-meals to the rest of the world.

Slower growth in the other main agricultural exports of the developing countries

4.22 There are well-known reasons why the generally unfavourable trends in the net exports of the major export commodities of the developing countries to the rest of the world may continue. For sugar, the reason is mostly the probable continuation of support and protection policies, market access restrictions and subsidized exports of major developed countries. Then, the former CPEs are likely to be much smaller net importers in the future. Therefore, net exports to the developed countries will, in all likelihood, continue to fall. This trend may be attenuated if further trade liberalization efforts lead to a more liberal trading environment. At the same time, the developing exporting countries will probably continue to expand exports as there are growing markets in the net importing developing countries, which increased their net imports nearly fourfold in the last 20 years.

4.23 Unlike sugar and some other major export commodities, coffee and cocoa are produced only in the developing countries and consumed mostly in the Western developed countries, where per caput consumption levels are already generally high. Therefore, efforts by developing countries to increase supplies in competition with each other translate into small increases in the volume of exports and large declines in prices. For the longer term, there is scope for the situation to improve given the low consumption levels prevailing in the former CPEs and the developing countries themselves. But little of this scope may materialize in the form of increased consumption and imports in the next 20 years. Therefore, growth in net exports of about 25 percent, and somewhat higher in production, is a likely outcome. For tea, there are somewhat better prospects for production growth, although not for exports, because a good proportion of production is consumed in the developing countries themselves and per caput consumption will continue to increase. Finally, exports of bananas have better prospects than those of the tropical beverages since there is still scope for per caput consumption to increase in the developed countries.

4.24 In general, for the traditional commodities produced only or mainly in developing countries competing with each other and consumed mostly in developed countries with nearly saturated consumption levels, the prospects for export earnings will continue to be dominated by movements in prices rather than volumes. The very long-term remedy to declining prices may be found in the growth of consumption in still unsaturated markets (former CPEs and developing countries themselves) and ultimately in the general development of the producing countries. The latter factor is important because it will create alternative income-earning opportunities and put a floor to how low the returns to labour in these commodity sectors may fall before supply contracts and prices recover. At the same time, there is scope for increasing agricultural export earnings if advantage is taken of the growing opportunities for trade in non-traditional products, such as horticultural produce, cut flowers, etc.

4.25 Finally, the prospects for some agricultural raw materials traditionally exported from the developing countries offer limited scope for growth in net export earnings, although for different, and not always negative, reasons. Thus, net exports of tobacco to the developed countries may not grow at all because their consumption is on the decline while it is on a rapid growth path in the developing countries. For cotton, the developing countries have recently turned from being net exporters to become net importers and will further increase their net imports in the future. This is, on the whole, a positive development because it reflects their growing and increasingly export-oriented textile industries. These trends could become even more pronounced if restrictions on textile exports are made less stringent or abolished. Similar considerations apply to the hides and skins sector and the associated expansion of exports of leather goods. Finally, natural rubber exports to the developed countries are expected to continue to grow, but also here the developing countries will gradually increase their share in world consumption and may, by the year 2010, account for over 50 percent of the world total, compared with less than 25 percent 20 years ago. Much of the expansion in consumption will be in East Asia.

Nearly stagnant fish production from capture fisheries, but better prospects for aquaculture

4.26 As noted earlier, the stagnation of fish production from capture fisheries, which peaked in 1989, is not a temporary phenomenon, but may persist, so that global per caput production of fish from this source can be expected to decline. It is possible for the effect on the fish supplies for human consumption to be somewhat mitigated by the addition of part of the catch of small pelagic fish, which are used in the production of fish-meal. However, the greatest scope for averting the decline in per caput production of food fish is to be found in further development of aquaculture. Continuation of the annual increase of about 1 million tonnes of fish from this source would be sufficient to maintain world per caput supplies for food at present levels, provided capture fishery management practices are improved and expanded, permitting capture fisheries production to remain at present levels. However, given that demand for fish products is expected to grow more rapidly than the population, particularly in Southeast Asia, unchanged per caput fish supplies will not suffice to avoid an increase in the real price of fish.

THE DEVELOPING COUNTRIES' LIKELY TURN FROM NET AGRICULTURAL EXPORTERS TO NET IMPORTERS

4.27 The prospective developments presented above for the major commodity sectors indicate that the developing countries' net imports of the agricultural (crop and livestock) commodities for which they are, or may become, net importers will be growing faster than their net exports of their major export commodities. While the individual developing countries face widely differing prospects in terms of changes in their net agricultural trade balances, these trends in import and export volumes point firmly in the direction of the developing countries' combined agricultural trade account switching from surplus to deficit. The movement in this direction has been evident for some time in the historical period. The positive net balance of trade on the agricultural account shrank rapidly in the 1970s, when food imports from the developed countries exploded. Although the trend was somewhat reversed in the 1980s, the overall surplus was only US$5 billion in 1988-1990 compared with $17.5 billion in 1969-1971 (both at 1988-1990 prices).

PROSPECTS FOR THE MAJOR COMMODITY SECTORS: SIGNIFICANCE FOR FOOD SECURITY

4.28 The preceding summary presentation of the prospects for the major commodities indicates clearly that the multiple role of agriculture in contributing to enhanced food security (by increasing food supplies, incomes and export earnings) will be conditioned by very diverse factors. These range from the more direct impacts of local production of cereals and of policies affecting their production and trade on a world scale, to the role of urbanization as a factor in the consumption of starchy foods (roots, tubers, plantains), to the world market prospects for the major food and non-food exportables of those countries with a high dependence on them.

5. Prospects to 2010: agricultural resources and yields in developing countries

AGRICULTURAL LAND AND IRRIGATION
The overall situation

5.1 Land currently used in crop production in the developing countries (excluding China) amounts to some 760 million ha, of which 120 million ha are irrigated, including 36 million ha of arid and hyperarid land made productive through irrigation. These 760 million ha represent only 30 percent of the total land of varying qualities with rain-fed crop production potential, which is estimated to be 2. 57 billion ha, including the 36 million ha of irrigated hyperarid land (Table 6). The remaining 1.8 billion ha would therefore seem to provide significant scope for further expansion of agriculture. However, this impression is severely redimensioned if a number of constraints are taken into account, such as:

- About 92 percent of the 1.8 billion ha of land with rain-fed crop production potential but not yet so used is in sub-Saharan Africa (44 percent) and Latin America and the Caribbean (48 percent). At the other extreme, there is little land for agricultural expansion in South Asia and the Near East and North Africa.

- Over two-thirds of the 1.8 billion ha of land not in crop production is concentrated in a small number of countries, e.g. 27 percent is in Brazil, 9 percent in Zaire and another 36 percent in 13 other countries (Angola, Argentina, Bolivia, Central African Republic, Colombia, Indonesia, Mexico, Mozambique, Peru, the Sudan, United Republic of Tanzania, Venezuela and Zambia).

- A good part of this land "reserve" is under forest (at least 45 percent, but probably much more) or in protected areas, and therefore it should not be considered as a reserve readily available for agricultural expansion. Forests play a fundamentally important role in conserving the resource base, i.e. in terms of soil and water conservation and by providing a habitat for plant and animal diversity. Production of timber, wood and non-wood products provides income and jobs thereby increasing the possibility of local communities to obtain or purchase food and other basic necessities.

- A significant part (72 percent, see Table 7) of the agricultural land of the two regions (sub-Saharan Africa and Latin America and the Caribbean) that share 92 percent of the total reserve suffers from soil and terrain constraints. This is a much higher percentage than encountered in the other regions. Overall, some 50 percent of the 1.8 billion ha of land reserve is classified in the categories "humid" or "marginally suitable for crop production" (see below). Only 28 percent of land in use at present falls into these two categories.

- Finally, human settlements and infrastructure occupy some of the land with agricultural potential, roughly estimated at about 3 percent. This proportion is expected to increase in the future, perhaps to 4 percent by 2010.

Table 6
LAND WITH RAIN-FED CROP PRODUCTION POTENTIAL IN DEVELOPING COUNTRIES (excluding China)

Class	Moisture regime (LGP in days)	Land quality	Potential	In use		Balance	
				1988-90	2010	1988-90	2010
				(million ha)			
Dry semi-arid	75-119	VS, S, MS	154	86	92	68	62
Moist semi-arid	120-179	VS, S	350	148	161	202	189
Subhumid	180-269	VS, S	594	222	249	372	344
Humid	270+	VS, S	598	201	232	915	883
Marginally suitable land in the moist semi-arid, subhumid, humid classes	120+	MS	518				
Fluvisols/Gleysols	Naturally flooded	VS, S	258	64	77	259	246
Marginally suitable Fluvisols/Gleysols	Naturally flooded	MS	65				
Total with rain-fed potential (of which irrigated)			2 537	721 (87)	812 (108)	1 816	1 725
Additional irrigation on non-suitable (arid and hyperarid) land			36	36	38		
TOTAL			2 573	757	850	1 816	1 725

LGP = length of growing period; VS = very suitable; S = suitable; MS = marginally suitable.

Table 7
SHARE OF LAND WITH TERRAIN AND SOIL CONSTRAINTS IN TOTAL RAIN-FED LAND WITH CROP PRODUCTION POTENTIAL

Constraint	Sub-Saharan Africa	Latin America & the Caribbean	Near East & North Africa	East Asia	South Asia	Developing countries (91)
			(%)			
Steep slopes (16-45%)	11	6	24	13	19	10
Shallow soils (<50 cm)	1	10	4	1	1	1
Low natural fertility	42	46	1	28	4	38
Poor soil drainage	15	28	2	26	11	20
Sandy or stony soils	36	15	17	11	11	23
Soil chemical constraints[1]	1	2	3	1	2	1
Total land in all land classes affected by one or more constraints[2]	72	72	43	63	42	67

[1] Salinity, sodicity and excess of gypsum.
[2] Individual constraints are non-additive, i.e. they may overlap.

5.2 It is against this background that the prospects of more land coming into crop production use in the next 20 years must be examined. A process of expansion on to new land has characterized the evolution of agriculture in the past, and there is no reason to think that it will not occur in the future in the countries in which a combination of potential and need so dictate. The fact that there is little scope for agricultural land expansion in many countries should not lead to the conclusion that this applies to the developing countries as a whole. In what follows, an attempt is made to project how much new land may be brought under crop production by the year 2010. Potential and need are the main factors that will determine the rate of expansion. The first step is to estimate the potential. This was done using FAO's georeferenced agro-ecological zones (AEZ) database. The results are shown in Table 6. These data give an idea as to how much of the total land can be classified as "suitable", "very suitable" and irrigated, or "high potential", land.

Future expansion of land in crop production, rain-fed and irrigated

5.3 Land under crop production in the developing countries, excluding China,[7] may expand from the 760 million ha in 1988-1990 to reach 850 million ha in 2010, an increase of 90 million ha or about 5 percent of the 1.8 billion ha land balance (Table 6). The bulk of the increase would be in sub-Saharan Africa and in Latin America and the Caribbean. The rest of the increase would be mainly in East Asia, and very little of it would be in South Asia and the Near East and North Africa (Table 8). The following observations may be made:

- Although the arable land may expand by 90 million ha, the harvested area could increase by 124 million ha because of a rise in cropping intensities (Table 8). The trend for the cropping intensities to increase and for fallow periods to become shorter is a well-established phenomenon (although there are no systematic comprehensive historical data on this variable) accompanying the process of agricultural intensification and reflecting, among other things, increases in population densities and the rising share of irrigation in total land use.

- Irrigated land in the developing countries may expand by 23 million ha, or by 19 percent in net terms (Tables 6 and 8), assuming that losses of existing irrigated land (because of, for example, water shortages or degradation caused by salinization) will be compensated for by rehabilitation or substitution of new areas for the lost ones. It has not been possible to project the rate of irrigated land losses. The few existing historical data on such losses are too uncertain and anecdotal and do not provide a reliable basis for drawing inferences about the future. If it is assumed that 2.5 percent of existing irrigation must be rehabilitated or substituted by new irrigation each year (that is, if the average life span of irrigation schemes was 40 years), then the total irrigation investment activity over the period of the study in the developing countries (excluding China) must encompass some 85 million ha, of which over 70 percent would be used for rehabilitation or substitution and the balance for net expansion.

- The projections of irrigation reflect a composite of information on existing irrigation expansion plans in the different countries, the potential for expansion and the need to increase crop production. The projections include

[7] China is excluded because of the lack of relevant data, i.e. the crop production patterns and land with agricultural potential, both of which are required by agro-ecological zone for the analysis. In addition, there are indications that the existing data understate the land in agricultural use and overstate yields. If this is true, there is apparently more potential for further growth of agricultural production than is commonly thought. Until such uncertainties are resolved, no evaluation of the future prospects for land use and yields can be undertaken. Discussion of this issue in the context of the recent concerns about China's rising cereal imports can be found in Alexandratos (1996).

Table 8
ARABLE LAND IN USE, CROPPING INTENSITIES AND HARVESTED LAND IN DEVELOPING COUNTRIES (excluding China)

	Total land in use			Rain-fed use					Irrigated use				
	Arable (million ha)	Cropping intensity (%)	Harvested (million ha)	Arable (million ha)	Cropping intensity (%)	Harvested (million ha)	On land with rain-fed crop production potential (million ha)	On arid and hyperarid land (million ha)	Total arable (million ha)	As percentage of total arable land in use	Cropping intensity (%)	Harvested (million ha)	As percentage of total harvested land in use
Sub-Saharan Africa													
(1969-71)	(124)		(98)						(3.6)				
(1988-90)	(140)		(114)						(5.3)				
1988-90	212.5	55	117.7	207.2	55	113.7	4.6	0.7	5.3	2	75	4.0	3
2010	254.7	62	158.1	247.7	61	152.2	6.2	0.8	7.0	3	84	5.9	4
Near East & North Africa													
(1969-71)	(89)		(53)						(16.3)				
(1988-90)	(93)		(62)						(20.1)				
1988-90	76.5	83	63.4	56.4	77	43.7	5.3	14.8	20.1	26	98	19.7	31
2010	80.5	93	74.8	57.9	85	49.0	6.5	16.2	22.7	28	114	25.8	34
East Asia													
(1969-71)	(68)		(64)						(11.0)				
(1988-90)	(82)		(85)						(20.0)				
1988-90	87.5	101	88.8	68.2	96	65.6	19.3	0.0	19.3	22	120	23.2	26
2010	102.8	105	108.4	81.2	100	81.3	21.5	0.0	21.5	21	126	27.1	25
South Asia													
(1969-71)	(197)		(187)						(44.8)				
(1988-90)	(204)		(205)						(65.2)				
1988-90	190.5	112	213.0	127.1	109	138.4	48.1	15.3	63.4	33	118	74.6	35
2010	194.9	122	237.0	118.6	113	133.6	60.5	15.8	76.3	39	136	103.4	44
Latin America & the Caribbean													
(1969-71)	(117)		(88)						(10.0)				
(1988-90)	(150)		(113)						(15.4)				
1988-90	189.6	61	115.6	174.6	58	101.5	9.9	5.1	15.0	8	94	14.1	12
2010	216.8	67	145.0	198.4	64	127.0	13.2	5.1	18.3	8	98	18.0	12
Developing countries													
(1969-71)	(595)		(488)						(85.7)				
(1988-90)	(669)		(579)						(126.1)				
1988-90	756.7	79	598.5	633.6	73	462.9	87.1	35.9	123.0	16	110	135.6	23
2010	849.7	85	723.3	703.8	77	543.1	108.0	37.9	145.9	17	124	180.2	25

Note: Data in parentheses are the historical data before adjustment to correct inconsistencies in the data of some countries. Adjustments were made only for 1988-1990.

some expansion in informal (community-managed) irrigation, which is important in sub-Saharan Africa. Cropping intensities on irrigated land are expected to continue to grow, particularly in the land-scarce regions. This would result in the harvested irrigated area increasing by 45 million ha, compared with the 23 million ha projected for the arable (physical) area in irrigation. The projected increase in arable irrigated land is well below that of the preceding 20 years, when it was 40 million ha (Table 8). It is even lower when considered in relative terms, with the projected growth rate being 0.8 percent per annum compared with 2.2 percent in the 1970s and 1.9 percent in the 1980s. The projected slow-down reflects the increasing scarcity of water resources, the rising costs of irrigation investment and, for the developing countries, the projected lower rate of agricultural production growth. Physical potential for faster expansion of irrigation exists in several countries and could be exploited if the socio-economic conditions so dictated (see WFS companion paper 7, *Food production: the critical role of water*).

LAND-YIELD COMBINATIONS FOR MAJOR CROPS

5.4 The aggregate crop production in the developing countries as a whole (excluding China) is projected to grow at 2.4 percent a year, down from the annual growth rate of 2.9 percent evident between 1970 and 1990. The reasons why future growth may be lower than in the past were explained in the preceding section. The overall combinations of harvested area expansion and yield increases underlying the projections for major crops are shown in Table 9.

5.5 The data and projections in Tables 8 and 9 are useful for forming an overall idea of the extent to which production projections depend on the further expansion of land and irrigation, their more intensive use (increasing cropping intensities) and the continuation of yield growth. In particular, they shed some light on the question of whether or not the future will be like the past, although the historical data do not always provide a sufficient basis for making this comparison. It must be emphasized that these land and yield projections are definitely not extrapolations of the historical trends. The reader is invited to contemplate what the projections would have been if this study had just extrapolated the explosive area growth rates of the historical period for soybean and sugar cane in a major country like Brazil, which were 10.8 percent per year and 7.4 percent per year, respectively, in the period from 1970 to 1990.

5.6 Three overall conclusions can be made. First, for the major crops (such as cereals and soybean), the growth rates of average yields can be expected to be much below those of the last 20 years, e.g. 1.6 percent per annum for wheat compared with 2.8 percent per annum in the past and 1.5 percent per annum for rice compared with 2.3 percent per annum formerly (Table 9). Second, harvested area expansion will continue to play a significant role in total crop production growth, although, like in the past, it will be much less significant than that of yield increases. At the same time, increases in the cropping intensities of mainly the irrigated areas will play a predominant role in the land-scarce regions (South Asia, the Near East and North Africa). And, third, as noted in the

Table 9

AREA AND YIELDS FOR MAJOR CROPS IN DEVELOPING COUNTRIES (excluding China)

	Production (P) (million tonnes)				Harvested area (A) (million ha)			Yield (Y) (tonnes/ha)			Growth rates (% per annum)					
											1970-90			1988-90 to 2010		
	1969-71	1988-90	1991-92*	2010	1969-71	1988-90	2010	1969-71	1988-90	2010	P	A	Y	P	A	Y
Wheat	67	132	144	205	58	70	77	1.2	1.9	2.7	3.8	0.9	2.8	2.1	0.5	1.6
Rice (paddy)	177	303	309	459	95	109	120	1.9	2.8	3.8	3.0	0.8	2.3	2.0	0.5	1.5
Maize	70	112	117	196	54	63	80	1.3	1.8	2.5	2.7	0.9	1.8	2.7	1.2	1.5
Barley	16	22	24	35	15	17	19	1.1	1.3	1.8	1.8	0.8	1.0	2.3	0.6	1.8
Millet	19	22	21	32	35	32	38	0.6	0.7	0.8	0.4	-0.6	1.0	1.8	0.9	1.0
Sorghum	28	37	37	62	38	37	50	0.7	1.0	1.2	1.7	0.3	1.5	2.5	1.4	1.1
TOTAL CEREALS	381	631	657	995	299	331	389	1.3	1.9	2.6	2.8	0.6	2.2	2.2	0.8	1.4
Cassava	95	153	149	223	11	15	18	8.3	10.1	12.2	2.4	1.3	1.1	1.8	0.9	0.9
Sugar cane	486	882	939	1 365	9	15	18	52.0	59.6	75.4	3.4	2.5	0.8	2.1	1.0	1.1
Pulses	24	30	32	48	46	52	61	0.5	0.6	0.8	1.3	0.7	0.6	2.2	0.7	1.5
Soybeans	3	38	37	79	3	22	33	1.0	1.7	2.4	11.8	9.4	2.1	3.6	1.9	1.7
Groundnuts	14	16	15	30	17	17	21	0.8	1.0	1.4	0.4	-0.4	0.9	3.0	1.2	1.7
Coffee	4	6	6	8	9	11	12	0.5	0.5	0.7	2.2	1.5	0.7	1.5	0.1	1.4
Seed cotton	16	21	22	42	22	19	22	0.7	1.1	1.9	1.3	-0.9	2.2	3.2	0.7	2.5

Note: Sometimes the changes in the annual growth rates between the historical and the projection periods appear to be large. Often this is a continuation of a change already begun in the historical period or an expected change in one country that has a large weight in the total. For example, annual growth in sugar-cane production in the developing countries excluding Brazil is projected to remain the same as in the historical period, namely 2.2 percent. Likewise, the area allocated to soybean in Brazil (currently more than 50 percent of total soybean area in developing countries) grew at 21.2 percent annually in the 1970s, but fell to 3.5 percent in the 1980s.

* Revised data for 1991-1992 as known in May 1994, but not used in this study.

preceding section, the expansion of irrigated land will probably proceed at a much slower pace than in the past.

Land-yield combinations in the cereals sector

5.7 The growth in production of wheat and rice is expected to slow down considerably over the projection period as compared with growth in the last two decades. Coarse grains should maintain their past annual growth in the future, reflecting in part the strong growth of demand for cereals used for feed. By far the greater part (82 percent) of the production of wheat in the developing countries (excluding China) is located in South Asia and the Near East and North Africa. Rice production is concentrated in South and East Asia (89 percent) and barley is produced mainly in the Near East and North African Region. These are land-scarce regions with higher-than-average dependence on irrigation. Both necessity and potential dictate that much of the production increases of these three cereals will come from higher yields. Maize and sorghum are produced mainly in Latin America and sub-Saharan Africa, while millet production is evenly distributed between sub-Saharan Africa and South Asia. By and large, the predominance of the two land-abundant regions with rain-fed agriculture in the production of coarse grains (except barley) indicates that area expansion will play a comparatively larger role in the growth of coarse grains production than in that of wheat and rice production.

5.8 The data and projections in Table 9 demonstrate this prospect. For example, a 2.0 percent annual increase in rice production may be achieved by a 0.5 percent annual increase in harvested rice area (and much less in arable area under rice). At the other extreme, a 2.5 percent annual growth rate in sorghum production will be based on the harvested sorghum area growing at 1.4 percent per annum. The fact that the production of these coarse grains is overwhelmingly rain-fed with, for millet and sorghum, a high proportion being in the two semi-arid land classes, explains why growth of yields may be expected to make a less-important contribution to production growth than for wheat and rice. The overall picture of possible area-yield combinations by agro-ecological land class underlying the production projections of cereals is shown in Table 10.

CONSIDERATIONS RELATING TO THE POTENTIAL FOR YIELD GROWTH

5.9 Given the high dependence of production increases on the growth of yields, the question is often raised as to whether or not, in the post-green revolution period, there is much scope left for further increases in yields. Particularly of interest is the extent to which yield increases may depend on the research system's generation of new varieties (e.g. those that would make possible quantum jumps in yields), or of varieties contributing to slower (evolutionary) growth of yields, for the periodic replacement of existing ones subject to the erosion of their yield potential. This is a central issue concerning research requirements and priorities to sustain the growth of production.

Table 10
PRODUCTION OF MAJOR CEREALS BY LAND CLASS IN DEVELOPING COUNTRIES (excluding China)[1]

	All land classes [2]			Dry semi-arid			Moist semi-arid			Subhumid			Humid			Fluvisols and Gleysols			Irrigated		
	A	Y	P	A	Y	P	A	Y	P	A	Y	P	A	Y	P	A	Y	P	A	Y	P
Wheat																					
1988-90	69.7	1.9	132.4	3.1	0.7	2.2	10.0	1.2	12.3	16.0	1.7	27.3	6.2	1.6	10.3	0.5	0.7	0.4	33.8	2.4	80.0
2010	77.1	2.7	205.0	3.2	1.0	3.3	11.0	1.8	20.3	17.4	2.1	37.1	5.2	2.3	12.1	0.5	1.0	0.5	39.7	3.3	131.7
Rice (paddy)																					
1988-90	109.2	2.8	302.7							10.5	2.1	22.4	21.4	1.6	33.3	29.7	2.4	71.7	47.5	3.7	175.3
2010	120.5	3.8	458.7							5.7	2.4	13.4	24.5	1.9	45.4	32.6	3.1	101.9	57.7	5.2	297.9
Maize																					
1988-90	62.6	1.8	112.2	0.8	0.6	0.5	7.6	1.2	9.0	30.1	1.8	54.9	15.3	1.3	19.5	1.6	1.0	1.7	7.2	3.7	26.7
2010	79.6	2.5	196.6	1.0	0.9	0.9	8.8	1.5	13.6	38.1	2.6	97.7	19.3	1.7	33.5	1.6	1.2	1.9	10.8	4.5	49.0
Barley																					
1988-90	17.2	1.3	21.9	4.7	0.7	3.3	3.9	1.2	4.8	2.8	1.7	4.8	2.3	1.4	3.2	0.6	0.7	0.4	2.9	1.8	5.3
2010	19.4	1.8	35.5	5.2	1.1	5.7	4.2	1.9	7.9	3.3	2.4	7.7	2.9	1.9	5.4	0.8	1.0	0.8	3.1	2.6	8.0
Millet																					
1988-90	31.9	0.7	21.7	10.2	0.4	3.9	9.8	0.6	6.4	6.3	0.9	5.8	2.9	0.5	1.5	0.9	0.8	0.8	1.7	1.9	3.3
2010	38.2	0.8	31.7	12.1	0.5	6.1	12.1	0.8	9.9	7.2	1.1	8.1	3.7	0.6	2.4	1.3	1.2	1.6	1.8	2.0	3.5
Sorghum																					
1988-90	37.1	1.0	36.9	8.8	0.5	4.1	11.3	0.8	8.9	9.4	1.3	11.9	2.5	0.7	1.9	2.0	0.8	1.7	3.0	2.8	8.4
2010	49.7	1.2	61.8	11.7	0.6	6.9	14.5	1.0	14.2	12.7	1.7	21.5	4.3	0.9	3.9	2.8	1.1	3.1	3.8	3.3	12.3

A = area in million hectares; Y = yield in tonnes per hectare; P = production in million tonnes.
[1] Data on land and yields by land class at the country level do not exist in any systematic form. They have been assembled for this study based on whatever information was available (country/project reports, expert judgement, etc.). They should therefore be interpreted with care.
[2] Land classes as defined in Table 5.

5.10 The agro-ecological characteristics used to classify agricultural land into categories in this study provide some useful background for addressing this issue. How useful they are depends on whether or not the resulting land classes may be considered to be representative of homogeneous physical production environments and their potential for yield growth. This is clearly not the case. For example, irrigated land in the Punjab in India is not necessarily the same as that found in Mexico, and so on for the other land classes.

5.11 These limitations of the agro-ecological classifications notwithstanding, their use in the analysis of this study, in association with the distinction of individual cereals rather than cereals or coarse grains as a group, is a useful step towards enlightening the debate on the extent to which future yield growth depends on new research breakthroughs. It certainly provides a sounder basis for judging this issue than the mere comparison of intercountry differentials in average yields, let alone differentials among large country groups, e.g. between average yields of the developed and the developing countries.

5.12 In examining the scope for production growth in the future through further increases in yields, the dominant factor is the realization that the scope for raising yield ceilings by quantum jumps through the introduction of new varieties is more limited now than it was in the past. Therefore, much of the growth in average yields must come less from raising yields of the countries with the highest yields today and more from raising those of the countries, particularly the large ones, at the middle and lower ranges of the yield distribution. This is why the yield projections imply a narrowing of the intercountry yield differences for each land class. The relevant data and projections by land class are shown in Table 11.

5.13 Does this pattern conform to the historical experience? It is not possible to investigate this issue for individual land classes because there are no relevant historical data. Such data exist only for average yields (over all land classes) in each country. They show that the gap between the countries with the highest yields and those with the lowest yields (simple averages of the top and bottom deciles of the countries ranked by yield level) had widened between 1969-1971 and 1988-1990 (Table 11). This occurred mainly as a result of a process whereby the yields of the countries in the top decile in 1969-1971 rose by more than those of the countries in the bottom decile. The projections for average yields (over all land classes) imply that the future may be unlike the past and that the yield gap may become narrower because the scope of yield growth in the top decile countries of 1988-1990 is more limited than it was 20 years ago.

5.14 This pattern is illustrated in Table 12 with data of individual countries for wheat and rice. For wheat, the countries in the top decile of the distribution in 1988-1990 had yields that were nearly twice as high as the countries in the top decile of 1969-1971. In contrast, there was much less yield growth in the countries in the bottom decile. These developments were even more pronounced for rice.

5.15 The dependence of the future growth of aggregate production of the developing countries on the narrowing of the intercountry yield gap (as measured

Table 11

CEREAL YIELDS IN MAJOR AGRO-ECOLOGICAL LAND CLASSES AND INTERCOUNTRY DIFFERENCES IN DEVELOPING COUNTRIES (excluding China)

Product/land class	Percentage of production coming from the given land class, 1988-90	Yields[1] (tonnes/ha)				
		Average (weighted)		Country range[2]		
		1988-90	2010	1969-71	1988-90	2010
Rice (paddy)/all land classes	100	2.8	3.8	0.9 - 4.6	0.9 - 6.6	1.5 - 7.2
Irrigated	58	3.7	5.2		1.7 - 7.2	3.4 - 8.0
Fluvisols and Gleysols	24	2.4	3.1		1.0 - 3.6	1.4 - 4.0
Wheat/all land classes	100	1.9	2.7	0.5 - 2.7	0.8 - 5.1	1.2 - 6.4
Irrigated	60	2.4	3.3		1.1 - 5.4	1.9 - 6.7
Rain-fed, subhumid	21	1.7	2.1		0.9 - 2.9	1.2 - 4.1
Maize/all land classes	100	1.8	2.5	0.6 - 3.1	0.6 - 4.9	1.1 - 6.0
Irrigated	24	3.8	4.6		1.6 - 7.9	2.2 - 8.4
Rain-fed, subhumid	49	1.8	2.6		0.6 - 3.7	1.2 - 4.1
Rain-fed, humid	17	1.3	1.7		0.4 - 2.8	0.8 - 3.6
Millet/all land classes	100	0.7	0.8	0.4 - 1.3	0.3 - 1.4	0.6 - 1.7
Rain-fed, dry semi-arid	18	0.4	0.5		0.1 - 0.6	0.3 - 0.8
Rain-fed, subhumid	27	0.9	1.1		0.6 - 1.8	0.7 - 2.2
Sorghum/all land classes	100	1.0	1.2	0.3 - 2.8	0.4 - 3.4	0.6 - 3.7
Rain-fed, dry semi-arid	11	0.5	0.6		0.3 - 1.0	0.4 - 1.2
Rain-fed, subhumid	32	1.3	1.7		0.6 - 3.5	0.9 - 3.9

[1] Yields of countries with at least 50 000 ha in the land class, crop and year shown.
[2] Simple averages of the yields of the bottom 10 percent and top 10 percent of the countries ranked by yield level (not always the same countries in the top or bottom deciles in each year).

here, the difference in the simple average of yields between the top and bottom deciles of countries) should not, however, be exaggerated. This is because the countries at the two ends of the distribution (top and bottom deciles) account for a relatively small part of the total production of the crop examined. This is true even when, as has been done for Tables 11 and 12, countries with less than 50 000 ha under the crop (and for Table 10 also under the given land class) are excluded from the analysis. In practice, the realism, or otherwise, of the projections of total production of the developing countries depends crucially on that for yield growth in the countries that account for the bulk of the area under each crop.

5.16 For this purpose, Table 12 also shows the relevant historical data and projections of the 10 percent of countries with the largest areas (top decile of countries ranked by area under the crop). It is seen that: these countries have yields that are less than 50 percent of those in the countries with the highest yields; for wheat, their (simple) average yield is projected to grow by 43 percent, which is below the 62 percent increase of the 20 preceding years; for rice, the corresponding percentages are 47 percent and 50 percent; and, even with such increases, these countries, whose performance carries a large weight in the total, would still have in 2010 (simple) average yields about 50 percent of those projected for the countries in the top decile. Thus, although the gap may narrow, particularly for rice, it would be the result of the more limited scope for yield growth in the countries in the top decile, and not because the large countries with middle yields are projected to have higher growth than in the past.

Table 12
INTERCOUNTRY GAPS IN AVERAGE YIELDS FOR WHEAT AND RICE IN DEVELOPING COUNTRIES
(excluding China)[1]

	Wheat					Rice				
	1969-71		1988-90		2010	1969-71		1988-90		2010
	(32)[2]		(33)		(34)	(44)		(47)		(50)
					(tonnes/ha)					
Top decile	Mexico	2.92	Zimbabwe	5.73		Egypt	5.27	Egypt	6.65	
	Egypt	2.74	Egypt	5.00		Korea (Rep.)	4.63	Korea (Rep.)	6.41	
	Korea (Rep.)	2.31	Saudi Arabia	4.65		Korea (DPR)	4.25	Korea (DPR)	8.11	
						Peru	4.14	Peru	5.16	
	Average	2.65	*Average*	5.12	6.37	*Average*	4.57	*Average*	6.58	7.25
Bottom decile	Algeria	0.61	Algeria	0.68		Ghana	1.00	Liberia	1.14	
	Myanmar	0.55	Bolivia	0.70		Tanzania	1.00	Mozambique	0.87	
	Libya	0.26	Libya	0.90		Guinea	0.89	Guinea	0.83	
						Zaire	0.76	Zaire	0.91	
	Average	0.47	*Average*	0.76	1.16	*Average*	0.91	*Average*	0.94	1.55
Decile of largest producers *(by area)*	Turkey	1.32	Turkey	2.02		Indonesia	2.35	Indonesia	4.22	
	India	1.23	India	2.12		Thailand	1.93	Thailand	2.00	
	Pakistan	1.11	Pakistan	1.81		Bangladesh	1.68	Bangladesh	2.57	
						India	1.67	India	2.63	
	Average	1.22	*Average*	1.98	2.84	*Average*	1.91	*Average*	2.86	4.20
Yield of top decile = 100	100		100		100	100		100		100
Bottom decile	18		15		18	20		14		21
Largest producers	46		39		45	42		43		58
Simple average, all countries	43		53		57	47		45		53

[1] Data and projections for countries with over 50 000 ha under wheat or rice in the year shown. Average yields are simple country averages (not weighted by area).
[2] Number of countries.

5.17 The preceding rather lengthy discussion was considered necessary in order to provide the reader with sufficient material to consider the issue of the potential for further growth in yields to underpin the growth of production. This issue is discussed further in the full study, but no attempt is made to translate these projected yields into concrete proposals for agricultural research (magnitude, modalities, priorities). No doubt, further growth in yields, even at the more modest rates projected for the future compared with the past, will not come about unless the research effort continues unabated. It is just that the effects of research on production growth may manifest themselves in different ways: greater impact through the results of evolutionary, adaptive and maintenance research and less through achievement of quantum jumps in yield ceilings.

6. Issues of agricultural resources, environment and sustainability

GENERAL CONSIDERATIONS

6.1 Concern with the state of the environment and the dwindling quantity (per caput) of land and water resources as well as their degradation requires that the conclusions of the paper be amplified to address questions such as the following: to what extent may the resource and environmental constraints impinge on the prospects for increasing food supplies and assuring access to food for all, the very essence of food security? And can such progress be achieved while ensuring that the gains made and the potential for further gains are maintained for future generations, the very essence of sustainability? This concluding section endeavours to put the overall issue in perspective.

6.2 The paper highlighted a number of interdependent factors as being instrumental in increasing per caput food supplies: poverty-reducing economic growth; the multiple role of agricultural growth in the majority of the developing countries (increasing food supplies and providing employment and income-earning opportunities for the poor, both directly and indirectly, via the growth linkages of agriculture); enhanced capacity to import food; and public policy. It follows, therefore, that as important as the agricultural resource constraints are in conditioning the prospects for food production and generation of incomes in agriculture, they are but one of the factors that affect the prospects of eliminating undernutrition. Other environmental factors (e.g. the capacity of the ecosystem to absorb the impact of increased use of energy) can condition the process of economic growth, poverty reduction and, ultimately, the prospects for eliminating undernutrition. In the end, the issue becomes one of sustainable paths to economic development and poverty elimination and not only one of increasing food production in sustainable ways. However, as noted, in the low-income countries with a high dependence on agriculture, it is the potential for exploiting sustainably their agricultural resources that will predominate for some time, until the process of development reduces this dependence.

LAND AND WATER RESOURCES IN THE QUEST FOR SUSTAINABLE RESPONSES TO THE FOOD PROBLEM

6.3 Reference is made to Table 6, which shows for the developing countries (excluding China) the data on land of varying qualities with potential to grow crops under rain-fed conditions and alternative levels of technology. The stark contrast between regions was noted earlier. Differences among countries become more sharply evident when expressed in terms of population densities, and even more so in terms of hectare per person in the population economically active in agriculture. This latter variable is the key to understanding the forces that may shape the future in terms of the population-resources balance. This balance has two main dimensions: how much more food must be produced, which is directly linked to the growth of total population and the per caput consumption of food, and how many people are, or will be, making a living from the exploitation of agricultural resources. The relevant variable here is the size of the population economically active in agriculture.

6.4 The continuous decline of agricultural resources per caput following population growth is one of the major reasons why concern is expressed about the population-food supply balance. The other reason has to do with the deterioration of the quality and production potential of the resources. The data discussed above may be used to shed some light on the nature and significance of the decline in the resources/person ratio (hereafter referred to as the land/person ratio). The values of this latter ratio in the different developing countries span a very wide range, from very low to very high. For example, at the very low end of the scale are countries such as Egypt, Mauritius and Rwanda, with ratios of land in use of under 0.1 ha per person in the total population and virtually zero reserves for further expansion. At the other extreme, countries such as Argentina and the Central African Republic have land-in-use ratios of close to 1 ha per person and considerable reserves.

6.5 With population growth, more and more countries will be shifting closer to values of the land/person ratios typical of those encountered currently in the land-scarce countries. Does this matter for their food and nutrition? An approach to obtaining a first partial answer is to examine if the currently land-scarce countries are worse off nutritionally (in terms of per caput food availabilities) than the more land-abundant countries. The picture emerging from this examination only confirms what is known, i.e. there is no apparent close relationship between the land/person ratios and per caput food supplies, even after controlling for differences in the quality of land. If anything, many land-abundant countries have low per caput food supplies, while most of the nutritionally better-off countries seem to be precisely those with the highest land scarcities. At the same time, most of these latter countries have considerable cereal imports.

6.6 Should this evidence be interpreted to mean that the perceived threat of ever-declining land/person ratios is misplaced? Not necessarily. In the first place, the national land/person ratio, even if adjusted for land-quality differentials, is just one of the many factors that determine per caput food supplies. Its importance cannot be evidenced without an analysis accounting for the role of these other factors (essentially respecting the clause "other things being equal"). Second, the land-scarce, nutritionally sound countries generally have a high dependence on imported cereals. This means that, for them, the perceived threat of the declining land/person ratios must be understood in a global context. That is, a decline in an individual country's land/person ratio may not threaten its own food welfare provided there is enough land elsewhere (in the actual or potential exporting countries) to keep the global land/person ratio from falling below (unknown) critical minimum values and, of course, provided that the people in the land-scarce country do not depend in a major way on the local land and water resources for a living. Countries such as Mauritius and the Republic of Korea are in this class.

6.7 It follows from the above that declining land/person ratios can threaten the food welfare of those land-scarce countries that greatly depend on agriculture for a living. And this is irrespective of the fact that their own population growth may not have a significant impact on the global land/person ratios. Only a combination of much more productive agriculture (in practice, the adoption of land-augmenting technologies that would halt or reverse the declines) and vigorous non-agricultural growth will free them from the bonds of ever-declining land/person ratios.

6.8 In conclusion, the declining land/person ratios do matter for per caput food supplies in two respects. In the global context, and for countries with high actual or potential dependence on food imports, they matter mainly if the declines threaten to push the global ratio below (unknown) critical values, even after allowing for the reprieve resulting from the use of land-augmenting technologies. Should this happen, the effects would be manifested in terms of rising food prices, which would mostly affect the poor. It has not happened so far, despite continuous declines in the global land/person ratios. How close the world is to eventual critical values and whether such values are likely to be reached before the world achieves stationary population and acceptable per caput food supplies for all is a matter of conjecture.

6.9 In the local context, declines in the land/person ratios do matter for food supplies, nutrition and incomes, mainly for the countries with limited access to imported food and with high dependence on agriculture for the maintenance and improvement of living standards and, consequently, of food welfare. If and when such dependence is reduced, the pressures on the global land/person ratios will assume increasing importance also for them.

6.10 The possible role of land-augmenting (in practice, yield-increasing) technologies was referred to above for the reprieve such technologies can afford in relation to the consequences of the inexorable declines of the land/person ratios. However, some of the perceived threats to progress towards solving the food problem have precisely to do with the risks to the productive potential of the agricultural resources stemming from the application of these very technologies, e.g. loss of rain-fed land to soil erosion and of irrigated land to salinization and waterlogging, loss of yield potential and increased risk of crop failures because of pest resistance, etc. In addition, efforts to bring new land under cultivation or to use existing agricultural land more intensively can often be associated with degradation (e.g. as a result of reduced fallows or from exposure of fragile soils to erosion following deforestation) and may not add permanently to total productive potential. An attempt is made below to address what are considered to be the more fundamental processes driving human activity towards degradation of the productive potential of agricultural resources.

AGRICULTURAL ACTIVITY AND THE DEGRADATION OF AGRICULTURAL RESOURCES

6.11 As noted, there is sufficient (although not comprehensive nor detailed) evidence establishing the fact that the productive potential of at least part of the world's land and water resources is being degraded by agricultural activity (e.g. soil erosion, waterlogging and salinization of irrigated lands). In addition, agricultural activity generates other adverse environmental impacts (e.g. the threat to biological diversity and the pollution of surface and groundwater sources). While recognizing that agricultural activity often contributes to maintaining or restoring the productive capacity of land and water resources, responding to the problem of resource degradation requires a framework of reflection on why human activity may end up destroying rather than preserving or enhancing this capacity. This is attempted below.

6.12 The most commonly held view is that these processes are somehow related to continuing demographic growth in two ways. First, more food must be produced, and this tends to draw into agricultural use land and water resources not previously so used and/or causes such resources to be used more intensively. Both possibilities may generate adverse impacts on the quality of the resources themselves as well as on the broader environment. Second, in many developing countries, population growth is accompanied by increases in the number of poor persons living off the exploitation of agricultural resources with the consequence that the amount of resources per person declines.

6.13 In the normal course of events, the decline in per caput resources would tend to increase their value to the persons concerned (often being their main or only income-earning asset) and would lead to their more efficient use, including maintenance and improvement of their productive potential. The fact that much of the agricultural resource base has been improved for agricultural use by human activity in the historical period is testimony to this process. Yet it is often observed that under certain conditions this caring relationship tends to break down, with the result that people destroy rather than conserve and improve the productive potential of the resources.

6.14 Understanding why this happens is the most important insight needed for policy responses to promote sustainable development. When this destructive relationship is observed in conditions of poverty, it is commonly taken for granted that poverty explains the behaviour of people *vis-à-vis* the resources. The hypothesized mechanism works (in economic parlance) in view of the shortening of the time horizon of the poor. In plain language, this means that, in conditions of abject poverty, the need for survival today takes high precedence over considerations of survival for tomorrow. The poor simply do not have sufficient means to provide for today and also invest in resource conservation and improvement to provide for tomorrow.

6.15 However, this proposition is far from being a sufficiently complete explanation of processes at work useful for formulating policy responses. For one thing, there is plenty of empirical evidence to show that this process is not at work in many situations of poverty. The Machakos district of Kenya provides an example of change towards more sustainable exploitation of poor agricultural resources under conditions of poverty and growing demographic pressure. For another, it is often observed that agricultural resource degradation occurs also when such resources are exploited by the non-poor (a matter discussed below). It also occurs, and often more so, in conditions where poverty is declining rather than increasing, for example, when the opening up of income-earning opportunities outside agriculture leads to the abandonment (because they are no longer worth it) of elaborate resource conservation practices, such as the maintenance of terraces to conserve small, poor-quality land patches on hillsides, etc.

6.16 It follows from the above that more complex processes are at work and that the simple correlation between poverty and environmental degradation can be an oversimplification. This is well recognized, and research work on understanding the role of other variables that influence the relationship between poverty and environmental degradation can provide valuable insights. Such work emphasizes, for example: the vital importance of institutions governing access to resources (e.g. to common property or open-access resources) and how such institutions come under pressure when population density increases; inequality of access to land and landlessness; policies that distort incentives to use technology that would contribute to resource conservation, e.g. by depressing the output/fertilizer price ratio and making fertilizer use uneconomic where increased use is vital for the prevention of soil mining; and the knock-on effects of policies that facilitate interactions between the non-poor and the poor in ways that lead to degradation, such as when deforestation and expansion of agriculture are facilitated by incentives to logging operations that open access roads into, and make possible agricultural settlement of, previously inaccessible forest areas that may have soils that cannot easily sustain crop production.

6.17 Understanding the role of these and other mediating variables and getting away from the simple notion that degradation can be explained by poverty alone is important for formulating and implementing policies for sustainable agriculture and resource conservation. It is important because the policy environment in the future will continue to be characterized by pressures on agricultural resources related, in one way or another, to rural poverty. Indeed, the numbers of rural poor depending on the exploitation of agricultural resources will probably increase further in some countries, although they may decline in others. It was noted earlier that both processes can be associated with resource degradation. Therefore, the key policy problem is how to minimize the adverse environmental impacts of both processes.

6.18 Poverty-related degradation of agricultural resources is only part of the story. It is well known that part of the degradation process is related to the actions of people who are not in the poor category. This issue has two aspects. The first aspect has to do with consumption levels and patterns of the non-poor, in both the developed and the developing countries. For example, some 30 percent of world cereals output is used as animal feed and a good part of the production of soybean and other oilseeds is also related to livestock production. Most of the livestock output produced in concentrate-feeding systems is consumed by the medium- and high-income sectors of society. To the extent that the production of cereals and oilseeds causes degradation (as indeed it does in some places, although not in others), it can be said that part of the degradation is caused by actions of the rich, not the poor. It would perhaps be more correct to say that it is caused by interactions between the rich and poor.

6.19 The second aspect has to do with the fact that resource degradation is also associated with agricultural practices of farmers who are not poor. Soil erosion believed to be associated with some of the grain production in North America is a case in point; excessive fertilizer and other agrochemical use in Europe is another; and effluents from intensive livestock operations are in the same category. These are all examples of actions by the non-poor with adverse environmental effects. It all goes to show that associating resource degradation with poverty addresses only part of the issue.

6.20 In the end, the focus of policy has to recognize that resource degradation has different consequences for different countries and population groups. For the poor countries, the consequences can be very serious because their welfare depends heavily on the productive potential of their agricultural resources. Therefore, from a purely developmental and conventional welfare standpoint, it is right that preoccupation with resource degradation problems focuses primarily on the developing countries. At the same time, it must be recognized that resource degradation not only in the developing countries but anywhere on the planet, particularly in the major food-exporting developed countries, can render more difficult the solution of the food security problems of the poor if it reduces the global food production potential. Therefore, controlling resource degradation in the rich countries assumes priority even in strategies focused primarily on the food security of the poor; and this is irrespective of the fact that the welfare of the rich countries, as conventionally measured by, for example, per caput incomes, may not be seriously threatened by moderate degradation of their own resources. There are, of course, other compelling reasons why the rich countries give high priority to controlling degradation of their own resources as an objective in its own right.

FUTURE DIMENSIONS

6.21 The projections to 2010 of production, land use and yields presented in this paper indicate rather modest expansion of land in agricultural use and further intensification (double cropping, reduced fallows and higher yields). As noted, in the past these processes have often been associated with resource degradation and wider environmental problems. Therefore, to the question of whether or not agricultural development will be, or can be made, sustainable in the period up to 2010, the broad answer can only be that the forces, briefly surveyed in this section, that generated unsustainable outcomes in the past cannot be assumed to disappear overnight. It follows that, at least for some time, the world will have to accept trade-offs between more production and the provision of means of sustenance for the growing rural population on the one hand and the need to preserve the ecosystem and avoid resource degradation on the other. This notwithstanding, there is much that can be done to minimize such trade-offs and set the stage for putting agriculture on a more sustainable development path. Selected examples are given here:

- The area under crop production can be increased by the projected 90 million ha while at the same time containing tropical deforestation, which in the 1980s amounted to 15 million ha per year. Policy, institutional and more general development failures in the past led to agricultural expansion having been associated with more deforestation than would have been the case otherwise. Correcting these failures, admittedly no small task, holds promise of containing further deforestation to the minimum necessary.

- The adverse effects on the environment of the increased use of fertilizers and pesticides can be minimized if the process of intensification is carefully managed in the context of the potential offered by approaches such as Integrated Plant Nutrition Systems (IPNS) and Integrated Pest Management (IPM). It is noted, however, that enhanced fertilizer use is a necessary ingredient in the move towards more sustainability in areas where too little fertilizer use is associated with nutrient mining and soil degradation. This is the case in many countries of sub-Saharan Africa, and the risk here is that the economic and policy environment may continue to be hostile to the adoption of practices to prevent soil nutrient mining.

- In a similar vein, there is scope for the enhanced pressures on freshwater resources from agriculture as well as from industrial and urban uses to be accommodated, at least in part, by the more efficient use of the resource, which, in many cases, is dismally low. It remains to be seen if the policy, economic and institutional environment can adapt fast enough to relax the constraints resulting from the increased scarcity of freshwater supplies.

6.22 The preceding are just a few examples of aspects of the sustainability (or unsustainability) of agricultural development and the need and options for policy responses to minimize trade-offs that appear to be unavoidable for some time. More examples (e.g. desertification, soil erosion, etc.) are not discussed in the interests of keeping this paper brief. But some reference needs to be made to the mutual impacts of agriculture and aspects of the global environment:

- Expansion and intensification of agriculture will contribute to intensified pressures on the global environment. In addition to adversely affecting the productive and protective functions of forests, deforestation will affect their role as habitats for biological diversity and as major carbon sinks. Biological diversity will also probably suffer from possible further draining of wetlands for conversion to agriculture, even though this conversion may affect only a minor proportion of total wetlands. Additionally, agriculture will continue to contribute to the growth of greenhouse gases in the atmosphere (biomass burning in the process of deforestation and methane emissions from rice cultivation and from ruminant livestock).

- The eventual impacts of climate change on the physical parameters of agriculture (temperature, rainfall, variability, impact on yields) are still uncertain, but, based on present evidence, they may affect particularly adversely those regions already vulnerable to climate variation, notably sub-Saharan Africa. The effects of an eventual rise in the sea level would also be severe for some countries and a good part of their high-quality land resources would suffer. At present, increased carbon dioxide levels appear to have a positive effect on agriculture in general, and will continue to do so in the immediate future, because they contribute to higher yields through faster growth of plant biomass and better water utilization in many crops. However, the socio-economic and food security effects of these eventual changes will ultimately depend on the state of development the countries affected will have reached at that time. It is reasonable to predict that, if today's low-income countries in the latitudes that may be adversely affected by climate change were still low-income with widespread poverty and undernutrition and highly dependent on their agriculture in the longer-term future, the adverse effects on their food security would be severe. Obviously this need not be the case. If these countries had reached by then higher levels of development, they would be less dependent on agriculture and have enhanced resilience to withstand shocks. Thus, they would be in a position to better defend themselves in a world environment with increased trade, unless, of course, the effects of climate change on agriculture were to be catastrophic on a global scale. But this will probably not occur, as the productive potential of the northern latitudes may actually be enhanced by rising temperatures.

6.23 Finally, the concerns and the debate about the longer-term prospects should be informed by some fundamental facts: the growth rate of world population is on the decline (1.5 percent per annum from 1990 to 1995, expected to fall to 1.0 percent per annum from 2020 to 2025 and further to 0.5 percent per annum from 2045 to 2050); even the annual absolute increases in world population are about to peak at about 90 million in the next five years, after which they may start declining, but very slowly, to 80 million from 2020 to 2025 and down to 50 million from 2045 to 2050 (United Nations medium variant projection); and more and more countries will be achieving medium-high levels of per caput food consumption, beyond which the scope for further increases is diminished accordingly.

6.24 All these possible developments point to the need for agricultural production to grow at declining rates, and, therefore, the buildup of pressures from this origin on resources and the environment will become less intense. At the same time, if development takes hold in the low-income countries, environmental conservation will be edging higher in the priorities of people, while the means for investing in it will also be less scarce. It remains to be seen if the world can tread a sustainable path to this stage of easing of pressures of agricultural origin on resources and the environment. There is no assurance that this will be so if development failures continue to plague numerous countries as they do at present.

7. Conclusions

7.1 In conclusion, the longer-term food security future of humanity need not be bleak if action is taken now to: first, bring about the needed changes in the political, policy and institutional factors responsible for development failures and protracted mass poverty; second, invest in infrastructure and technology generation and diffusion to enhance the productive potential of agriculture in sustainable ways; and, third, address the population-development problem in accordance with the Programme of Action of the 1994 International Conference on Population and Development.

7.2 Is this message, that humanity has the potential to take action to make progress towards resolving the world's food security problems, overly optimistic? It could be put in the negative: "... the long-term food security future of humanity will be bleak if action is not taken now ...". Whatever the formulation, this paper makes it clear that, in a business-as-usual scenario, severe food insecurity problems will persist for a long time. This is far from being an optimistic assessment, on the contrary; and the emphasis is on action to avert such an outcome. This is indeed what the World Food Summit is about.

7.3 As noted earlier, the world cereals markets have, over the last two years, been emanating signals (rising prices) that the world balance between supply and effective demand has been deteriorating. It is, therefore, a legitimate question to ask whether or not even the limited progress foreseen for up to 2010 under the business-as-usual scenario presented in this paper can be achieved. In other words, have the fundamentals changed significantly? Since this question is raised mostly in relation to the decline in the growth rate of world cereals production, any attempt at an answer must involve comparing and analysing recent developments in production with what was implied for the mid-1990s by the *WAT2010* projections.

7.4 The broad conclusion made from the more precise discussion of this question in Box 2 is that, on balance, the recent production shortfalls and developments in the world markets provide no compelling reason for revising the cereals production levels projected for 2010 for the world and the major regions identified here. The principal factors responsible for the divergencies of actual outcomes from those implied by a smooth projection are reversible. But the risk of increased volatility can prove to be a more permanent structural change in the system, calling for appropriate policy responses.

7.5 The paramount food security problem in overall terms persists: the pace of improvement in raising the per caput food supplies (i.e. consumption) of the poor in the developing countries as a whole is too sluggish and the risk of outright stagnation or reversals in several of the most needy nations is a strong one.

Box 2
THE CEREALS SECTOR OUTLOOK TO 2010 SEEN FROM MID-1996

Developments from 1990 to 1995

The cereals projections of the FAO study *World agriculture: towards 2010 (WAT2010)* are presented in Table 5. World production was projected to be 2 334 million tonnes in 2010 compared with 1 679 million tonnes in the three-year average 1988-1990, the base years of the study. If world production had evolved along a smooth expansion path (but this was not what the study said, on the contrary), it should have reached a level of 1 840 million tonnes in 1995. In the end, world production was only 1 713 million tonnes in 1995 (or, more appropriately, 1 772 million tonnes in the three-year average 1994, 1995 and forecast 1996). This significant shortfall raises the question as to whether or not the level projected for 2010 is still a realistic one.

To answer this question, the evolution of production must be observed at a more disaggregated level. This is done in the Figure on p. 47, which distinguishes three country groups, two of the groups of developed countries in Table 5 and one for the developing countries as a whole. It is clearly seen that the world shortfall is mostly attributable to developments in the Eastern Europe and former Union of Soviet Socialist Republics (USSR) region and to a much lesser extent in the group "Other developed countries". The reasons for this shortfall and the implications for world market prices and stock levels were discussed earlier and are not repeated here.

It is also seen in the Figure that the actual production of the developing countries has been tracking very closely the projection trajectory; their net imports for the average of the latest two years (July/June 1994/95 and forecast 1995/96) are estimated to be 107 million tonnes, i.e. again close to what could be deduced from a smooth interpolation for 1995 along the net-imports trajectory of the study (from 90 million tonnes in 1988-1990 to 162 million tonnes in 2010). By implication, also their total cereals consumption (production plus net imports) has been evolving as indicated by the study.

Re-evaluating the world production outlook for 2010

The extent to which these recent developments will lead to any significant revisions of the above-indicated world cereals production projections for 2010 depends on whether any or all of the factors behind the production shortfalls in recent years (reforms in the former centrally planned economies, weather shocks, policy reforms in the major exporting countries leading to lower publicly held stocks) can be considered to be in the nature of a permanent structural change in the fundamentals of the world cereals economy, naturally beyond the changes already incorporated in the projections. Obviously, the production declines in the Eastern Europe and the former USSR region are not in that category. It can be fairly safely assumed that the eventual recovery will put the region on a trajectory that would lead its production to be near the just over 300 million tonnes projected for 2010 (Table 5). However, part of the declines in the region's apparent consumption (mostly in feed and waste) are likely to prove permanent and this would lead to the emergence of the region as a small net exporter, compared with its status as a large net importer in the pre-reform period, as foreseen by the study.

Box 2 *(continued)*

There is no hard evidence that weather-induced production shortfalls are likely to be more frequent in the future than in the past, nor that weather may affect the foreseen trend in production *per se*. Therefore, there is no compelling reason to assume that the projected world production for 2010 (to be understood as an average of at least three years) needs to be revised for this reason alone.

Finally, whatever the pattern of weather fluctuations in the future, their importance for world markets must be examined in conjunction with the third above-mentioned factor, i.e. the policy reforms away from the production of surpluses and towards reduced publicly held stocks in major exporting countries. This is indeed a factor that may prove to be a permanent structural change in the fundamentals of the world cereals economy. There is at least a risk that for this reason the world cereals markets could become more volatile in the future, despite the stabilizing effect of an increasingly liberalized trading system. The magnitude of this risk is a moot point at the moment, but it is the subject, together with the required measures to safeguard world food security, of particular concern to FAO.

Figure
ACTUAL VERSUS PROJECTED CEREALS PRODUCTION (WITH RICE IN MILLED EQUIVALENT)

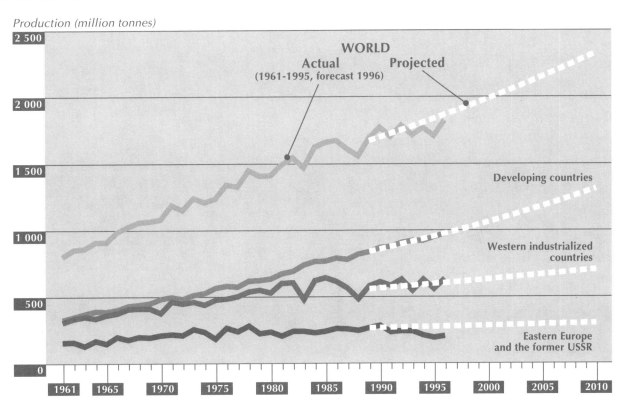

Source: 1961-1995 data, FAOSTAT; 1996 forecast, *Food outlook*; 1988/90-2010 projections from *World agriculture: towards 2010 (WAT2010)*, (FAO, 1995), p. 145-150.

Bibliography

Alexandratos, N. 1996. China's future cereals deficits in a world context. *Agric. Econ.* (In press)

FAO. 1992. *Nutrition and development, a global assessment.* Rome.

FAO. 1995. *World agriculture: towards 2010.* N. Alexandratos, ed. Rome, FAO and, Chichester, UK, John Wiley. (Published also in French by Polytechnica, Paris, and in Spanish by Mundi-Prensa Libros, Madrid and Mexico.)

FAO. 1996. *The sixth world food survey.* Rome.

Lewis, W.A. 1953. *Report on industrialization and the Gold Coast.* Government Printing Office, Accra,Ghana.

United Nations. 1974. *Assessment of world food situation, present and future.* World Food Conference Document E/CONF. 65/3. New York, NY, USA, United Nations.

United Nations. 1991. *World population prospects 1990.* Population Studies No. 120. New York, NY, USA, United Nations.

United Nations. 1993. *World population prospects: the 1992 revision.* New York, NY, USA, United Nations.

United Nations. 1994. *World population prospects: the 1994 revision.* Annex tables. New York, NY, USA, United Nations.

World Bank. 1996. *Global economic prospects and the developing countries, 1996.* Washington, DC, World Bank.

2
Success stories in food security

Contents

Acknowledgements

The preparation of the World Food Summit technical background documents (TBDs) has mobilized, in addition to FAO's own staff contribution, a considerable amount of expertise in the international scientific community, drawn from partner international institutions and governmental or non-governmental circles. The process has been monitored at FAO by an internal Reading Committee, composed of staff selected ad personam *and established to ensure that the whole collection meets appropriate quality and consistency criteria.*

The present document has been edited by FAO's A.A. Gürkan and K. Stamoulis using contributions elicited from K. Savadogo and T. Reardon (Burkina Faso); J.Y. Lin (China); A.A. Buainain (Costa Rica and Ecuador); N.S. Randhawa (India, Indonesia and Thailand); D. Tschirley and M.T. Weber (Mozambique); M. Allaya (Tunisia); H. Kasnakoglu (Turkey); B. Weisel (Zimbabwe); T.S. Jayne, L. Rubey, M. Chisva and M.T. Weber (Zimbabwe); and M.M. Mamba (southern Africa). After initial review within the Reading Committee, the case-studies were circulated to peer reviewers in the countries included in the study. Much appreciated comments and advice have been received from J. Mora (Costa Rica), F. Recalde (Ecuador), C. Gopalan (India), A. Valyasevi and A. Siamwalla (Thailand), T. Jaouadi (Tunisia), A. Eryilmaz (Turkey) and M. Smulders (Zimbabwe and southern Africa).

While grateful for the contributions received from all reviewers, the FAO Secretariat bears responsibility for the content of the document.

Executive summary

This paper provides a sample of country experiences in improving food security. Each example summarizes the major food security issues specific to the case and analyses briefly the various approaches adopted through time to tackle them. Most of the countries presented have realized significant and sustained betterment in the national level of food availability and household food security since the early 1960s. A few others provide an occasion to illustrate achievements in certain aspects of food security, although not exhibiting a general improvement in average food availability or household food security. Finally, an example of a successful international effort to prevent a major food security crisis in southern Africa illustrates the nature of actions that can avert widespread famine following a natural disaster.

FAO's Committee on World Food Security defined its objective as ensuring "that all people at all times have both the physical and economic access to the basic food they need". To this end, it was recognized that three conditions need to be met: ensuring adequacy of food supply or availability, ensuring stability of supply and ensuring access to food at the household level, particularly by the poor. The International Conference on Nutrition in 1992 added a nutrition dimension in expressing the objective that "all people at all times have access to safe and nutritious food to maintain a healthy and active life".

If it were possible to differentiate the effects of sanitation, health and care from those of food security, indicators of nutritional status would provide the most direct way of assessing the status of food security at the individual level. However, given the severe restrictions on data related to the phenomenon, per caput food availability (known as the average daily energy supply, or DES) and measures based on FAO estimates of proportions of the population who are chronically undernourished are used as the main indicators of food (in)security in this paper.

Burkina Faso fully realized its vulnerability in the wake of the drought spell that hit the Sahelian zone from the late 1960s to the mid-1970s. Since then, a mix of policy measures, including macroeconomic policies (the restructuring of public finance), soil conservation and water harvesting, new land settlement, household-level income generating and transfer measures, have been successful in curbing food insecurity and promoting human welfare. Indeed, despite the extensive variability over the years in both DES and food production, since the early 1990s the household food security situation in the country has improved significantly.

China is highly acclaimed for its ability to feed over one-fifth of the global population with only one-fifteenth of the world's arable land. Starting from a level of 1 500 Calories at the beginning of the 1960s, China had increased average DES to over 2 700 Calories by the early 1990s, achieving this almost exclusively through increases in domestic production. The Chinese experience, especially the post-1978 reforms, demonstrates the importance of incentives and of a conducive institutional framework in maximizing the effects of agricultural infrastructure, as well as of research on new technologies and their successful dissemination.

Costa Rica has steadily improved its food security over the past 30 years. Part of the reason for this has been the strong policy emphasis on anti-poverty. Although macroeconomic problems led to policy adjustments that reduced the production of some traditional crops, the shift in emphasis to export-driven growth allowed financing of food imports which facilitated progress in improving average DES, currently close to 3 000 Calories.

In Ecuador, where the main indicators of food security show substantial improvement over the last three decades, per caput food production and availability have developed along a cyclical path similar to that of macroeconomic indicators and policies. The impact of changing macroeconomic and sectoral policies was especially strong on per caput food supply, which declined under increasing macro imbalances prior to the 1980s and has significantly improved with the implementation of stabilization and structural policies since then.

India is considered a low-income country with a per caput gross national product (GNP) of approximately US$300. It has had an economic growth of around 5.2 percent per annum since the early 1980s, three points above the average annual population growth for the same period. Despite rather wide variability in food availability since the 1960s, India has maintained a determined effort to develop domestic food production, reduce aid dependency and improve household food security throughout this period. DES currently stands at only 2 400 Calories and the prevalence of poverty is still high, but extensive use of targeted anti-poverty measures has reduced vulnerability to famines and preserved a minimum status of food security even in poorer areas of the country.

Indonesia, where economic growth has been strong in the past two decades, has pursued a successful policy of self-sufficiency in rice, the major food staple of the country, since the late 1960s. This has been successful in achieving food security, as DES increased from just under 2 000 Calories by that time to around 2 700 by the early 1990s, and the status of household food security improved significantly. Part of the success can be attributed to the holistic approach to agricultural policy adopted by the government so that marketing interventions were complemented by research, dissemination and provision of high-yielding varieties of rice and requisite modern input packages.

Mozambique, after nearly a decade of economic liberalization, and only four years after the country's devastating civil war, remains among the poorest countries in the world. Hunger is a stark fact of life for large numbers of households. Yet this should not hide the promising progress made in recent years towards sustainable food security, which can be seen in increased DES despite rapid dramatic reductions in food aid; lower and more stable prices for the principal domestically produced staple, white maize; and a food system that now provides consumers with a broader range of low-cost staples from which to choose.

Thailand's use of macroeconomic stability, an outward-looking development strategy and universal primary education, among other ingredients, allowed its economy to grow at about 7 percent per annum over three decades. While food production growth paralleled overall economic development, neither DES nor household food security improved to the same extent. In fact DES hovered above 2 000 Calories until the late 1980s, but had not yet reached 2 500 Calories by the early 1990s. The increased production has been made possible by extensive land expansion without a substantial improvement at the intensive margin.

Increasing intensity, tackling environmental threats, improving diversity and addressing rural poverty remain important policy objectives towards sustainable food security.

Tunisia has undergone rapid food security improvement since the beginning of the 1960s, thanks to a sound underlying economic and social process significantly influenced by public action. DES increases, from about 2 000 Calories at that time to nearly 3 500 today, were achieved essentially through food imports because of severe natural constraints affecting agricultural production. With extensive social safety nets at the household level, it has been possible to translate increased food availability into improved food security for much of the population.

Turkey is one country in this paper that has maintained a relatively high level of food availability and security throughout the period reviewed. Most of the achievements in this respect took place prior to the 1960s, with extensive government intervention in all aspects of the most important agricultural markets. Currently, food security problems relate to achieving a nutritionally balanced diet rather than to energy availabilities. Despite increased efforts to liberalize agricultural markets, reducing public intervention continues to be difficult, placing considerable strain on government budget and general price levels.

Zimbabwe did not witness significant improvements in average food availability and household food security over the past three decades, which placed the country among those still vulnerable. Productivity in the food sector has been on the decline since the early 1970s, and especially in the 1980s as a result of changing agricultural policies. More recently, structural changes in the marketing of maize, the principal food crop, removed some of the constraints on the markets, resulting in substantial betterment for the food security of the most vulnerable population groups through reduction in the prices of the staple food crop.

Southern Africa has periodically been wrecked by droughts, most recently in 1991/92 and 1994/95. The 1991/92 drought, in particular, which devastated the subregion's agricultural production and induced unprecedented import requirements, will probably be remembered as the worst for several decades. During this disaster, the subregion experienced a reduction of aggregate food crop production of up to 50 percent less than the normal output. The cereal deficit of the subregion more than doubled and some 18 million people were facing the spectre of starvation. Efficient early warning, rapid regional coordination and adequate international support resulted in a successful relief effort, avoiding widespread food shortages and famine.

These case-studies illustrate the importance of the policy environment in shaping the economic and social processes that ultimately determine the food security status of the people in any country. Where implemented, direct measures aimed at the vulnerable have proved their worth, but the multiplicity of policy objectives pursued within any setting must be politically, socially and economically feasible in order to succeed. For most of the countries reviewed, the 1980s was an era when financial and economic constraints were most binding. In countries that reduced protection to the agricultural and food sector, the transition has been painful during the initial phases, with food insecurity increasing. Whatever the appropriate policy, however, establishing safety nets for the vulnerable, and preserving them in times of economic hardship, continues to be an indispensable component for alleviating food insecurity.

1. Introduction

1.1. This paper provides a sample of country experiences in improving food security. Each country example summarizes the major food security issues specific to the case and analyses briefly the various approaches adopted over time to tackle them. Most of the countries selected for presentation have achieved significant and sustained betterment in the national level of food availability and household food security since 1961, or currently enjoy high levels of food security. Others illustrate achievements in certain aspects of food security, although not exhibiting a general improvement in average food availability or household food security. Finally, an example of a successful international effort to prevent a major food security crisis in southern Africa illustrates the nature of actions that can avert widespread famine following a natural disaster.

1.2 Chapter 2 discusses the conceptual framework of food security in the context of development strategies. It also reviews the question of characterizing the status of, and progress in, food security through appropriate measurement. Against this backdrop, the survey of specific country experiences is given in Chapter 3, with a summary and conclusions provided in Chapter 4.

2. Food security issues at the country level

2.1 The conceptual framework for food security has undergone considerable evolution, reflecting the changes in perception over time of the world food problem as a whole. In the aftermath of the world food crisis of the early 1970s, the concept of food security was closely linked to the view that food security for individual countries could be ensured if larger grain stocks were available globally and if fluctuations in international grain prices could be contained within reasonable limits.

2.2 Thus, in the strategy recommended by the World Food Conference in 1974, laid out in the *International undertaking on world food security*, special emphasis was placed on maintaining the stability of supplies to ensure the physical availability of food in the event of widespread crop failure, and particularly in order to sustain levels of consumption in the most vulnerable countries. The undertaking envisaged internationally coordinated, nationally held stocks as well as food aid programmes and other measures, including long-term trade agreements. At the same time, the undertaking recognized that, in a broad sense, the attainment of world food security depends on the growth of food production, particularly in the low-income food-deficit countries (LIFDCs).

2.3 While food production at the global level has kept pace with, and even surpassed, population growth over the years, the food supply-demand gap and, as a consequence, hunger and malnutrition persist on a large scale, especially in the LIFDCs. Given the background to the present world food security situation, the Committee on World Food Security (CFS), at its eighth session in 1983, reappraised the concept of food security and adopted a broadened concept. According to this broadened concept, "The ultimate objective of world food security should be to ensure that all people at all times have both physical and economic access to the basic food they need"(FAO, 1983). To achieve this objective, it was recognized that three conditions would need to be fulfilled: ensuring adequacy or availability of food supply; ensuring stability of supply; and ensuring access to food at the household level, particularly by the poor.

2.4 The International Conference on Nutrition (ICN), held in 1992, added a nutrition dimension, expressing the objective that "all people at all times have access to safe and nutritious food to maintain a healthy and active life", which is the concept most widely recognized at present. In addition, concern that the drive for accelerated food production across the world should not lead to degradation of natural resources and the environment has meant that this goal should be achieved "without compromising the productive capacity of natural resources, the integrity of biological systems, or environmental quality".[1]

---

[1] FAO/UNDP Cooperative Agreement, September 1994.

2.5 For the purposes of analysis, the processes that underlie nutritional well-being can be broken down into separate subsystems that respectively determine the quantity, quality and nature of food that a household has access to; its allocation among the individuals belonging to the household; its intake by the individual; and its subsequent physiological utilization. The first two constitute household food security, while the last two are related more to factors such as sanitation, health and care. These interdependent subsystems are influenced by a common set of technological, economic, social, political, legal and cultural processes, which are parts of development in its broadest sense. Indeed, whatever the immediate causes of undernutrition and household food insecurity, the factors that hinder their improvement are basically the same as those hindering poverty alleviation and development.

2.6 The majority of the world's food insecure and poor live and earn their living in the rural areas of the developing world, where agricultural activity makes a substantial contribution to their daily subsistence and where most produce food directly to meet some of their own nutritional needs, despite the accelerated urbanization observed in most of the developing countries. Moreover, in the least developed among these countries, employment and income opportunities in all sectors, not just in agriculture, are significantly limited by the level of agricultural productivity, the relative endowments of natural resources and the availability of human-made physical capital and economic, social and institutional infrastructure in the rural areas. In order to allow the realization of the full productive potential of rural people and to eradicate pockets of food insecurity and poverty that exist in rural areas, it is necessary to eliminate inequities in the distribution of land, income and political power, to provide education and training and to bring down barriers to access to inputs, services and markets. These measures are likely to address some of the problems of urban food-insecure people as well, by easing rural-urban migration pressures and expanding demand for non-agricultural goods, etc., although specific policies will continue to be needed to alleviate the food insecurity and poverty of the rapidly growing number of vulnerable people in urban areas.

2.7 Provided that it is possible to differentiate between the effects of sanitation, health and care and those of household food security, indicators of nutritional status can provide the most direct way of assessing the status of food security at the household level. In this respect, the best measure is obtained from direct surveys of dietary intake, used in conjunction with appropriate adequacy norms. These surveys are usually expensive and not readily available, especially in those regions and countries where vulnerability is the greatest. However, there are rough methods of estimating the number of people who are likely to be deficient in certain required food components at the country level. These estimates usually proxy, not the incidence of food security, but the incidence of food deficiency, since they do not take into account those who may not necessarily be food deficient but nevertheless are exposed to a relatively large risk of becoming food deficient because of fluctuations in availability and affordability of food (FAO, 1996a).

2.8 FAO has developed an aggregate household food security index (AHFSI) based on the work of Sen (1976) and Bigman (1993), which attempts to incorporate directly all of the three elements of food security mentioned earlier, namely, availability and stability of food supplies and access to food (see Box 1 for technical details). It has also introduced an intuitively more appealing indicator that measures the extent of inadequacy in food availability at the country level (see Box 2 for a more detailed definition), utilizing FAO estimates of the prevalence of the chronically undernourished. These two measures, combined with those of food availability obtained from food balance sheets, provide the background that threads together the policy experiences of the individual countries in so far as they have influenced the economic and social determinants of food security.

Box 1
THE AGGREGATE HOUSEHOLD FOOD SECURITY INDEX

The aggregate household food security index (AHFSI) uses FAO estimates of the prevalence of undernutrition in developing countries as its basis and combines these with measures of the extent of the food gap of the undernourished from national average requirements for dietary energy, the inequality in the distribution of food gaps and instability in the annual availability of dietary energy, which is a rather crude indicator of the risk of food deficiency at the aggregate level. The methods used in calculating the prevalence of undernourishment (see FAO, 1996a for detailed explanations) reflect only the number of chronically undernourished, who on average in the course of a year have a food intake below that required to maintain body weight and support light activity. People who are affected by seasonal and acute food insecurity are not directly taken into account, although the inclusion of a measure of variability in food availability may, to a certain extent, represent the risk being faced in the country.

The form of the index is:

$$AHFSI = 100 - [H(G+(1-G)I^p) + \frac{1}{2}\sigma\{1 - H(G+(1-G)I^p)\}]100,$$

where:
   H is the head count ratio, which measures the proportion of the undernourished in the total population, expressing the extent of undernourishment;
   G is the food gap, which measures the proportion of shortfall of the average daily dietary energy intake of the undernourished from average national nutritional requirements, expressing the depth of undernourishment;
   I^p is a measure of inequality in the distribution of the food gaps;
   σ is the coefficient of variation in dietary energy supplies, measuring the likelihood of facing temporary food insecurity.

The values of AHFSI range from 0 to 100, the higher values representing higher levels of food security. It should be noted that AHFSI is essentially an ordinal index. Thus, it is difficult to attach an intuitive meaning to any particular value, except its two extreme values.

Box 2
EXPLANATION OF THE STANDARD DIAGRAMS USED IN EACH COUNTRY CASE-STUDY

In order to link the food security histories briefly told for each selected country, two standard diagrams are presented, constructed on the basis of data collated by FAO. One of the diagrams summarizes the salient features of the food balance sheets generated by FAO, based on data furnished by its members. For purposes of exposition, production, apparent consumption, total use and imports of all reported food crops are weighted by their respective energy content, aggregated and then normalized by estimates of total population, to generate time series in units of Calories per caput per day for the period 1961-1992.

The other diagram reports the values of two similar composite indexes that measure the status of food security in the countries concerned for three distinct periods: 1969-1971, 1979-1981 and 1990-1992. The first of the indices is the AHFSI, which is described in detail in Box 1. Based on estimates reported by FAO (1994a), countries having an AHFSI above 85 are considered to enjoy a high level of food security. There were 25 countries reported to be in this category. Seven countries had AHFSI values below 65 and were thereby considered to have critically low levels of food security. A further 35 countries, having an index between 75 and 65, were considered as having low levels of food security. The remaining 26 countries were considered as having medium levels of food security.

The second of the indexes is more intuitive and measures food inadequacy (FA) in a country (FAO, 1996a), which is defined as:

$$FA = \left[\frac{P_{UNNUR}(C_{AVREQ} - C_{AVUNNUR})}{P_{TOTAL}C_{AVAVAIL}} \right] 100$$

where:

P_{UNNUR} is the number of undernourished individuals;

P_{TOTAL} is the total population;

C_{AVREQ} is the average Calorie requirement norm;

$C_{AVUNNUR}$ is the average availability of Calories for the undernourished in the population;

$C_{AVAVAIL}$ is the average Calorie availability.

As can be seen, the measure takes into account not only the head count measure of undernutrition but also the food gap of the undernourished. It expresses, in percentage terms, the extent of total Calories needed to bring all the undernourished people in the population up to a certain level, assuming perfect targeting.

3. Summaries of country experiences in food security

3.1 No country can claim that it has completely eliminated chronic hunger and food insecurity. Therefore, there is as yet no country that can present itself as an example of complete success in this regard. Even if it were possible to find such a country, the paths followed to success are not likely to be replicated in, or appropriate to, other countries, given the complexity of the food security problem already mentioned and the diversity of its dimensions, causes and consequences. Yet despite this, the discovery of significant, and indeed meaningful, general consistencies at the global level linking status of food security and level of economic and social development suggests that there may be many success stories to be told.

3.2 Successes may be about specific experiences of countries in improving certain, but not necessarily all, aspects of their food security, and they can be accompanied by shortcomings in other aspects, sometimes being involved even in trade-offs with competing objectives not necessarily related to immediate food security considerations. This section of the paper tells the success stories about the food security experiences of a selected set of countries, highlighting wherever necessary shortcomings and even outright failures that can prove to be as instructive.

3.3 The collection of country cases presented illustrates policy experiences in large and small countries from different regions and with varied policy orientations, where domestic production, commercial imports and food aid play different roles in ensuring food security and where there is high or low economic dependence on agriculture.

BURKINA FASO[2]

3.4 Achieving food security has become a major goal of Burkina Faso. The vulnerability of the country to weather conditions was fully manifested in the wake of the drought that hit the Sahel region from the late 1960s to the mid-1970s. Since then, a variety of policy measures have been taken to address the problem including macro policies (the restructuring of public finance), policies for soil conservation and water harvesting, new land settlements, household-level income-generation policies and transfers. Such measures have been successful in curbing food insecurity and improving human welfare.

3.5 The daily per caput energy availability at the national level over the 1961-1992 period averaged close to 1 800 Calories, with a moderate annual growth (0.9 percent), but was also marked by important swings. Three periods can be discerned. From 1961 to 1967, there was a small rise in per caput energy availability. This was followed by a declining trend over 1968-1974, the main

[2] This section is an edited and condensed version of FAO (1996c).

Sahel drought period. An upward trend is visible over the 1975-1991 period, with strong year-to-year fluctuations (Figure 1). These underlying developments in food availability closely follow those of the productivity of rural labour. Total cereal production per person living from agriculture, for example, has increased from about 180 kg in 1961 to over 300 kg in 1991, albeit with substantial year-to-year fluctuations.

3.6 However, since the early 1970s (post-drought period) the importance of food imports has also increased, reflecting in part the changing consumption patterns of urban consumers towards rice and wheat. Over the whole period, the contribution of domestic production to the growth in food availability is slightly more than one-half, only marginally higher than the contribution of imports. Commercial imports (mainly of rice and wheat) have shown the greatest variability, suggesting that they are the major variable that adjusts to keep total supply at the desired level. Future movements in the level of commercial imports will depend on income and price factors. Although the effect is not yet apparent, the recent (1994) devaluation of the national currency, together with price increases in world cereal markets, may lead to higher relative border prices and induce a reverse substitution of urban consumers towards domestic cereals. There is evidence of a strong supply response of rural production to higher prices provided that a conducive government policy in the area of inputs and infrastructure provision is in place (Saradogo, Reardon and Pietola, 1994).

3.7 Burkina Faso has a history of fairly low household food security. The AHFSI and the food inadequacy index (see Figure 2) indicate that, up until the beginning of the 1990s, Burkina Faso had severe food insecurity problems, with an energy deficit of nearly one-third of the national requirements. The situation since then has improved significantly and the country is no longer considered to have a critically low level of household food security, i.e. the value of AHFSI is nearly 70, with the food inadequacy level reduced to about one-tenth of the national requirements.[3]

3.8 The trend in food security identified above is the net result of many factors, the most important of which are: restructuring of public financing in favour of the rural sector; changes in agricultural sector and food security policies; and demographic factors and State-sponsored or spontaneous rural-to-rural migration.[4]

3.9 Over the 1983-1989 period, the government undertook major macroeconomic and sectoral policies aimed at restoring macroeconomic equilibria. A system of expenditure redistribution was implemented to allow the financing of sectoral programmes, including agriculture, while adhering to government deficit reduction targets. To reduce the deficit, budget cutting was mostly geared towards civil servants' salaries (60 percent of the total budget), leading to a cumulated savings over the 1984-1990 period of about CFAF 14 billion, or 4 percent of the CFAF 300 billion cumulated receipts over the same period (Zagré, 1992; Savadogo, 1994). The effect of the combined stabilization measures was to reduce the government budget deficit from CFAF 24.5 billion in 1984 to CFAF 4.5 billion in 1985, effectively enabling the financing of the rural sector as discussed below.

[3] It should be noted that vulnerability across the country is not uniform. According to International Crops Research Institute for the Semi-Arid Tropics (ICRISAT) data collected in 1985 (a good year), in the populous, agriculture-based but degraded central plateau, average per caput daily energy intake (2 000 Calories) is lower than in the northern, drought-prone and livestock-based Sahel region (3 200 Calories). Moreover, the variability, and hence vulnerability, is higher in the central plateau. The CEDRES data, ten years later, confirm the regional disparity, by comparing the central plateau and the most productive zone, the Sudano-Guinean zone. The annual average energy consumption of 2 900 Calories for the Guinean zone exceeds the 2 500 Calories in the central plateau. Overall, the micro data suggest higher energy access but are not out of range with the national data and underline the importance of both regional and seasonal dimensions in designing food security programmes.

[4] The period covered in this case-study (1961-1991) is prior to the 1991 signing of an adjustment programme with the International Monetary Fund (IMF)/World Bank, and therefore the potential impact of the changing macroeconomic environment on food security is not addressed. Likewise, the government has recently (1993) initiated specific food security, poverty-reducing programmes in selected rural areas that are supported by the World Bank. These income-generating activities target mainly women, on the assumption that female-controlled income is more likely to raise food security than is male-controlled income. It is however too early to assess the net impact of these programmes.

Figure 1
PER CAPUT FOOD AVAILABILITY – BURKINA FASO (1961-1992)

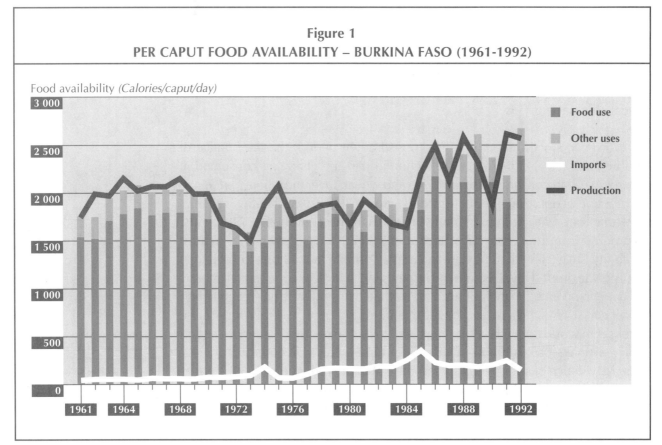

Figure 2
STATUS OF FOOD SECURITY AS MEASURED BY LEVEL OF FOOD INADEQUACY[a]
AND AHFSI[b] – BURKINA FASO

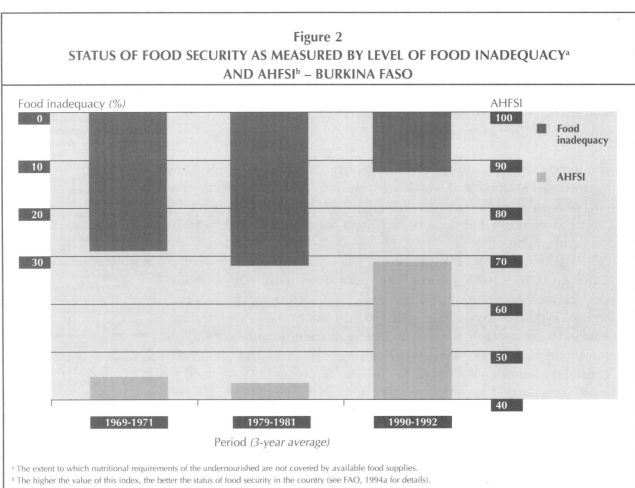

[a] The extent to which nutritional requirements of the undernourished are not covered by available food supplies.
[b] The higher the value of this index, the better the status of food security in the country (see FAO, 1994a for details).

3.10 As Burkina Faso suffered through the major drought years of the late 1960s to mid-1970s, an awareness at the political level of the vulnerability of the country to natural conditions developed, leading to an increasing policy effort to stabilize and increase land productivity. Soil conservation measures (primarily the use of manure and compost and the construction of stone dykes to reduce water runoff) were promoted through the provision of government trucks and food-for-work programmes. Although soil conservation measures were initiated in the 1960s, they were accelerated during the 1983-1989 self-imposed adjustment period (Sanders *et al.*, 1987; Savadogo and Wetta, 1992). The conservation policies led to increased yields on the degraded soils of the central plateau, thus increasing and stabilizing production (Cleaver, 1993).

3.11 With regard to demographic changes, the urban population has been increasing at a much higher rate than the rural population, while the latter has been characterized by important migrations from the low-potential central plateau to the southwestern areas. The consequence of an increasing urban population is a changing dietary pattern at the national level. Over the 1980s, the share of non-traditional cereals (rice and wheat) in total imported cereals has been growing at the expense of traditional cereals (sorghum and maize). The key demographic change, however, has been the massive migration from the overpopulated and low-potential central plateau to the more fertile but river blindness-infected agricultural land of the Volta River basins (south and southwest). Migrations had started early in the 1960s but were accelerated in the late 1970s to the early 1980s after the vector of river blindness, blackfly, was brought under control through a major public health programme sponsored by the World Health Organization (WHO) (McMillan and Savadogo, 1996). The need to claim new land was an immediate consequence of the 1968-1974 drought and was amplified by the major 1984 drought. Migrants were more willing to adopt improved technologies than indigenous people, which resulted in an increased agricultural output per person and per land unit at the national level (Savadogo, 1990).

3.12 Despite significant successes in food security as described above, household-level studies also reveal that seasonal food insecurity still prevails, raising the issue of an interseasonal food arbitrage. Because of the need for cash, households typically sell grain at harvest and have to repurchase when prices are higher. Off-farm income appears to be a way out of this vicious circle, but poor households in rural areas, which represent the primary food-insecure population group, are also poor in off-farm physical and financial assets. The non-agricultural income-generating programme initiated by the government in 1993 aims at addressing this issue by raising incomes and hence access to food.

CHINA[5]

3.13 China is highly acclaimed for its ability to feed over one-fifth of the world population with only one-fifteenth of the world's arable land. Starting from a level of 1 500 Calories per caput per day at the beginning of the 1960s, China increased food availability to over 2 700 Calories per caput per day by the beginning of the 1990s, achieving this almost exclusively through increases in domestic production. The Chinese experience, especially the post-1978 reforms, demonstrates the

[5] This is a condensed and edited version of Lin (1995).

importance of incentives and a conducive institutional framework in maximizing the effects of agricultural infrastructure, and of successful research on, and dissemination of, new technologies. Over the years, China has successfully met the challenge of achieving universal food security in the face of increasing population.

3.14 After the formation of the People's Republic of China in 1949, its war-torn agrarian economy was rebuilt through a development strategy oriented towards heavy industry. To facilitate the rapid capital accumulation necessary in the face of a low domestic savings rate, a policy of surplus transfer from agriculture to industry was implemented mainly by keeping wages for industrial workers at low levels. Such a policy made necessary the establishment of low prices for food, energy, transportation and other necessities. For food, this was achieved by compulsory grain procurement and strict food rationing policies.

3.15 However, a number of factors raised concerns about food security and prompted the pursuit of food self-sufficiency: increasing population, rising demand for food by the urban/industrial sectors, a severe famine that caused the death from malnutrition of millions of people between 1958 and 1961, and foreign exchange constraints. Such concerns prompted the government to adopt a strategy that would permit and foster the simultaneous development of agriculture and industry. For agriculture, the strategy consisted of a massive labour-intensive programme of investments in irrigation, land reclamation and flood control. At the same time, research and dissemination of high-yielding varieties (HYVs) and improved farming practices were promoted. Collectivized agriculture was considered to be the ideal system to coordinate such functions as well as to carry out the procurement of grain and other products deemed necessary for the implementation of the industrial development strategy (Lin, 1995).

3.16 The strategy was successful in so much as it allowed China to eliminate famine and feed its population at a reasonable level. Two nationwide food consumption surveys carried out in 1959 and 1982 show that both energy and protein intakes per caput increased in this period, energy from 2 060 to 2 485 Calories per caput per day and protein from 57 to 67 g per caput per day. Both increases were attributed to an increase in grain production, since a very high proportion of energy and protein is provided by cereals (71 percent of energy and 78 percent of protein, in 1982).

3.17 The developments in the food security situation in China are illustrated in Figure 3. Both food production and total food availability per caput followed similar paths, since food imports have been relatively small, averaging around 2.5 percent of per caput availability up to about the mid-1970s and around 3.5 percent since then. The widening gap between the availability of food for all uses and human consumption also reflects the changing structure of demand towards increasing meat consumption and thus of foodstuffs. The growth in per caput production of food energy averaged around 7 percent per annum between 1961 and 1966, declining sharply to approximately 3 percent since then (until 1992). During the intervening period, growth stagnated from 1967 to 1977, increased annually by about 6 percent from 1977 to 1984, and grew by less than 0.5 percent per annum between 1985 and 1992.

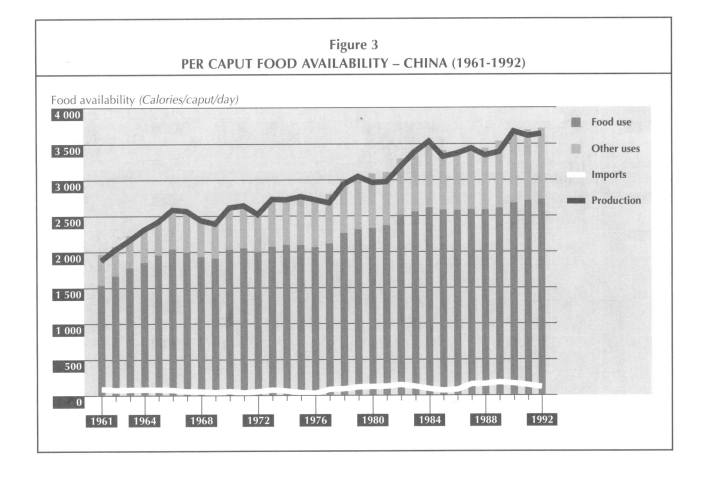

Figure 3
PER CAPUT FOOD AVAILABILITY – CHINA (1961-1992)

3.18 Taking distributional considerations into account, the household food security situation in the country from the beginning of the 1970s as measured by the AHFSI and the level of food inadequacy (see Figure 4) indicates a similar improvement to that observed for average food availability at the national level. From being considered a country with a low level of food security during 1969-1971, China has come close to being considered a country with a high level of food security. This is better illustrated with the more intuitive measure of food inadequacy, which essentially measures the depth and extent of undernourishment in the country. The total shortfall in energy requirements for the undernourished was nearly 15 percent at the beginning of the period considered, falling to below 5 percent in most recent years. This information is confirmed by evidence from two large-scale national surveys, conducted in 1975 and 1985. A comparison of data from the two studies shows an improvement in nutritional status in this period. Children observed were both heavier and taller in 1985 than in 1975, indicating an improvement in both acute and chronic malnutrition (Capital Institute Paediatrics, 1985).

The role of changes in the institutional structure of farming

3.19 Following the period of crisis and famine of 1959-1961 a number of reforms took place. Tight controls of the agricultural commune system were relaxed in favour of a more decentralized management system. Infrastructural investment continued alongside a remarkable effort and achievements in the

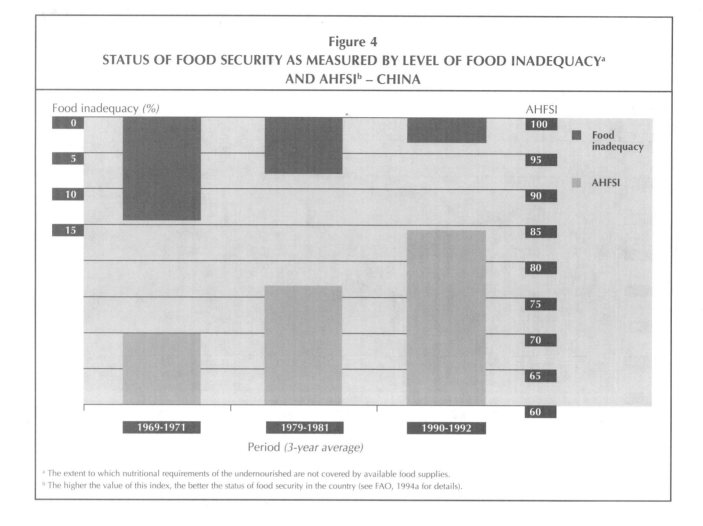

Figure 4
STATUS OF FOOD SECURITY AS MEASURED BY LEVEL OF FOOD INADEQUACY[a]
AND AHFSI[b] – CHINA

Food inadequacy (%)   AHFSI

■ Food inadequacy

■ AHFSI

1969-1971   1979-1981   1990-1992

Period *(3-year average)*

[a] The extent to which nutritional requirements of the undernourished are not covered by available food supplies.
[b] The higher the value of this index, the better the status of food security in the country (see FAO, 1994a for details).

area of seed improvement. The combination of a decentralized research system and successful extension resulted in the replacement by the end of the 1970s of 80 percent of the traditional varieties of rice and wheat by modern dwarf varieties. For more than a decade China was the only country in the world in which hybrid rice was commercially produced. Modern varieties of corn, cotton and other crops were also introduced and promoted in the 1960s and 1970s. The pace of mechanization also accelerated after 1965, especially during the 1970s.

3.20 The combination of infrastructural development, mechanization and the spread of modern inputs and seeds enabled China to eliminate famine and maintain a reasonable energy intake, but grain production growth was barely kept above population growth. Between 1952 and 1978 grain production growth per caput was 0.4 percent, with per caput availability of grain increasing only 10 percent in a quarter of a century, while no substantial improvements of living standards were attained after 30 years of socialist revolution. Despite dramatic increases·in modern inputs in the 1960s and 1970s, the total factor productivity of Chinese agriculture in the 1980s remained about 20 percent lower than the level reached before the collectivization movement (Wen, 1993). The weak relationship between work effort and reward had detrimental effects on work incentives, which, combined with inefficient management and uneconomic resource use, contributed to the low technical efficiency in Chinese agriculture.[6]

[6] Because of the difficulty in supervising agricultural teamwork, the success of an agricultural collective depends on a contract of self-discipline which can only be sustained in a voluntarily formed team. Before the communal movement in the autumn of 1958, a farmer's participation in an agricultural collective was voluntary. After the movement started, participation became compulsory. As a result, the self-enforcing contract could not be sustained and agricultural productivity collapsed (see Lin, 1990, 1993 , 1995).

3.21 Frustrated by the inability to raise living standards substantially after 30 years of socialist revolution, the Chinese leadership initiated in 1979 a series of sweeping reforms in agriculture. Such reforms included both increased incentives in the form of higher State procurement prices and a series of institutional reforms. These included diversification of the rural economy, production specialization, expansion of rights to land, increased flexibility in employment choice, crop selection in accordance with regional comparative advantages and enhancement of the role of markets. The most important change, however, was the emergence and eventual predominance of the household responsibility system (HRS), which restored the primacy of the individual household in place of the collective team system as the basic unit of production and management in rural China.

3.22 Relaxation of controls on private and market initiative unleashed the potential of the Chinese agricultural sector. While the population grew at 1.3 percent per year on average between 1979 and 1984, the value of agricultural output and grain output respectively grew by 11.8 and 4.1 percent annually in the same period. It is empirically assessed that about half of the increase in the agricultural output in 1978-1984 can be attributed to the improvement of incentives arising from changes of farming institutions from the collective system to the household system. As the real value of China's agricultural output more than doubled since 1978, rural per caput income increased rapidly, reducing by two-thirds the number of people living in absolute poverty. The most rapid increase in rural per caput income occurred between 1979 and 1984, when the increase averaged 15 percent per year (FAO, 1994b). The number of rural poor declined from 260 million in 1978 to 100 million in 1990 or from 33 to about 12 percent of the rural population.

Keeping the pace: prospects and problems for Chinese agriculture

3.23 While agricultural production still grew remarkably after the completion of the HRS reform in 1984, grain production in China declined and then stagnated for several years in 1984-1989. This stagnation was mainly a result of the fact that, as individual households were given more autonomy to produce after the HRS was instituted, peasants began to allocate greater resources to the production of specific crops that were decontrolled and commanded higher profits. Perhaps an additional factor may have been that the marketing of grain was not fully liberalized. Farmers are still required to sell certain quotas of grain below market prices to the government. Therefore, farmers' incentives for grain production are suppressed. Further growth of grain output to meet the increasing demand for both foodgrains and feedgrains in the future requires the liberalization of remaining market impediments and the government's strong support for agricultural research.

3.24 Poverty alleviation issues will continue to be important in China. While the strong rural sector growth played an important role in bringing down poverty levels during the first half of the 1980s, the subsequent slowdown in agricultural growth after 1985 coincided with a stagnation of poverty levels. In 1978 most of the poor resided in areas where rapid productivity gains were feasible through an increased use of farm inputs and hybrid seeds. By 1985, however, China's remaining poor were concentrated in the less productive rain-fed areas. While some increases in productivity were achieved in these resource-poor areas, more needs to be done, as available evidence suggests that gains in agricultural growth have so far been largely offset by population growth.

COSTA RICA[7]

3.25 Food security in Costa Rica, in terms of both per caput food availability and production and direct indicators of household food security status, has steadily improved through the period studied. Part of the reason for this is the strong policy emphasis on poverty alleviation. Although macroeconomic problems were encountered and policy adjustments were made that reduced the production of some traditional crops, the shift in emphasis to export-driven growth allowed increases in food imports to maintain per caput food availability, which is currently just below 3 000 Calories per day.

3.26 The Costa Rican economy experienced high rates of growth for nearly three decades until the early 1980s, despite its relatively narrow export basis consisting mainly of traditional tropical products (bananas and coffee). Contrary to what happened in many Latin American countries, fast economic growth was accompanied by significant social development, reducing the incidence of poverty to around 20 percent by the end of the 1970s. However, at the beginning of the 1980s the Costa Rican economy was severely hit by sharply worsening terms of trade and unfavourable conditions in the international financial markets. Institutional reforms – to open the economy to external competition, to reduce price distortions and government intervention and to diversify exports as a response to the crisis – allowed the economy to adjust to the new context without exacting high social costs.

3.27 During the 1960s and 1980s the government of Costa Rica implemented a series of successful policies aimed at promoting agricultural growth, with particular emphasis on increasing food production. The set of instruments used in this effort included setting minimum prices, subsidizing interest rates and inputs and providing agricultural extension and technical assistance. These measures proved to be extremely successful in promoting staple food production. (Figure 5 conceals this development because of the dominating influence of banana production in the food sector.) The increasing trend in per caput food imports of the 1960s was thus reversed in the early 1970s. However, by 1982 the cost of the agricultural programme had reached 30 percent of total current government expenditure and the programme was the first to be hit by the severe crisis faced by the country. Policy emphasis shifted from import substitution, food self-sufficiency and growth-cum-debt to export-driven sustainable growth. Although production of traditional crops declined during this period, production and exports of non-traditional crops increased rapidly, allowing an increase in per caput imports to nearly 30 percent of total food availability as the result of this policy shift.[8]

[7] This is a condensed and edited version of FAO (1995c).
[8] One interesting aspect of food imports in Costa Rica is the importance of food aid. Over the 1971-1991 period, cereal food aid constituted more than one-quarter of the food imports in energy equivalents. Although this share has recently fallen to around 23 percent (1990-1992), cereal aid still makes up 6 percent of per caput food availability for human consumption.

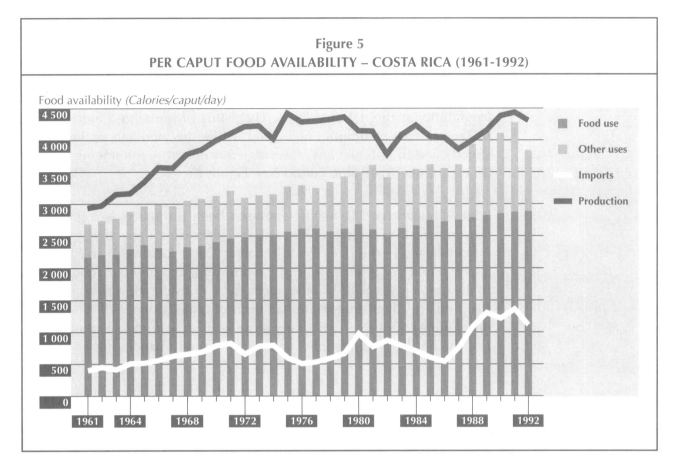

Figure 5
PER CAPUT FOOD AVAILABILITY – COSTA RICA (1961-1992)

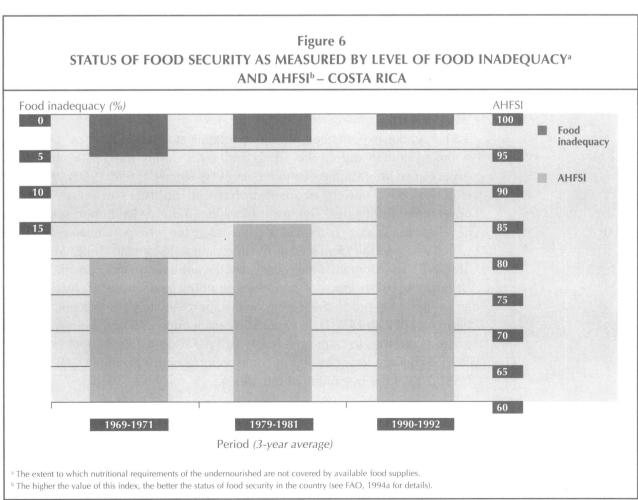

Figure 6
STATUS OF FOOD SECURITY AS MEASURED BY LEVEL OF FOOD INADEQUACY[a]
AND AHFSI[b] – COSTA RICA

[a] The extent to which nutritional requirements of the undernourished are not covered by available food supplies.
[b] The higher the value of this index, the better the status of food security in the country (see FAO, 1994a for details).

3.28 The net result of these developments was an average annual increase in per caput food availability of close to 1 percent, from around 2 200 Calories in 1961 to around 2 900 Calories in 1992. Although there are important regional differences in food intake in the country, improvements in AHFSI and food adequacy have closely followed those of average availability at the national level. The status of household food security increased from medium to high level, while the food gap declined from slightly less than 6 percent of average nutritional requirements to about 2 percent over the same period (see Figure 6).

3.29 Although food self-sufficiency has been dismissed as a goal to be pursued at all costs, the continued and increasing dependence on food imports leads to the question of whether Costa Rica has a solid enough export base to afford the increasing import bill and improve food security in the coming years. This issue needs to be considered in the light of the traditionally adverse international terms of trade between developed and developing countries, particularly those with large primary export sectors, and the level of indebtedness and recent global financial instability.

ECUADOR[9]

3.30 Although the main indicators of food security in Ecuador show a steady improvement throughout the three decades studied in this paper, per caput food production and availability followed a path similar to that followed by macroeconomic indicators and policies. The impact of changing macroeconomic and sectoral policies was especially strong on per caput food supplies, which were declining with increasing macro imbalances prior to the 1980s but which have significantly improved with the implementation of stabilization and structural policies since then.

3.31 Ecuador experienced phases of relative stagnation prior to the 1970s, booming growth during the 1970s and crisis during the 1980s, and it has experienced an unstable economic recovery since the mid-1980s. It has also experienced a variety of institutional and political arrangements and development strategies. The inward-looking, industry-led import substitution development strategy of the 1960s gave way to the oil export drive of the 1970s which was gradually replaced by the International Monetary Fund/World Bank (IMF/WB) development strategy in the last decade as economic growth slumped. During the 1970s Ecuador registered stunning and unprecedented rates of gross domestic product (GDP) growth (approximately 18 percent per year between 1972 and 1981). In about 30 years, it improved from being one of the poorest countries in Latin America, with a per caput GDP of about US$200 in 1961, to being a lower-middle-income country, with a per caput GDP of about US$1 200 at the beginning of the 1990s.

3.32 Ecuador's rather uneven growth experience was accompanied by important structural changes in the economy. From what was a traditional, rural-based economy and a typical tropical fruit-exporting country in much

[9] This is a condensed and edited version of FAO (1995d).

of the 1950s and 1960s, Ecuador has developed in the 1990s into a typical Latin American urban and industry-based economy. Agriculture's share in GDP declined from 26.4 percent at the beginning of the 1960s to less than 15 percent in the early 1990s, when industrial activities (including oil extraction and refining) accounted for almost 35 percent of total value added.

3.33 The underlying policy thrust that underpinned this development was characterized by a macroeconomic environment that was not particularly favourable to agricultural growth, especially during the 1960s and 1970s. The overvaluation of the Ecuadorian sucre and heavy taxation of traditional export crops, i.e. coffee and bananas, reduced the competitiveness of the sector as a whole. As a result, exports stagnated while imports of cheaper raw materials were encouraged. Food imports were subsidized, especially during periods of high international prices, to ensure the supply of cheap food to urban consumers. Although there were times when food imports were taxed to encourage local production of food crops, on balance, policies resulted in an average decline in food production per caput (expressed in energy equivalents) of about 2.8 percent per annum during 1961-1983 (see Figure 7). Livestock production, fisheries (shrimp cultivation) and rice production were the only food production sectors exhibiting some dynamism during this period. The production of maize, wheat, barley and potatoes as well as that of banana and coffee declined as a result of an extraordinary expansion of pastureland at their expense. Such shifts in resource allocation reflected reduced incentives for crop production and moves by large landowners to undermine agrarian reform.

3.34 The worsening of macroeconomic imbalances in early 1980 led to the need to implement stabilization and structural adjustment measures. From 1984 onwards, the government gave up attempts to regulate the economy. International trade, financial markets and foreign investments were liberalized; a floating exchange rate system was introduced; domestic markets and labour relations were deregulated; and agricultural policy shifted focus from direct intervention in markets to market assistance to foster greater private-sector participation. Although the government retained control in some agricultural markets, such as rice, soybean and sorghum, the negative trend in per caput food production was reversed, from -2.8 percent per annum before 1983, as noted above, to +4.1 percent per annum thereafter. In parallel, the share of food imports in total food availabilities for direct human consumption (in energy equivalents), which had grown from 8 percent in the 1960s to nearly 20 percent by the early 1980s, has since stabilized around that level (see Figure 7).

3.35 The economic developments briefly described above have also been reflected in food availabilities over the same period. Daily per caput food availability grew by an average of 0.7 percent per annum between 1961 and 1992, increasing from just less than 2 000 Calories to around 2 600 Calories.

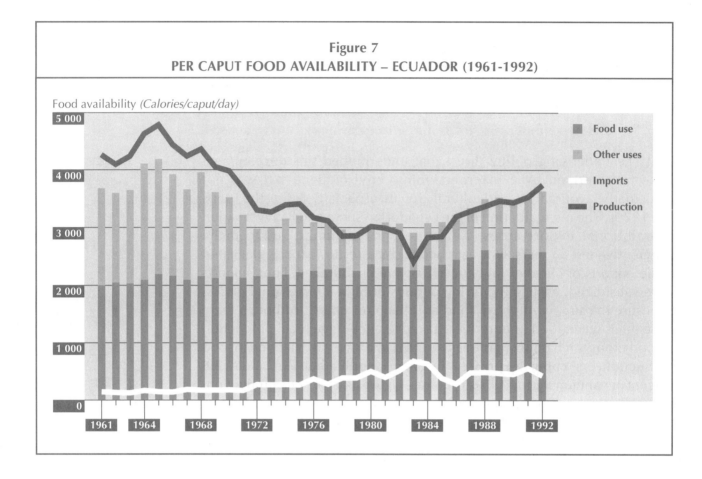

Figure 7
PER CAPUT FOOD AVAILABILITY – ECUADOR (1961-1992)

Food availability *(Calories/caput/day)*

Food use
Other uses
Imports
Production

It should be noted that the annual growth observed since 1983 is 1.1 percent, significantly greater than the 0.6 percent estimated for the period prior to 1983. Ecuador is currently considered to have a high level of food security, with an AHFSI greater than 85 and food inadequacy less than 5 percent (see Figure 8). However, within the food-insecure group, pregnant women, lactating mothers and children below five years of age continue to be especially vulnerable.

3.36 Despite progress in food security, the prevalence of malnutrition remains high among marginalized groups, whether in rural or urban areas. Micronutrient deficiencies (particularly iron, iodine and vitamin A) are widespread. The government, in collaboration with non-governmental organizations (NGOs), is currently embarking on an intersectoral approach to improve food security, linked to the existing food and nutrition surveillance system. This approach combines general development programmes with interventions focusing on marginal groups. The approach includes the diversification of food production for national consumption, the prevention of post-harvest losses, food quality and safety measures, the improvement of the food distribution systems, the promotion of linkages between the food industry and nutrition institutions, food fortification and nutrition education and communication to raise awareness on food and nutrition issues at all levels (family, community and school). Support to marginalized groups concentrates on increasing and diversifying household food production and consumption and promoting income-generating activities. Particular attention is given to the training and organization of women's groups.

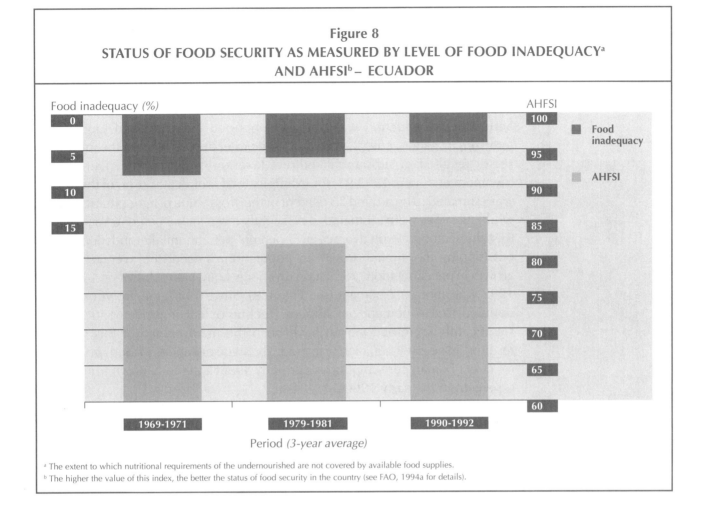

Figure 8
STATUS OF FOOD SECURITY AS MEASURED BY LEVEL OF FOOD INADEQUACY[a]
AND AHFSI[b] – ECUADOR

a The extent to which nutritional requirements of the undernourished are not covered by available food supplies.
b The higher the value of this index, the better the status of food security in the country (see FAO, 1994a for details).

INDIA[10]

3.37 India is a vast country covering a total area of over 297 million hectares and with a population of just over 935 million people. It is considered a low-income country with a per caput gross national product (GNP) of about US$300, according to most recent estimates. India has experienced moderately high economic growth of around 5.2 percent per annum since the early 1980s, well above the average annual population growth rate of slightly above 2 percent for the same period. Despite rather large variability in per caput food availability since the 1960s, India has maintained a determined effort to achieve self-sufficiency and improve household food security throughout this period. Per caput food availability currently stands at 2 400 Calories per day and the prevalence of poverty is still relatively high, but the extensive use of targeted anti-poverty measures has reduced vulnerability to famines and maintained the status of food security in the country.

3.38 India still has an agrarian-based economy, in which the share of agriculture in GDP is slightly less than one-third. The performance of the Indian economy has been largely conditioned by its founders' economic and political philosophy, which is firmly rooted in democratic principles and finds its expression within a mixed-economy environment.

[10] This section is a condensed and edited version of FAO (1995h).

3.39 Soon after independence in the mid-1950s India entered an era of ambitious industrialization that emphasized import substitution and a central role for the public sector, which was expected to occupy the "commanding heights" of the economy through investments in heavy industry and social infrastructure. Throughout this period, industry was heavily protected by overvalued exchange rates, quantitative restrictions and import tariffs. Although agricultural production was directly supported by subsidized inputs, i.e. fertilizer, irrigation, energy, seeds etc., the protection afforded to the industrial sector resulted in substantial indirect taxation of agriculture. During the triennium ending in 1992/93, for example, total indirect taxation of the sector was estimated to be around 28 percent of the gross value of agricultural output, while subsidies were estimated to be slightly more than 5 percent. Yet, despite this, the sector grew on average by 3 percent per annum after independence, outstripping the annual growth in population. Indeed, the average annual growth in per caput food production (in energy equivalents) between 1961 and 1992 was about 0.7 percent (see Figure 9). Since 1980, the growth rate has doubled to 1.4 percent per annum. Technological improvements (which significantly increased yields) have been the main engine of this growth, resulting in near self-sufficiency in food. The share of imports in food availability for direct human consumption is currently about 1 percent, down from about 6 percent in the early 1960s.

3.40 Although average per caput food availability is currently slightly less than 2 400 Calories per day, up from around 2 000 Calories in the early 1960s, and food adequacy and aggregate household food security are at respectable levels (see Figure 10), the prevalence of poverty is still relatively high, at about 40 percent. This means that improvements in per caput food consumption have not been uniform among all households. Concerns about such vulnerability, which tends to be exacerbated by relatively greater year-to-year variability in food availabilities, have led to the establishment of policy instruments that directly target groups at greater risk. The Integrated Rural Development Programme, the National Rural Employment Programme and the more recent Employment Assurance Scheme, as well as other policies targeting the health and nutrition sectors, have resulted in gains in the elimination of famine, declines in the prevalence of severe and moderate protein-energy malnutrition, a steep decline in kwashiorkor, only rare appearances of micronutrient diseases such as beriberi and pellagra and a significant reduction in the incidence of nutritional blindness.

3.41 Micronutrient deficiencies such as vitamin A or iron deficiency are still significant public health problems in the country, especially for vulnerable groups in marginalized areas. Present development policies emphasize the need for an integrated and intersectoral approach. The sectoral plan for agriculture includes the diversification of food production to reflect nutritional needs, the prevention of post-harvest losses, the promotion of local horticulture projects for improved nutrition, nutrition education, and training and organization of women farmers. The public distribution system strives to ensure household food security through the distribution of essential foods in disadvantaged areas. Food processing industries at all levels are encouraged to prepare and facilitate markets of a variety of safe and ready-to-use foods,

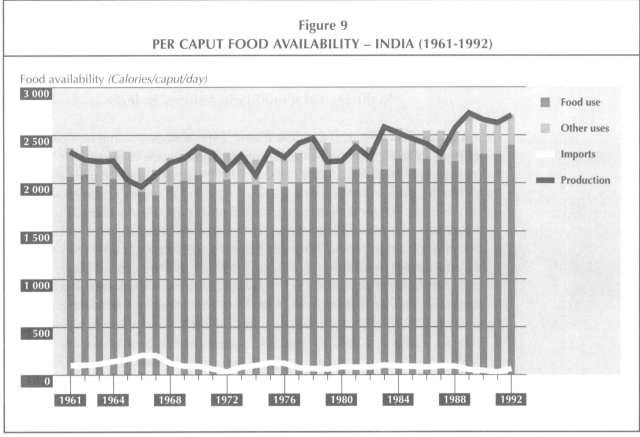

Figure 9
PER CAPUT FOOD AVAILABILITY – INDIA (1961-1992)

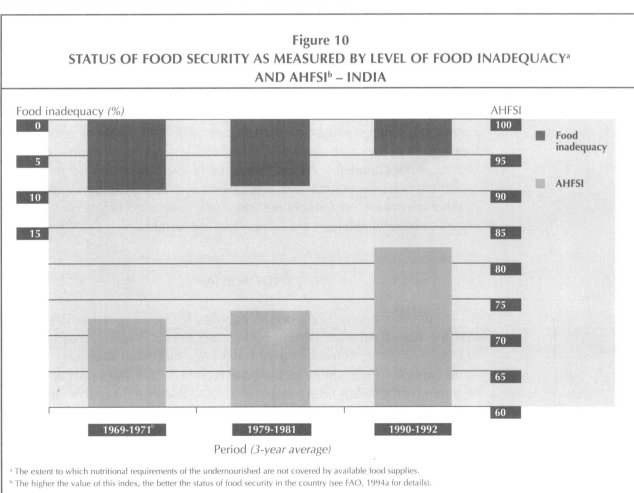

Figure 10
STATUS OF FOOD SECURITY AS MEASURED BY LEVEL OF FOOD INADEQUACY[a]
AND AHFSI[b] – INDIA

[a] The extent to which nutritional requirements of the undernourished are not covered by available food supplies.
[b] The higher the value of this index, the better the status of food security in the country (see FAO, 1994a for details).

with an emphasis on traditional foods, and to fortify and enrich common processed foods. Welfare programmes seek to address basic needs, including food needs, of disadvantaged sections of society.

Reducing vulnerability to famines in India[11]

3.42 India has managed to avoid major famines since gaining independence in 1947. Although gains in productivity and production in the food sector and an extensive public food distribution system have been important elements in this endeavour, India's experience with rural employment schemes seems to be the critical factor differentiating it from other countries that frequently suffer the drastic consequences of famines. The schemes tend to vary across states, but they all aim at providing employment to the rural poor who are willing to do unskilled manual work on a piece-rate basis. Self-selection is usually built in, as no choice of work is offered, the wage rate is usually below the agricultural wage rate and workers may have to travel long distances to participate. The projects chosen are usually labour-intensive and create productive assets. The scheme in Maharashtra, for example, where there is a rural workforce of 20 million people, can provide up to about 100 million person-days of employment in a typical year (Gaiha, 1995).

3.43 The extent of general participation in the schemes has been found to be related to economic conditions in the states concerned, increasing during times of difficulty and declining when conditions improve. Despite the fact that the piece-rate payment system may not be very appropriate for all the poor, for example the physically weak or women if they have to travel long distances, the welfare gains for those who participate may well be substantial during lean and slack periods. The Indian authorities, encouraged by the presence of democratic institutions, have had the political will to commit the necessary resources to support these schemes, especially during times of severe food security crises associated with a rapid loss of food entitlements, so as to reduce, if not completely eliminate, mortality associated with famines. This aspect of India's experience stands out when compared with the experiences of other countries. India, of course, has a long way to go before poverty and chronic undernourishment are completely eliminated.

INDONESIA[12]

3.44 Indonesia has pursued a persistent policy of achieving self-sufficiency in rice, the major food staple of the country, since the late 1960s and early 1970s in order to improve its food security. It has been successful in achieving both, as per caput food availability increased to around 2 700 Calories per day at the beginning of the 1990s from just under 2 000 Calories at the end of the 1960s and the status of household food security improved significantly during the same period. Part of the success can be attributed to the integrated approach adopted by the government whereby marketing interventions were complemented by research on and dissemination of HYVs of rice as well as the provision of the requisite modern input packages.

[11] This section is a highly stylized summary of the conclusions contained in Drèze and Sen (1989).
[12] This is a condensed and edited version of FAO (1995i).

3.45 Having enjoyed nearly three decades of rapid economic growth with macroeconomic, political and social stability, Indonesia has earned the reputation of being a tiger along with the other two second-generation high-performing Asian countries, Malaysia and Thailand. Although Indonesia is considered a lower-middle-income country, with a per caput GNP of US$740 in 1993, it has achieved an average annual growth rate of above 6 percent over the past three decades, compared with annual growth of only 2 percent during the 1955-1966 period. The implementation of stabilization policies during 1966-1972, particularly those that pertained to exchange rate adjustments and liberalization of foreign capital flows, initiated this process. The oil boom that ensued from 1973 to 1982 sustained the improvements as exports earnings and investment rose.

3.46 The agricultural sector, particularly the rice subsector, received significant support during this boom period. There were substantial investments in irrigation, infrastructure, research, extension and education. These were supplemented by market stabilization and support programmes through BULOG, the parastatal National Logistics Agency, responsible for price stabilization and support and for food security, while other marketing agencies were responsible for intensification programmes, including the dissemination of HYVs and the provision of modern input packages. The direct support provided to the sector, as demostrated by continuing positive nominal and effective protection rates for many important crops, places Indonesia among a small number of developing countries where agriculture has been given positive protection.

3.47 The effects of these developments on the food sector are illustrated in Figure 11. Stagnating per caput food production and availability in the early 1960s were transformed into significant increases, from an annual average decline of about 2 percent to an annual increase of 2 percent for food production and from zero growth to an annual growth about of 1.5 percent in food availability for human consumption. Overall, food imports continue to be important, averaging about 6 percent of total per caput food availability during 1988-1992. However, the special focus on the rice sector resulted in rice production more than doubling over a period of 25 years, turning Indonesia into a rice-exporting country, although it continues to import when there is a need.

3.48 These developments resulted in a significantly improved food security status in the country. Indonesia has been able to move from a low to high food security status (AHFSI nearly 90). Indeed, the shortfall in the food gap for the average undernourished person was slightly less than 10 percent in the beginning of the period under consideration, falling to about 2 percent in recent years (Figure 12). Indonesia's integrated approach to agricultural development and timely and effective adjustments to macroeconomic policies and programmes in the face of emerging new challenges have been the cornerstones of this success.

3.49 An applied nutrition programme survey conducted in 1973 found the average energy consumption to be 1 528 Calories per person per day and

Figure 11
PER CAPUT FOOD AVAILABILITY – INDONESIA (1961-1992)

Food availability *(Calories/caput/day)*

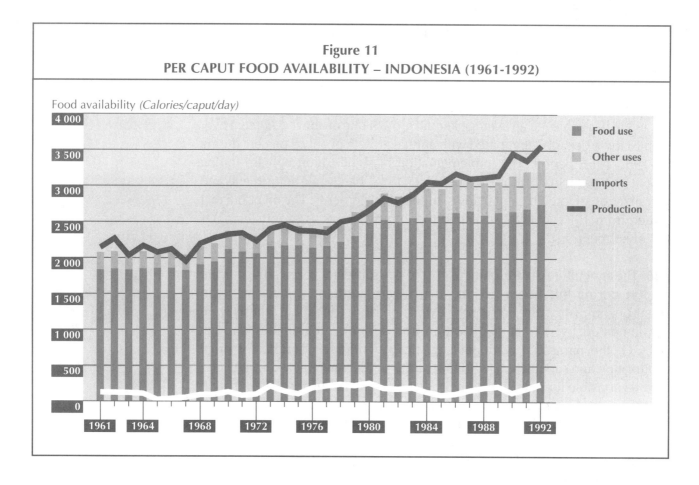

average protein consumption to be 42.8 g per person per day. Data from the Household Expenditure Surveys of 1980, 1981 and 1984 put the average daily per caput consumption at 1 800 Calories and 43 g of protein. Although these low intakes, which are considerably below the national figures for food availability (about 2 500 Calories), serve to highlight that there are food insecurity problems in the country, the above increase in food intake is matched by a recorded improvement in nutritional status. A longitudinal study comparing results of 1979 and 1986 surveys conducted among children under five years of age in 27 provinces shows a decrease in the rate of severe malnutrition (<70 percent of standard weight for height) from 5.9 percent in 1979 to 4.2 percent in 1986. However, the national diet of Indonesia is grossly unbalanced, with 82 percent of dietary energy supplied by cereals, roots and tubers and nuts and oilseeds. This diet provides 8.5 percent of energy from protein and 15 percent from total oils and fats while the rest comes from carbohydrates. Improvements in the availability of animal products, oils and fats, pulses and beans and fruit and vegetables need to be considered by agricultural planners.

3.50 The Government of Indonesia, through the National Plan of Action for Nutrition, notes with great concern the prevalence of undernutrition among the poor, particularly the elderly. It emphasizes the need for political will and decentralization, focusing on farmers' welfare, and promotes an intersectoral approach to poverty alleviation. Specific attention is given to improving household food security and nutrition as an integral part of development policy. Timely warning and intervention systems in provinces prone to food shortages are also being developed.

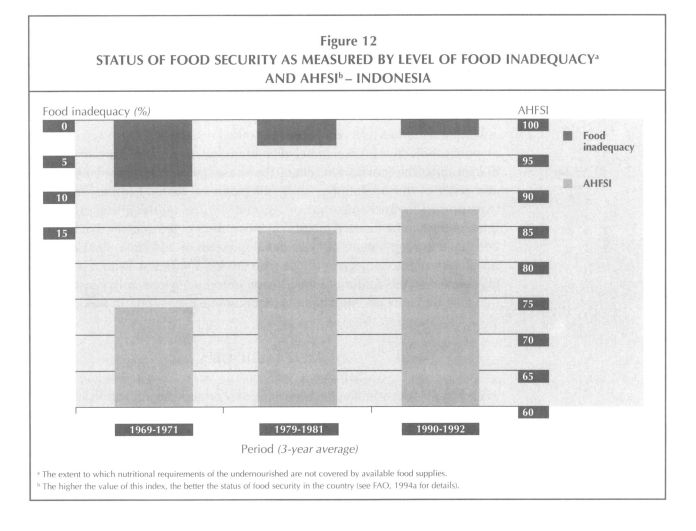

Figure 12
STATUS OF FOOD SECURITY AS MEASURED BY LEVEL OF FOOD INADEQUACY[a]
AND AHFSI[b] – INDONESIA

Food inadequacy (%)   AHFSI

■ Food inadequacy

■ AHFSI

Period (3-year average)

1969-1971   1979-1981   1990-1992

[a] The extent to which nutritional requirements of the undernourished are not covered by available food supplies.
[b] The higher the value of this index, the better the status of food security in the country (see FAO, 1994a for details).

Producer price polices for rice[13]

3.51 Since its inception in 1967, BULOG has implemented price policies for the principal food crops in Indonesia. While the various intensification programmes were crucial in disseminating the new technology that enabled Indonesia to become self-sufficient in rice, BULOG's approach to rice marketing and distribution aimed at complementing the policies on the production side by establishing a positive incentives system. Such efforts were undertaken at a time when marketing channels were severely disrupted and the transportation system and other marketing infrastructures were in disrepair. BULOG not only controlled international trade in rice but also provided the functions of supporting and stabilizing domestic prices of rice. Through its vast provincial and district-level organization, BULOG procured, stored and distributed rice, using floor prices to support producers and ceiling prices to protect consumers. Although the private sector usually handled 90 percent of rice production, its operations were restricted by BULOG's marketing margins, which were in turn determined by the agency's financial resources and readiness to intervene in the rice market.

3.52 Initially, the agency's principal achievement was the stabilization of interannual and interseasonal fluctuations in rice prices. It also had the responsibility for distributing rice to the armed forces and civil servants, which

<hr />

[13] Based on World Bank (1992).

may, at times, have forced it to behave as a target-driven procurement agency. In the early 1970s, rice prices were kept below import parity and rice consumption was subsidized. The resulting tax on producers was gradually lifted to encourage productivity increases, employment generation and poverty alleviation in rural areas. Between the mid-1980s and early 1990s, Indonesian rice prices were at or above world parity, inevitably exerting pressure on the government budget as it competed for limited resources serving a multiplicity of policy objectives. Over time, developments in the structure of the rice market and of the economy in general may have significantly altered the benefits and costs of the operations. Thus, for example, general improvements in transportation and information infrastructure could allow BULOG's interventions to be focused mainly on those areas of the country that have not been able to keep abreast of these developments, or distribution of rice could be altered so as to target only those who are food-insecure. Within politically feasible limits, the authorities are already introducing new policy instruments that take into account the changing economic environment in Indonesia.

MOZAMBIQUE[14]

3.53 Nearly a decade after the beginning of economic liberalization and nearly four years after the end of the country's devastating civil war, Mozambique remains among the poorest countries in the world. Hunger remains a stark fact of life for a large number of households. Despite adverse conditions, dramatic progress towards sustainable food security has been achieved in recent years. Three dimensions of this progress are evident: first, increasing per caput food energy availability in the face of drastic reductions in food aid; second, lower and more stable prices for the principal domestically produced staple, white maize; and third, a food system that now provides consumers with a broader range of low-cost staples from which to choose. Figure 13 illustrates the substantial decrease in both per caput food production and availability, despite the increase in per caput imports, almost all of which were in the form of food aid, since the early 1970s. The significant drop in AHFSI (which puts Mozambique among the five least food-secure countries in the developing world) and the increase in food inadequacy contributed to a grim food security situation in the country prior to the ending of hostilities (see Figure 14). Not shown in the figure is the fact that total cereal production and per caput energy availability from cereals in Mozambique have increased substantially in recent years, while the contribution of food aid to availability has fallen dramatically. Production for 1996/97 is forecast to be more than double that of 1989 and 25 percent higher than that of 1995/96. Per caput energy availability from all cereals in 1996 is projected to be equal to or higher than that of any year since at least 1989. Food aid's contribution is projected to fall to only 2 percent during 1996, down from 72 percent during the 1992 southern African drought and from an average of 49 percent for the three years prior to the drought.

3.54 Increased availability has been accompanied by lower and more stable staple food prices in key urban centres. The mean price of white maize in the capital city of Maputo for the post-drought period of March 1993 to January 1996 was 40 percent lower than the corresponding price for the pre-drought

14 This section is based on FAO (1996e).

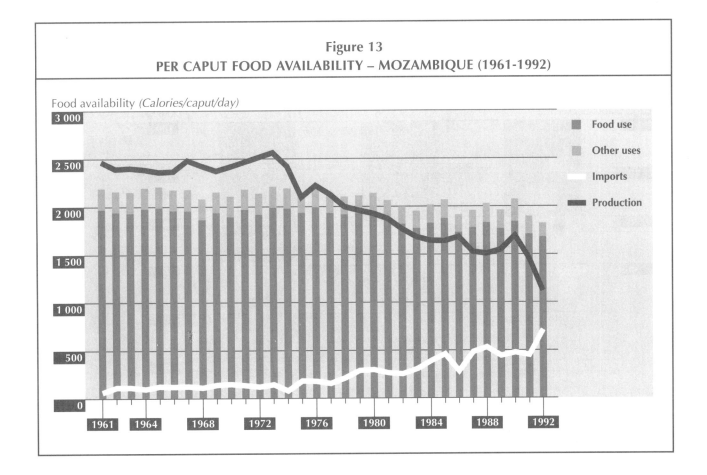

Figure 13
PER CAPUT FOOD AVAILABILITY – MOZAMBIQUE (1961-1992)

Food availability *(Calories/caput/day)*

Legend: Food use, Other uses, Imports, Production

period of March 1990 to March 1992. With excellent cereal production anticipated throughout southern Africa this year, white maize prices in Maputo are likely to fall near or below historical lows. Added to improved availability and lower and more stable white maize prices for urban consumers has been the continued availability of low-cost food staples such as whole ("99 percent") yellow and white maize meals, which low-income consumers tend to prefer when given the choice.

Correlatives of progress in food security

3.55 The ending of the war was the precondition for improvements in food security, yet the rapid progress the country has made in the past three to four years has been based on more than just the end of the war. Policy choices made prior to the peace accords created the conditions for rapid recovery once hostilities ceased. The key policy changes relate to general food marketing policy as well as to specific policies on the monetization of yellow maize food aid.

3.56 Starting in 1987, the country embarked on a programme of donor-financed economic reform under the Economic Rehabilitation Programme (ERP), which removed restrictions on product movement across district and provincial boundaries and eliminated the geographical monopolies for registered private traders. This led to the rapid entry of new traders, who dominated the food marketing system in Maputo by 1992. These traders, nearly all of them unlicensed, handled most of the domestic production that was able to reach

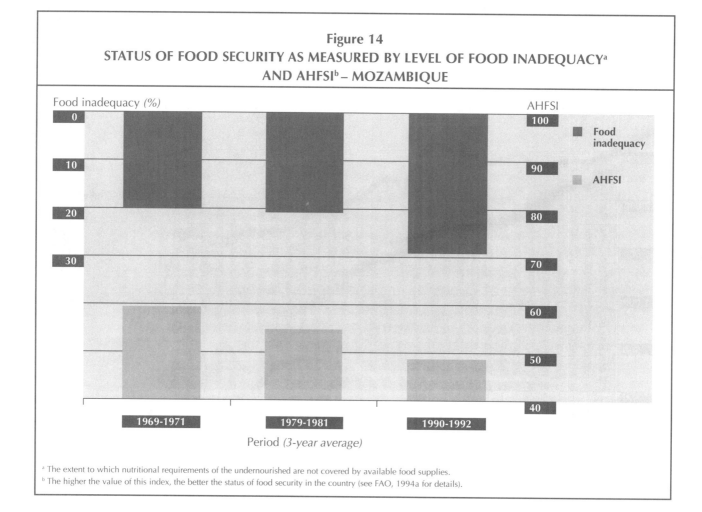

Figure 14
STATUS OF FOOD SECURITY AS MEASURED BY LEVEL OF FOOD INADEQUACY[a]
AND AHFSI[b] – MOZAMBIQUE

[a] The extent to which nutritional requirements of the undernourished are not covered by available food supplies.
[b] The higher the value of this index, the better the status of food security in the country (see FAO, 1994a for details).

the city and regularly brought maize meal, wheat flour, sugar, vegetable oil and other food products to the city from Swaziland and South Africa. Concurrently with the disintegration of the ration shops and the emergence of the informal trading sector, donors were looking for more market-oriented means of distributing monetized food aid. Beginning with shipments in mid-1991, donors negotiated with the Government of Mozambique for the grain to be sold directly to registered private wholesalers (called consignees) at fixed prices in the port cities. Many consignees were included, ensuring a competitive system at this level. These consignees then sold into the highly competitive informal market. The combined effects of liberalized food markets and a competitive trading system contributed decisively to the improvements in food security by:

- linking rural and urban areas through trade flows and providing increased incentives to producers, channelling maize through the small-scale milling sector, which ensured access by poor urban (and, increasingly, rural) consumers to cheap white and yellow wholemeals, stretching their limited purchasing power;

- engaging in active cross-border trade (nearly all imports) in food products, which played a key role in containing price increases in southern Mozambique during the 1995/96 hungry season.[15]

[15] It is important to note that Mozambique had no history of free private markets prior to the late 1980s. Private trade under both the colonial and Frelimo (Mozambique Liberation Front) regimes was highly controlled, with fixed prices at all levels of the system.

3.57 Despite this impressive progress, significant challenges remain in order for the move towards sustainable food security to continue. Among these challenges the most important are: consolidating reforms in the trading sector; investing in cost-reducing marketing infrastructure; and investing in the country's ability to identify and disseminate improved production technologies.

THAILAND[16]

3.58 Strong leadership, macroeconomic stability, an outward-looking development strategy and universal primary education are among the ingredients of the economic success that allowed Thailand's economy to grow steadily at about 7 percent per annum over the past three decades. Food production growth paralleled overall economic development although for a long time neither per caput food availability nor household food security improved dramatically. In fact, per caput food availability hovered just slightly above 2 000 Calories per day until the late 1980s, when it increased to just below 2 500 Calories. Increased production has been made possible by extensive land cultivation. Increasing intensity, improving diversity and reducing poverty remain important policy issues to be addressed.

3.59 Growth in the past three decades was led by developments in agriculture. Contributing to growth were stable macroeconomic management, infrastructure development and the promotion of better social integration. The spectacular expansion in agricultural land was the crucial factor for agricultural and overall economic growth, which in turn contributed to stability of Thailand's currency, the baht, during this period. Growth in the agricultural sector continued after the oil shock of 1972 with rising international agricultural prices despite increases in energy prices and growing indebtedness. By the time of the second oil shock of 1979, however, the rate of expansion of agricultural land had slowed down as the land frontier became exhausted, shifting the emphasis to an industry-led development strategy. With the restructuring of the economy completed, declining energy prices and a depreciating United States dollar, an industrial boom of unprecedented proportions occurred after the mid-1980s, allowing exports of manufactured goods to surpass those of agricultural commodities for the first time.

3.60 These developments have also been felt in the food sector, with per caput food production remaining relatively stable during the 1960s, increasing rapidly by more than 3 percent per annum until the mid-1980s and stagnating once again since then. Figure 15 shows clearly Thailand's food exporting status. It is also obvious from the figure that developments on the food production side have not been replicated on the availability side, at least until the beginning of the industry-led development phase in the mid-1980s. The average annual growth rate in food availability for human consumption was less than 0.5 percent during the earlier period but increased to over 1.5 percent in the latter. The rapidly widening gap between food availability for all uses and that for human consumption is also an indication of the changing consumption patterns resulting from the rapid industrialization during this period.[17] However, the fact that the average per caput availability for human consumption was still below 2 500 Calories as late as 1992 points to possible food insecurity problems in the country.

[16]This is a condensed and edited version of FAO (1995g).
[17] It should be noted that the sharp increases in cassava production for industrial use and as animal feed were also important for the apparent widening of the gap between food availability for all uses and human consumption.

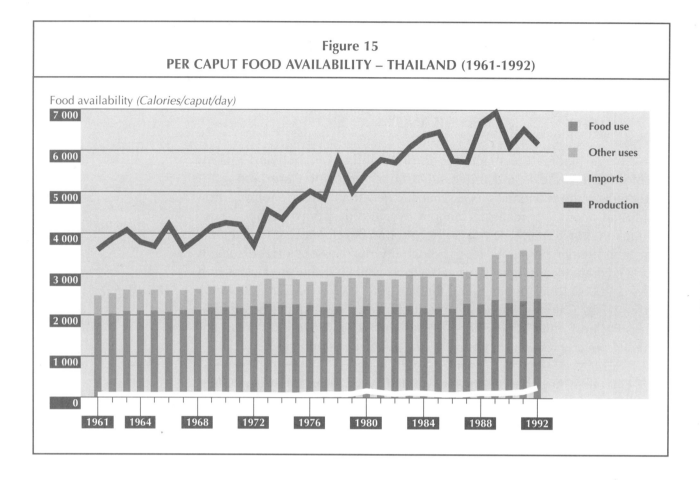

Figure 15
PER CAPUT FOOD AVAILABILITY – THAILAND (1961-1992)

Food availability *(Calories/caput/day)*

3.61 Support for this supposition is provided by recent estimates which place about 25 percent of the population among the poor, with most concentrated in rural areas. From the perspective of household food security, the estimates of AHFSI and food inadequacy paint a similar picture: the former indicates that the status of household food security in Thailand has hovered just above the level considered low food security, although food inadequacy has not surpassed 8 percent of average nutritional availability (Figure 16).

3.62 Malnutrition was recognized by the government as an important social problem: two national social and economic plans gave high priority to the alleviation of nutritional problems. In the 1980s Thailand managed to reduce the incidence of malnutrition dramatically through an integrated approach. Consequently, figures from the Ministry of Public Health's national growth monitoring programme (based on Thai standards) showed improvements in nutritional status of children from birth to 60 months in all parts of the country. The proportion of children with weight for age of less than 75 percent (using Thai standards) decreased from 15.1 percent in 1978-1982 to 2.8 percent in 1986. Essential among the factors that produced this success were political commitment and the recognition that food and nutrition are indispensable elements of human development. Certainly, success in Thailand was also facilitated by a favourable economic environment, but eliminating the nutrition problem was also seen as a prerequisite for overall development.

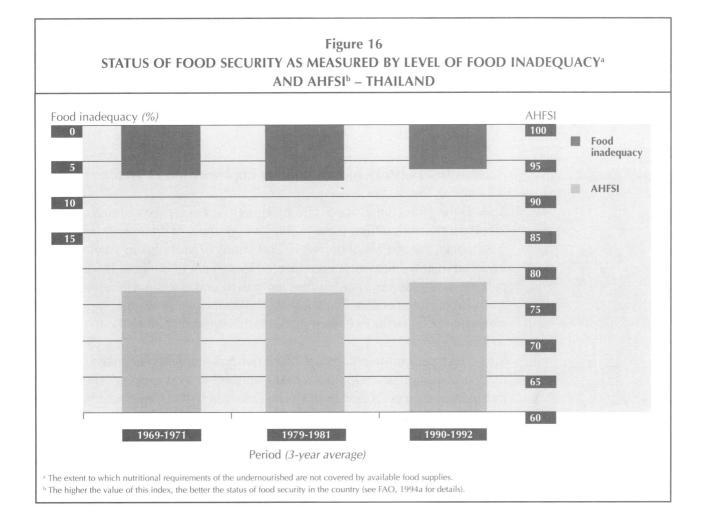

Figure 16
STATUS OF FOOD SECURITY AS MEASURED BY LEVEL OF FOOD INADEQUACY[a]
AND AHFSI[b] – THAILAND

Food inadequacy (%)

AHFSI

Food inadequacy

AHFSI

1969-1971   1979-1981   1990-1992

Period *(3-year average)*

[a] The extent to which nutritional requirements of the undernourished are not covered by available food supplies.
[b] The higher the value of this index, the better the status of food security in the country (see FAO, 1994a for details).

3.63 Thailand's Plan of Action for Nutrition (1994) expresses concern over the persistence of micronutrient deficiency diseases such as iodine deficiency disorders among young children and women of reproductive age in some rural areas and iron deficiency in rural areas nationwide. The thrust to strengthen multisectoral integration and adapt conventional programme planning and budgeting is actively pursued. Community-based nutrition programmes and the Poverty Alleviation Plan (combining rural job creation, agricultural production programmes, village development projects or activities and provision of basic services) are given high priority for reducing micronutrient deficiencies. Rural development policies give priority to areas of high poverty concentration and emphasize people's participation. Food processing and preservation and distribution are encouraged as important means to improve household food security. Programmes to ensure consumer protection and promote appropriate food habits are under way. Increased attention is given to high-risk groups such as small children and the elderly.

3.64 Perhaps of equal concern in regard to the current food security problems in the country are the sustainability issues that have been pushed to the fore because of the way past gains in agricultural outputs were achieved. The main source of such gains, as already noted, was the growth in agricultural land area achieved through extensive deforestation.

3.65 The forest cover dwindled from 60 percent of total land area in the early 1950s to around 30 percent in the late 1980s. Yields, especially of the main staple, rice, still remain well below those of Thailand's competitors in the international markets. Thus diversification, sustainability, poverty alleviation, increasing productivity and addressing unbalanced development are challenges to be tackled on the road to improving food security in the future.

A brief history of rice policies implemented in Thailand[18]

3.66 During the 1980s, rice accounted for 40 percent of agricultural GDP and 30 percent of agricultural exports and for two-thirds of the energy in the Thai diet. In fact, 98 percent of the 4 million farming households in Thailand were involved in growing rice, accounting for 55 percent of the population and 66 percent of the labour force. Furthermore, rice was the most important wage good affecting the cost of living for the Thai consumer. Therefore, pricing and marketing policies for rice were particularly important before the mid-1980s.

3.67 The most prominent feature of the policies implemented at the time was the various implicit and explicit taxes applied to rice exports. The diverse instruments of intervention in rice prices ultimately had the effect of lowering the price to producers. This, in turn, had a substantial effect on the urban real wage and the direction and magnitude of intersectoral transfers. Mills, retail outlets, industry in general and final consumers benefited directly in varying degrees from lower rice prices, although the real thrust of the policies was to stabilize domestic prices, mainly by clipping price peaks. The pro-consumer bias of these policies was strengthened through a cheap rice sales programme, funded from export taxes, until the mid-1970s. Increased rice production was sustained through area expansion, despite the heavy taxation of rice producers.

3.68 With area expansion reaching its limit, the focus of rice policy shifted to raising producer prices, essentially to encourage intensification and promote yield increases. However, the producer subsidies were costly and largely self-defeating because they were funded from rice export taxes. This fact, combined with a reduced reliance on tax revenues collected from rice exports and a softening of the international rice markets, resulted in the complete liberalization of rice exports in 1986.

TUNISIA[19]

3.69 Food security in Tunisia has improved very rapidly since the beginning of the 1960s. Per caput food availability has increased from about 2 000 Calories per day then to nearly 3 500 Calories per day at present (Table 17). Such a high level of food availability has been achieved essentially through food imports, which have been necessary because of severe natural constraints affecting agricultural production. Government intervention has succeeded in translating high food availability into improved food security for the majority of the population through the establishment of extensive social safety nets at the household level. In addition, policies for containing demographic growth have

[18] Extensive use has been made of World Bank (1984) and Siamwalla and Setboonsarng (1992) in the preparation of this section.
[19] This section is largely edited and condensed from FAO (1995b).

resulted in Tunisia being the first country in Africa to achieve a population growth of less than 2 percent.

3.70 Since independence, the public sector in Tunisia has gradually come to play a significant role in the economy. By the end of the 1980s government employees accounted for about 25 percent of all employed wage-earners; the public sector's share in total fixed investment approached nearly 60 percent and its share in value added nearly 50 percent; and public enterprise expenditure was over 40 percent of GDP. At the same time, the State also devoted higher public expenditures to social polices than do most middle-income countries. As a result, the literacy rate today stands at 65 percent; life expectancy is 68 years; and income inequality has declined, although significant regional disparities exist (World Bank, 1995). Poverty estimates derived from consumption expenditure surveys indicate that the incidence of poverty is currently fairly low, at slightly less than 7 percent of the total population, down from about 22 percent in 1975.

3.71 The substantial reduction in the incidence of poverty has also brought with it significant improvements in the status of aggregate household food security, as evidenced by the increase in the value of the AHFSI over the 1961-1992 period. Also, food inadequacy is currently less than 1 percent (see Figure 18). During the same period, average per caput food availability increased as mentioned above from around 2 000 to nearly 3 500 Calories per day, representing an average annual growth rate of slightly more than 1.5 percent (see Figure 17). Nutritional status, for both children and adults, has also gradually improved.

3.72 Increases in food imports including food aid have accounted for much of these successes. The share of food imports in food availability for human use has, on average, increased 1 percent per year during the period under consideration. However, since 1971 food aid receipts have averaged about 8.5 percent (reaching levels as high as 50 percent) of food availabilities for human consumption. Food aid was provided partially to offset the effects of droughts. Tunisia's vulnerability to drought results mainly from the severity of land and water constraints. Available water resources are expected to be fully utilized by the end of the century, while only 6 percent of agricultural land is under irrigation and irrigated agriculture accounts for 30 percent of the sectoral output. Moreover, land degradation affects over 60 percent of the country's usable land resources and is leading to the permanent loss of about 0.5 percent of agricultural land per year (World Bank, 1995).

3.73 Further efforts are being made to improve household food security and diversify diets, including redefining agricultural policy to satisfy the population's needs with local foods and to reduce consumption of imported foods. Encouraging the food industry is seen as an essential means for job creation and the production of convenience foods. Efforts to improve food marketing, distribution and quality control are under way. Nutrition education is being emphasized as a means to influence consumption. Parallel integrated interventions (e.g. safety nets and poverty alleviation) are being developed at local level to help vulnerable population groups. Programmes to mitigate natural disasters (such as drought) are also being developed.

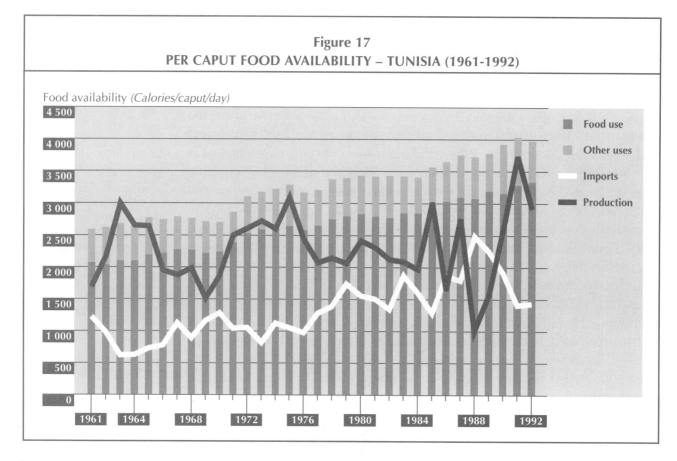

Figure 17
PER CAPUT FOOD AVAILABILITY – TUNISIA (1961-1992)

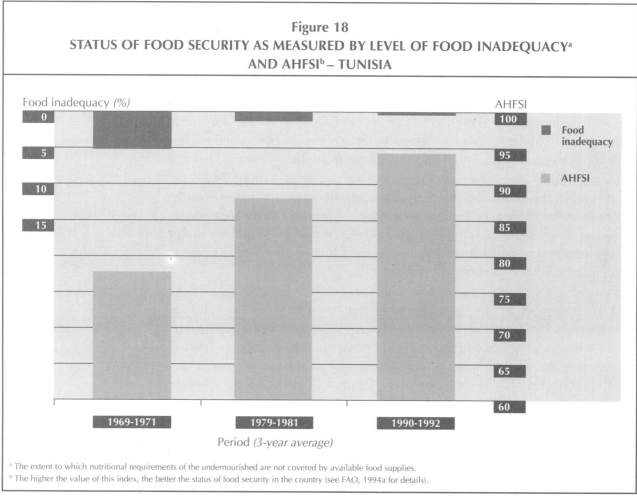

Figure 18
STATUS OF FOOD SECURITY AS MEASURED BY LEVEL OF FOOD INADEQUACY[a]
AND AHFSI[b] – TUNISIA

[a] The extent to which nutritional requirements of the undernourished are not covered by available food supplies.
[b] The higher the value of this index, the better the status of food security in the country (see FAO, 1994a for details).

Merging structural adjustment and food security concerns[20]

3.74 By the mid-1980s, pervasive public involvement in economic activity had resulted in the creation of fairly large imbalances in domestic and external accounts, fanning inflationary tendencies and slowing down economic growth. Stabilization and structural adjustment policies adopted after 1986 were designed to correct such unsustainable imbalances by reducing public spending and demand. Privatization and divestment of public enterprises, banking reforms and liberalization of international trade and domestic markets have indeed achieved a substantial degree of macroeconomic stability, lowering inflation levels to those observed in the countries of the European Union and increasing the per caput GDP growth rate from an annual average of 1.2 percent for the period 1981-1986 to 2.4 percent for the period 1987-1994.

3.75 The change in policy orientation was also reflected in agriculture. Subsidies on fertilizers, animal feed, pesticides and herbicides, seed, irrigation and mechanized services have been substantially reduced since 1989. Although the Caisse Générale de Compensation (CGC), the main agency created in 1971 to support food prices at both the consumer and producer levels, continues its activities, its deficits, which had contributed to the financial crisis of the mid-1980s, are now under control. Moreover, there has been an observable change in the structure of the support that CGC provides, with relatively more resources being allocated to support the consumption of cereals. Anti-poverty programmes targeting the vulnerable have also been developed, utilizing existing maternity and health centres, school canteens, regional rural youth employment centres, etc. Tunisia is one of the few countries in Africa that has established social safety nets alongside structural adjustment programmes (SAPs). At the producer level, prices of some products, such as poultry and bovine meat, have been completely liberalized, while markets for wheat, olive oil, sugar, tea, coffee and reconstituted milk continue to be controlled by parastatals.

3.76 The continued presence of the government in the food sector, along with a significant change in policy emphasis, appears to be an important reason for the underlying positive trend in food availability and food security in Tunisia. Nevertheless, extreme volatility of agricultural production[21] continues to be an important cause for concern and will continue to do so as long as water and land constraints remain. Thus, diversification (not only in the agricultural sector but also in the economy as a whole) will be crucial for the future of food security in Tunisia.

TURKEY[22]

3.77 Turkey is a developing country that has maintained a relatively high level of food availability and food security since the 1960s. Much of the improvement in this respect took place prior to the 1960s, with extensive government intervention in all aspects of the operations of the most important agricultural markets. Currently, food security problems are related more to achieving a nutritionally balanced diet than to increasing or maintaining energy availability.

[20] This section is based on World Bank (1995) and Khaldi and Naili (1995).
[21] The coefficient of variation (CV) of per caput food production, measured in energy equivalents, for Tunisia is around 30 percent. The country with the next highest CV included in this study is Turkey, with 7.5 percent. The CV is the ratio of the estimated standard deviation of per caput food production around a complex trend line to its mean for the period 1961-1992.
[22] This section is a condensed and edited version of FAO (1996c).

However, despite increased efforts to liberalize agricultural markets, public intervention continues to be important, placing considerable strain on the budget and on general price levels.

3.78 Turkey started its industrialization efforts quite early. It is customary to compare the country's modernization with that of Japan, as conscious development efforts started in both countries at more or less the same time. However, the natural resource base of Turkey was sufficiently large and a development path that involved pursuing a goal of agricultural self-sufficiency and import substitution, rather than one of export-led economic development, was chosen at a very early stage of the industrialization process. Although self-sufficiency in agriculture was taken to mean security in a strategic sense, it also provided a good base for industrialization. In fact, the first factories established during the early republican era were all agriculturally based.

3.79 Initially, the push towards agricultural self-sufficiency started with price support to wheat, the main staple crop, as early as the onset of the great depression in the early 1930s. The support programme was subsequently extended to cover more than 20 crops. The ensuing growth in agricultural output, which averaged over 3.5 percent per annum, well above the growth in population, was sustained first by extension in the area cropped and then by improvements in yields. Although the growth in per caput food production for the 1961-1992 period (averaging less than 0.5 percent) was modest, food availability for human consumption was already at a high level, over 2 800 Calories per person at the beginning of the period and rising still further to about 3 400 Calories by 1992 (see Figure 19).

3.80 The household food security situation has paralleled developments on the supply side, as Turkey has been consistently among those countries having a high food security status over the past 25 years (see Figure 20). With the completion of a major irrigation scheme in the southeastern region of the country (the GAP Project), it is not likely that the country will be troubled significantly by food insecurity problems in the future.

3.81 Food balance sheets show satisfactory aggregate food availability, yet unequal distribution among socio-economic, gender and age groups, inadequate food habits and poor quality of foods through contamination remain problems in many areas. The prevalence of malnutrition has decreased in the last ten years but is still high in some small, extremely poor areas of the country. Micronutrient deficiencies persist, in particular those of iron, calcium and riboflavin, and are attributed to inadequate intakes of milk and milk products, meat and meat products and eggs. Efforts to enhance consumer protection through strengthened food legislation and control programmes and appropriate consumer information are under way. Food fortification is encouraged according to local needs. The improvement of food distribution systems, particularly of street foods, is seen as one of the means to improve access to a safe and diversified diet. The sustainable use of natural resources, through

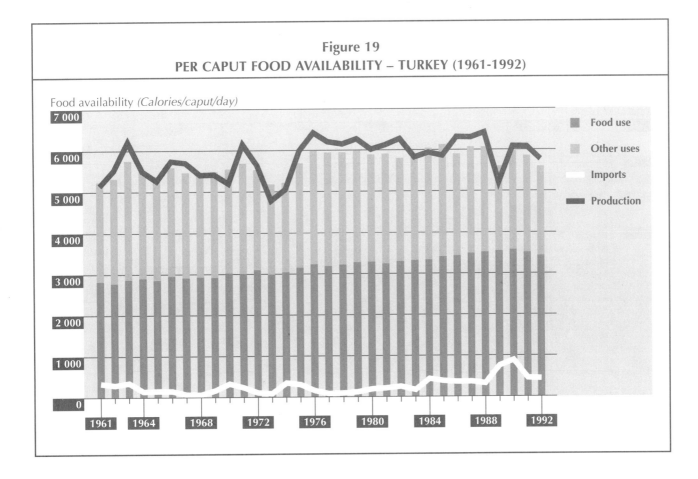

Figure 19
PER CAPUT FOOD AVAILABILITY – TURKEY (1961-1992)

more appropriate agriculture practices, is seen as a precondition for ensuring future food security. Priority development areas have been established to promote self-sustained development in disadvantaged areas. Emergency preparedness for natural and human-caused disasters has been given specific attention.

3.82 Turkey has been contributing food commodities to other countries in times of urgent need from its own production and is implementing a policy of sharing its expertise, knowledge and other resources with them. Turkey continues to support the efforts of the food-deficit countries in Africa, the Near East, the Balkans and the Caucasus to attain food security through training, education and increased production and productivity.

An overview of agricultural support policies in Turkey

3.83 Output support prices, input subsidies, subsidized credits, quotas, tariffs, taxes, land distribution, investments in infrastructure and extension services have all been employed in Turkey to achieve objectives ranging from income and price stability, stimulating output and income and satisfying demand, to improving the balance of payments. Five ministries and about 20 semi-autonomous agencies, i.e. State enterprises, State monopolies and unions of cooperatives (sales, credit, or both), have been involved in the formulation and administration of agricultural pricing policies. At the beginning of the 1980s, almost all major agricultural products, apart from

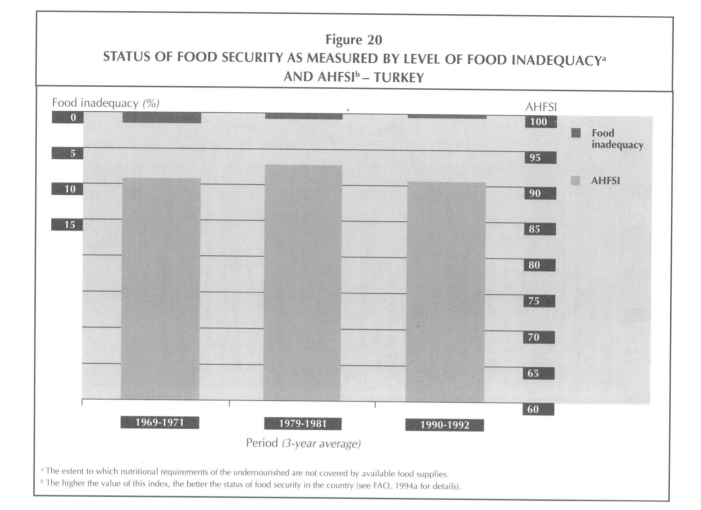

Figure 20
STATUS OF FOOD SECURITY AS MEASURED BY LEVEL OF FOOD INADEQUACY[a]
AND AHFSI[b] – TURKEY

a The extent to which nutritional requirements of the undernourished are not covered by available food supplies.
b The higher the value of this index, the better the status of food security in the country (see FAO, 1994a for details).

fresh fruit and vegetables, were under some form of government support, which constituted over 90 percent of the total value of agricultural production. Similarly, most modern inputs were either produced, distributed or priced by the government. Infrastructural investments, irrigation schemes, land development and conservation and extension services continue to provide inputs to agriculture free of charge or at subsidized prices.

3.84 Although these measures were not motivated by food security concerns alone, their contribution to the achievement of high levels of food security cannot be denied. Through such measures, the use and adoption of new technologies has been encouraged while demand for agricultural labour, agricultural productivity and incomes has also increased (Kasnakoglu, Akder and Gürkan, 1990). Nevertheless, such achievements have been brought about at a high cost. Data show that by 1991-1993, government expenditure on agriculture through commodity price support measures had reached about 35 percent of agricultural GDP, peaking at US$8.9 billion in 1992 (FAO, 1996b). The pressure that such massive intervention creates on government's budgetary resources, and subsequently on the general level of prices, is recognized by policy-makers, and attempts are currently being made to reduce the level of intervention, thus eliminating market distortions and emphasizing the targeting of specific groups who are most in need.

ZIMBABWE

3.85 There have been no significant improvements in average food availability and household food security in Zimbabwe over the past three decades, which places the country among those that can be considered vulnerable. Productivity in the food sector has been on the decline since the early 1970s. The economic and financial imbalances that were created following full national independence in 1980 necessitated the implementation of an SAP in the early 1990s. Although the country faced two severe droughts during the same period (1991-1992 and 1994-1995), those crises have been managed without large-scale hunger and malnutrition as a result of the aid of the international community and a remarkably successful coordination of activities with other countries in the southern African subregion. Moreover, the structural changes implemented after 1993 in the marketing of the principal food crop, maize, removed some of the constraints on the markets. They also resulted in substantial improvements in the food security status of the most vulnerable population groups by reducing the price of the staple food crop.

3.86 Zimbabwe gained full independence in 1980. Restricted by the requirements of the Lancaster House Constitution, which granted independence to the country, and by the need to consolidate its political base, the new government did not immediately change the agricultural policies followed by the white minority administration in earlier years. During the first few years of independence, the government devoted much of its resources and attention towards increasing agricultural output within the existing communal areas (formerly the Native Reserves). Credit facilities, extension services, crop package programmes and marketing opportunities (particularly the number of depots) were all increased within the first five years. As a result the communal areas' contribution to the national marketed output of maize rose from 7 to 50 percent between 1980 and 1985, although there was no perceptible improvement in the underlying trends in overall per caput production. By 1985, communal farmers produced and sold more cotton than the large-scale farmers.

3.87 After 1985, the ruling party became more dominant and introduced some of the socialist policies espoused during the pre-independence days. Maize prices were government controlled and subsidies were established. The buying of maize was closely controlled by the Grain Marketing Board (GMB), with a minimal role played by private traders. Although more inputs were provided to the communal and remote rural areas, severe restrictions were imposed on the marketing of maize. Maize could not be moved or traded between non-contiguous communal areas. White maize, in particular, could not move across commercial and communal boundaries. Maize could be bought only by the GMB at subsidized official prices, so there was limited movement of surplus grain to deficit regions. This often resulted in maize being transported significant distances from the points of purchase to storage depots before it was processed into roller meal and super-refined meal at one of four large roller-milling firms. These milling firms supplied almost all the commercially available maize meal to both the urban and rural areas. The objective of the government's control of the grain market was to ensure a consistent flow of maize meal to urban areas at prices that could be controlled and, if necessary, subsidized. Such a system involved transporting maize sold by communal farmers to urban areas for milling and then retransporting it to the rural areas to be resold. This type of marketing organization turned out to be highly inefficient.

3.88 The impact of these developments can be traced in Figure 21. Throughout most of the 1961-1992 period, Zimbabwe was able to produce more food than it used domestically. Nevertheless, however, the average energy availability and the status of household food security (see Figure 22) in the country were not very impressive, nor did they improve significantly throughout the period. Average food availability hovered around 2 100 Calories per caput per day and the country had low household food security status for much of this period. Despite wide fluctuations, per caput food production exhibited significant growth of about 2.5 percent per annum from 1961 to 1974. From then until 1992, however, per caput food production declined on average by about 4 percent per annum, with the exception of a few short-lived upward hikes. The decline was accentuated by the 1991-1992 drought.

Improving household food security through market reform[23]

3.89 By the early 1990s, the government of Zimbabwe recognized that there were serious imbalances in the economy. For a number of years, Zimbabwe had imported more than it exported and had built up a serious foreign debt. Continuous borrowing was needed to finance public-sector deficits. Fiscal deficits of around 10 percent of the national income crowded out private investment and created inflationary pressures. During the first decade following independence, the economy in fact stagnated with real per caput income remaining unchanged.

3.90 In October 1990, the initiation of the Economic Structural Adjustment Programme (ESAP) was announced. The measures taken were similar to those adopted in other countries: liberalizing the economy, reducing the fiscal deficit, reducing and reshaping the government workforce and creating the conditions for attracting foreign investment. Cuts in government spending caused hardship, especially for the poor. To address this problem, the government established the Social Dimensions of Adjustment Programme in November 1991, drawing upon the Social Development Fund (SDF).[24]

3.91 Relaxing the policy and constraints, especially those on the marketing of maize, had a significant positive impact on household food security. The maize meal subsidies prior to ESAP were limited exclusively to roller meal, a refined maize meal produced by the large-scale millers. Wholemeal, an unrefined maize product widely consumed in rural areas from maize that has been custom-milled from farmers' own production, was viewed by large-scale milling firms as an unsophisticated product for which there was little demand. Consequently, wholemeal was not produced by large-scale millers.

[23] This section is a condensed and edited version of Jayne *et al.*, 1995.
[24] It has been unfortunate that, since the introduction of ESAP, the country has suffered two serious droughts. In both cases, although response to the early indications of a drought was delayed, the country successfully implemented several food aid programmes which prevented starvation and suffering of the population, largely thanks to the grain storage system of the parastatal marketing board. It has been difficult, however, to separate the effects of ESAP and the drought.

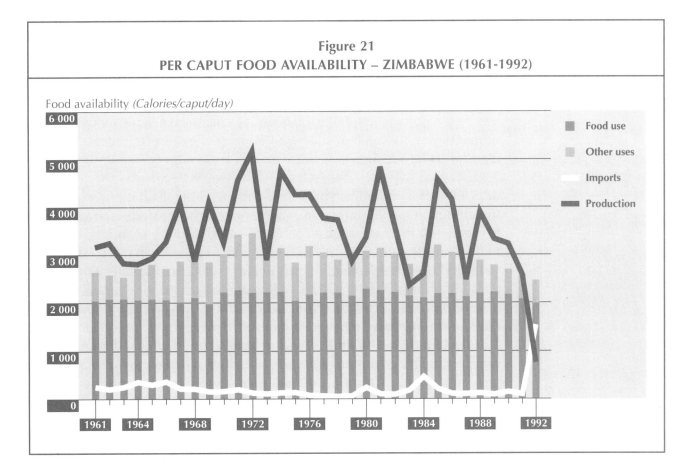

Figure 21
PER CAPUT FOOD AVAILABILITY – ZIMBABWE (1961-1992)

Food availability *(Calories/caput/day)*

Food use
Other uses
Imports
Production

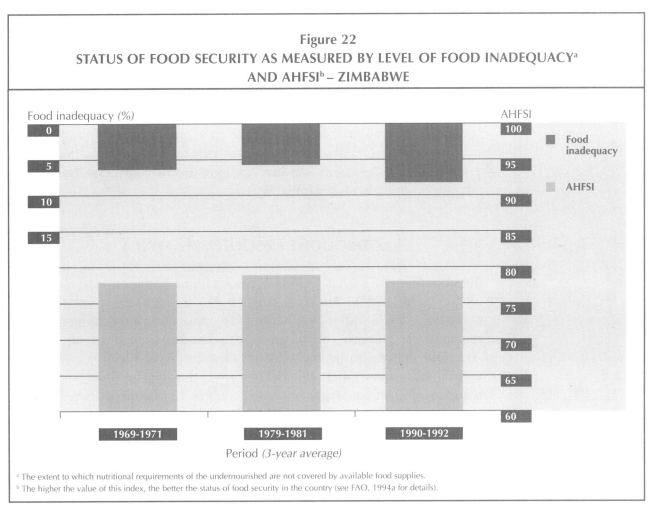

Figure 22
STATUS OF FOOD SECURITY AS MEASURED BY LEVEL OF FOOD INADEQUACY[a]
AND AHFSI[b] – ZIMBABWE

Food inadequacy (%)

AHFSI

Food inadequacy

AHFSI

Period *(3-year average)*

[a] The extent to which nutritional requirements of the undernourished are not covered by available food supplies.
[b] The higher the value of this index, the better the status of food security in the country (see FAO, 1994a for details).

3.92 When supplies of grain were available to consumers, whole meal was produced by small-scale custom hammer mills. For example, in 1991, small-scale hammer mills in Harare processed 8 percent of the city's maize meal requirements (Jayne *et al.*, 1991). Yet the set of policy restrictions before ESAP resulted in small-scale custom millers and urban consumers having difficulty in obtaining the quantities of maize needed for wholemeal production. Gross margins for whole maize meal are significantly lower than for roller meal.[25]

3.93 Research undertaken before food market liberalization predicted that the elimination of controls on maize movement into urban areas would substantially increase access to, and the affordability of, maize by small millers and low-income urban households. Household survey data also indicated that the demand for wholemeal was much greater than actual consumption as a result of prevailing policy restrictions on consumers' access to maize. Based on these findings, the Ministry of Lands advocated the removal of maize movement controls between smallholder and urban areas in June 1993. At about the same time, the roller meal subsidy, which was costing the government the equivalent of 2 percent of GDP annually, was eliminated. The price of roller meal without the subsidy quickly increased by 53 percent.

3.94 Urban consumers were publicly encouraged to avoid the effects of subsidy removal by obtaining maize grain and having it milled into wholemeal at local hammer mills. Research undertaken after the reforms has documented that first, within a span of two years, the proportion of staple maize meal procured through informal distribution channels soared from 8 percent to about 50 percent; second, the market reforms allowed urban household to acquire maize meal at 60 to 70 percent of the cost of maize meal manufactured by large-scale millers; and third, the cost saving to consumers was 7 to 13 percent of average household income among the lowest income quintile in the capital city, Harare (Rubey, 1995; Jayne *et al.*, 1995). Government policy-makers and the general public widely regard these maize market reforms as being among the most successful aspects of structural adjustment in Zimbabwe.

DROUGHT IN SOUTHERN AFRICA

3.95 Southern Africa has periodically been hit by droughts, most recently in 1991/92 and 1994/95. However, the 1991/92 drought, which devastated the subregion's agricultural production and induced unprecedented import requirements, will probably be remembered as the worst in several decades. As a result of that disaster, the subregion experienced a reduction in aggregate cereal production by more than 50 percent of the average. The cereal import requirements of the subregion more than doubled and some 18 million people faced the possibility of starvation. Fortunately, early warnings, rapid regional coordination and adequate international support resulted in a successful relief effort which effectively overcame widespread food shortages and the threat of famine.

[25] The limited quantities of maize available in urban areas for processing by hammer mills from official channels were supplemented by additional quantities of maize brought into urban areas illicitly.

Evolution of the 1991/92 crisis

3.96 The 1991/92 rainy season started on time in several countries of the subregion (in October 1991), but subsequent precipitation was below normal, seriously retarding crop development, notably in South Africa, Zimbabwe and central and southern parts of Mozambique. Until early January 1992, crop conditions were still good in Angola, Malawi, Namibia, the United Republic of Tanzania and Zambia, and about average elsewhere. However, prolonged hot and dry conditions in January and February during the crucial pollination stages severely affected crop growth throughout the subregion except in Angola and the United Republic of Tanzania, causing widespread crop failures or seriously reducing yield potential. Rains in March came too late to save crops in most countries as, although they did benefit pastures and limit the drought's impact on the livestock sector in some countries, irreversible damage to food crops and livestock had already occurred in most areas.

3.97 By December 1991, the early warning systems in the subregion supported by FAO signalled developing drought conditions. By the end of February 1992, it was confirmed that the situation looked critical. Apart from severe food shortages, the drought put at risk dwindling water supplies, the livestock sector and the general well-being of the population.

3.98 Mozambique was the most seriously affected country, as drought compounded the adverse effects of years of civil strife on food production. The almost complete crop failure in many areas of the country resulted in significant movements of drought-affected and war-displaced people in search of food and water, and some 3 million people were exposed to famine. Adding to the food shortages created by the drought was the low level of cereal stocks in the subregion. Traditionally, most of the coarse grain deficits in the countries of the subregion have been met by exports from South Africa and Zimbabwe and, to a much lesser extent, from Malawi, Zambia or the United Republic of Tanzania. However, following mediocre harvests in 1991, both South Africa and Zimbabwe had depleted their maize stocks and were themselves severely hit by the drought. As a result, these exporting countries were faced with the prospect of having to import substantial quantities of maize in 1992/93. Crop conditions were somewhat better in the United Republic of Tanzania, but the country did not have any surplus for export.

Action taken and results: the 1991/92 drought

3.99 Following the initial early warning alerts of the impending drought emergency, a series of joint FAO/World Food Programme (WFP) Crop and Food Supply Assessment Missions visited the subregion in March and April 1992 when crops were nearing maturity. These missions, in cooperation with the governments and the Southern African Development Community (SADC), reviewed the outcome of the 1992 cereal harvest and assessed the cereal import and food aid requirements for the 1992/93 marketing year. The missions also undertook a comprehensive logistic assessment of all major ports in the region, including those of South Africa.

3.100 The missions confirmed that the worst drought in decades had devastated crops in most countries of the region. The aggregate cereal import requirement of the ten SADC countries was estimated to be 6.1 million tonnes, compared with about 2 million tonnes in a normal year. In addition, it was found that South Africa (not a member of SADC at the time) would need to import 4.5 million tonnes of maize and 1 million tonnes of wheat. The total food aid requirement of 4 million tonnes included emergency assistance of 1.6 million tonnes, while a further 232 000 tonnes of supplementary food was also needed for targeted and vulnerable group feeding programmes.

3.101 Clearly, most of the countries affected would not have been able to acquire the unprecedented amount of food imports required for the 1992/93 period on a commercial basis. The FAO/WFP missions concluded that only a massive international relief effort would avert widespread food shortages and famine later in the year. With international attention focused on the deteriorating food situation in the former USSR, Eastern Europe and the Horn of Africa, special efforts were needed to mobilize the required international assistance for southern Africa.

3.102 The resulting Special Alert issued by FAO's Global Information and Early Warning System (GIEWS) in April 1992 brought the severity of the drought to the attention of the donor community and was used as a basis for preparing a United Nations-SADC Consolidated Appeal.

3.103 The SADC countries reacted promptly in April 1992 by establishing a regional task force to coordinate their relief efforts, including procurement, allocation and transport of food imports. Six corridor groups were formed, taking into account ports, connecting railways, roads and other transport-related services, including the private sector, in order to coordinate efforts to move the massive amount of drought relief imports smoothly into the region. In addition, a regional Logistic Advisory Centre was established, with WFP participation and funding from several donors to collect and disseminate information regularly on all matters relating to port and transport activities in the region to avoid congestion and other associated problems.

3.104 Collaboration between the United Nations (UN) and SADC in assessing emergency food aid and non-food aid requirements and in planning for delivery operations culminated in the launching of the 1992 UN-SADC Consolidated Appeal for Southern Africa. Participants in this effort also included the World Bank, IMF and several NGOs.

3.105 The appeal was effective in capturing world attention on the plight of the region. International assistance was requested for a total of 4.1 million tonnes of food aid, including 1.8 million tonnes of targeted food aid and 2.3 million tonnes of programme food aid. The appeal also included US$223 million of non-food assistance for water, health care and agricultural and livestock inputs as well as assistance for coordinating transport and logistics.

3.106 The donors' response to the UN-SADC appeal was very positive as pledges covered some 82 percent of the requests for targeted food aid and 89 percent for programme food aid. Contributions were more than sufficient for transport and logistics, as twice the amount requested by the SADC countries was obtained and many donors, NGOs and concerned institutions actively participated in the various relief activities. Consequently, rates of delivery of the goods were generally good, although it was noted that the cost of deliveries could have been reduced if planning, scheduling and transport operations had been better.

3.107 Non-food assistance related to water, health and agricultural inputs and rehabilitation received less attention, but efforts to mobilize resources for non-food assistance extended well beyond 1992 and funds were provided through various bilateral and multilateral channels. Concessional loans from institutions such as the World Bank allowed countries to import food on commercial terms.

3.108 Overall, as a result of effective coordination among the countries of the subregion and with the UN system, in addition to the very positive reaction by donors, the drought-induced emergency in southern Africa was resolved and the threat of famine was overcome.

Lessons learned: the 1994/95 drought

3.109 As a result of the experience of the 1991/92 crisis, the impact of the 1994/95 drought emergency in southern Africa, while serious, was much less devastating than the previous one. The drought was severe in Lesotho, where production was virtually wiped out, and serious in South Africa, Zambia and Zimbabwe, both with respect to domestic food production shortfalls and loss of exports. Other countries also suffered the effect of drought to varying degrees.

3.110 A number of favourable factors helped to mitigate the full impact of the 1994/95 drought on the food supply position of the countries in the subregion.

3.111 The Special Alerts on the crisis issued in December 1994 and January 1995 were released to the international community by FAO's GIEWS. These were followed by a series of joint FAO/WFP Crop and Food Supply Assessment Missions in the subregion in March/April 1995 in cooperation with the governments and SADC. These missions confirmed the earlier warnings and provided quantitative estimates of food needs in the subregion.

3.112 The governments of the affected countries and the international community heeded these early warnings of impending food supply shortfalls and made timely and adequate contingency plans. Large stocks held from the previous year's bumper harvest by national marketing boards, farmers and the commercial sectors in several countries, particularly South Africa and Zimbabwe, provided a welcome cushion before harvest and the arrival of imports.

3.113 FAO and WFP took the initiative of advancing approvals of emergency operations for the seriously affected countries in order to avoid delays in the mobilization of relief assistance. The countries in the subregion undertook a number of measures to control crop losses by plant pests and diseases.

3.114 In June 1995, SADC launched an international appeal to donors to combat the severe drought in parts of southern Africa and to overcome the anticipated food shortages in member countries. Several donors responded generously to this call for assistance. Working with governments, UN agencies, NGOs and local partners, donors undertook a range of measures across the region to help vulnerable groups in particular, some of whom had not yet recovered fully from the effects of the 1992 drought.

3.115 Since the 1991/92 drought emergency, a number of positive institutional and economic changes have also taken place in the subregion. South Africa became a member of SADC in 1994. Angola and Mozambique achieved peace, and several countries have instituted more liberal market policies. These developments are now contributing to a strong recovery in food production and substantially facilitate marketing and trade in the subregion.

4. Conclusions

4.1 This short collection of country case-studies demonstrates how a variety of countries with different economic and social structures, natural and social resource endowments and political orientations have managed to cope with some of the problems posed by national and household food insecurity. They illustrate the relative importance of the policy environment in shaping the economic and social processes that ultimately determine the food security status of the people in any country. Despite the varied nature of the specific policies employed in different countries and at different times, it is clear that there are always trade-offs involved in securing the food security of vulnerable groups. Moreover, the multiplicity of policy objectives that have to be pursued within any setting must ultimately be politically, socially and economically feasible if they are to have any chance of succeeding.

4.2 In any period, however, the orientation and nature of the policies implemented are usually shaped by the nature of the constraints that are viewed as binding by the policy-makers in the country. For most of the countries reviewed in this paper, the 1980s has been the era when financial and economic constraints appear to have dominated policy agendas. Some of those countries, such as China, Turkey and Indonesia, which have traditionally attached importance to measures for increasing productivity in the agricultural and food sector by promoting research, extension and the adoption of new production technologies, have gone a long way towards improving their food security situation. There have, however, been others, such as Thailand, Tunisia and Costa Rica, where the road to strengthening food security has meant devising measures to target vulnerable groups directly. Still others, for example Mozambique, Zimbabwe and Burkina Faso, more vulnerable than those already mentioned, have been able to alleviate the food security concerns of population groups particularly in need by removing some of the policy impediments that were constraining freer operations of food markets.

4.3 Generally speaking, most of the countries treated in the study at one time or another between the early 1960s and the 1990s faced financial and macroeconomic imbalances that jeopardized the sustainability of their public expenditures and affected the performance of their economies. In some, heavy protection afforded to agricultural producers and/or food consumers contributed in a major way to the creation of such imbalances. Experiences with the structural adjustment and economic liberalization programmes implemented to deal with the imbalances seem to be mixed. To the extent that these measures reduce support provided to vulnerable producers and consumers, the initial impact on food security is likely to be negative. However, increased economic efficiency may subsequently have beneficial impacts on food security in general. Experiences in Burkina Faso, Costa Rica, Ecuador, Mozambique, Tunisia and Zimbabwe, described above, have shown that such programmes really have improved food security. If, moreover, they are supplemented by appropriate policies that establish safety nets for vulnerable groups, as has been done in Costa Rica and Tunisia, the improvements tend to be more pronounced. Indeed, policies that are designed to target vulnerable groups, as in the case of food-for-work programmes in India, also tend to reduce distortions and imbalances.

Bibliography

Bigman, D. 1993. The measurement of food security: chronic undernutrition and temporary food deficiencies. *In* P. Back & D. Bigman, eds. *Food security and food inventories in developing countries,* p. 238-251. Wallingford, UK, CAB International.

Capital Institute Paediatrics. 1985. *Investigation on the physical development of children under 7 years of age in the rural districts of ten provinces of China.* (Mimeo)

Cleaver, K. 1993. *A strategy to develop agriculture in sub-Saharan Africa and a focus for the World Bank.* Technical Paper No. 203. Washington, DC, World Bank.

Drèze, J. & Sen, A. 1989. *Hunger and public action.* Oxford, UK, Clarendon.

FAO. 1983. *Report of the eighth session of the Committee on World Food Security.* CL 83/10. Rome.

FAO. 1993. *Progress report on the development of a household food security index.* CFS:93/2. Rome.

FAO. 1994a. *Assessment of the current world food security situation and recent policy developments.* CFS:94/2. Rome.

FAO. 1994b. *The State of Food and Agriculture.* 1994. Rome.

FAO. 1995a. *World agriculture: towards 2010.* N. Alexandratos, ed. Rome, FAO and Chichester, UK, John Wiley.

FAO. 1995b. *Evolution de la sécurité alimentaire en Tunisie,* by M. Allaya. Rome. (Mimeo)

FAO. 1995c. *Costa Rica: food security success story,* by A. Buainain. Rome. (Mimeo)

FAO. 1995d. *Ecuador: food security success story,* by A. Buainain. Rome. (Mimeo)

FAO. 1995e. *Agricultural policies and food security in China,* by J.Y. Lin. Rome. (Mimeo)

FAO. 1995f. *China: food security success story,* by J.Y. Lin. Rome. (Mimeo)

FAO. 1995g. *Food policy: frameworks for analysis and action. Achievements of outward oriented development strategy for food and agriculture in Thailand.* N.S. Randhawa & B. Huddleston, eds. Rome. (Mimeo)

FAO. 1995h. *Development of food and agriculture in India: a moderate performance,* by N.S. Randhawa. Rome. (Mimeo)

FAO. 1995i. *Genesis of agricultural and food development in Indonesia,* by N.S. Randhawa. Rome. (Mimeo)

FAO. 1996a. *The Sixth World Food Survey.* Rome.

FAO. 1996b. *Planning commodity exchanges – agricultural support policies in Turkey.* AG:TCP/TUR/4451. Rome.

FAO. 1996c. *Food security concerns in Turkey,* by H. Kasnakoglu. Rome. (Mimeo)

FAO. 1966d. *Burkina Faso: food security success story,* by K. Savadogo & T. Reardon. Rome. (Mimeo)

FAO. 1996e. *Mozambique: food security success story,* by D. Tschirley & M. Weber. Rome.

FAO/World Health Organization (WHO). 1992. *Major issues for nutrition strategies.* ICN/92/INF/7. Rome.

Gaiha, R. 1995. *Wages, participation and targeting – the case of the Employment Guarantee Scheme in India.* New Delhi, India. (Mimeo)

García, J.G. 1991. Colombia. *In* A.O. Krueger, M. Schiff & A. Valdés, eds. *The political economy of agricultural pricing policy – Latin America,* p. 144-202. Baltimore, MD, USA, The Johns Hopkins University Press, for the World Bank.

Gürkan, A.A. 1995a. Determining the structure of food insecurity at the global level: a cross country framework for analysing policy issues for the agro-food sector. *Econ. Soc.*, 22(3-4): 51-65.

Gürkan, A.A. 1995b. The mathematics of hunger. *CERES*, 27(2): 31-33.

Jayne, T.S., Rukuni, M., Hajek, M., Sithole, G. & Mudimu, G. 1991. Structural adjustment and food security in Zimbabwe. *In* J. Wyckoff & M. Rukuni, eds. *Toward an integrated national food policy strategy: proceedings of the second national consultative workshop.* Harare, Zimbabwe, University of Zimbabwe.

Jayne, T.S., Rubey, L., Tschirley, D., Mukumbu, M., Chisvo, M., Santos, A., Weber, M. & Diskin, P. 1995. *Effects of market reform on access to food by low-income households: evidence from four countries in eastern and southern Africa.* International Development Paper No.19. East Lansing, MI, USA, Michigan State University.

Kasnakoglu, H., Akder, H. & Gürkan, A.A. 1990. Agricultural labor and technological change in Turkey. *In* D. Tully, ed. *Labor and rainfed agriculture in West Asia and North Africa,* p. 103-133. Dordrecht, the Netherlands, Kluwer.

Khaldi, R. & Naili, A. 1995. Analyse des politiques de la sécurité alimentaire en Tunisie. *In* Centre international de hautes études agronomiques méditerranéennes (CIHEAM), ed. *La sécurité alimentaire en Méditerranée.* Montpellier, France, Options méditerranéennes, Série A: *Séminaires méditerranéens,* 26: 91-109.

Lin, J.Y. 1990. Collectivization and China's agricultural crisis in 1959-1961. *J. Polit. Econ.*, 98: 1228-1252.

Lin, J.Y. 1993. Exit rights, exit costs, and shirking in the theory of cooperative team: a reply. *J. Comp. Econ.,* 17: 504-520.

Lin, J.Y. 1995. *The role of agriculture in the transition process in China.* Paper presented at the Symposium on the Role of Agriculture in the Transition Process Towards a Market Oriented Economy, Wildbad Kreuth, Germany, 2-6 May.

McMillan, D.E. & Savadogo, K. 1996. Disease control, new land settlement and technological change. *In* J.H. Sanders, B.I. Shapiro & S. Ramaswamy, eds. *The economics of agricultural technology in semi-arid sub-Saharan Africa.* Baltimore, MD, USA, The Johns Hopkins University Press.

Maxwell, S. & Frankenberger, T. 1992. *Household food security: concepts, indicators, measurements – a technical review.* New York, NY, USA, United Nations Children's Fund (UNICEF) and Rome, International Fund for Agricultural Development (IFAD).

Pinstrup-Anderson, P. 1986. An analytical framework for assessing nutrition effects of policies and programs. *In* C.K. Mann & B. Huddleston, eds. *Food policy: frameworks for analysis and action,* p. 55-66. Bloomington, IN, USA, Indiana University Press.

Rubey, L. 1995. *Maize market reform in Zimbabwe: linkages between consumer preferences, small-scale enterprise development and alternative marketing channels.* Ph.D. dissertation. East Lansing, MI, USA, Michigan State University.

Sanders, J.H., Wright, P., Granier, P. & Savadogo, K. 1987. *Resource management and new technologies in Burkina Faso: a stable agricultural development.* Final report to the West African Division of the World Bank. West Lafayette, IN, USA, Department of Agricultural Economics, Purdue University.

Savadogo, K. 1990. *Production systems in the southwestern region of Burkina Faso.* Ouagadougou, Burkina Faso, School of Economics, University of Ouagadougou.

Savadogo, K. 1994. *Endogenously induced adjustment and poverty alleviation in sub-Saharan Africa.* Paper presented at the United States Agency for International Development (USAID)/Cornell University Conference on Poverty, Accra, Ghana, March.

Savadogo, K., Reardon T. & Pietola, K. 1994. *The determinants of agricultural productivity and supply response in Burkina Faso.* Michigan State University Staff Paper. East Lansing, MI, USA.

Savadogo, K. & Wetta, C. 1992. The impact of self-imposed adjustment: the case of Burkina Faso, 1983-89. *In* G.A. Cornia, R. Van der Hoeven & T. Mkandawire, eds. *Africa's recovery in the 1990s. From stagnation and adjustment to human development.* New York, NY, USA, St. Martin.

Sen, A.K. 1976. Poverty: an ordinal approach to measurement. *Econometrica*, 44: 219-31.

Siamwalla, A. & Setboonsarng, S. 1992. Thailand. *In* A.O. Krueger, M. Schiff & A. Valdés, eds. *The political economy of agricultural pricing policy – Asia,* p. 206-281. Baltimore, MD, USA, The John Hopkins University Press, for the World Bank.

Speth, J. 1993. *Towards sustainable food security.* Sir John Crawford Memorial Lecture. Washington, DC, Consultative Group on International Agricultural Research (CGIAR).

United Nations Children's Fund (UNICEF). 1990. *Strategy for improved nutrition of children and women in developing countries – a UNICEF policy review.* New York, NY, USA.

United States Agency for International Development (USAID). 1992. *World Food Day Report.* Washington, DC, USA. Office of Food for Peace.

Wen, G.J. 1993. Total factor productivity change in China's farming sector: 1952-89. *Econ. Dev. Cult. Change,* 42: 1-47.

World Bank. 1984. *Thailand: pricing and marketing policy for intensification of rice agriculture.* Report No. 4963-TH. Washington, DC, USA.

World Bank. 1986. *Poverty and hunger: issues and options for food security in developing countries.* Washington, DC, USA.

World Bank. 1992. *Indonesia: agricultural transformation – challenges and opportunities.* Washington, DC, USA.

World Bank. 1995. *Republic of Tunisia – towards the 21st century.* Country Economic Memorandum. Washington, DC, USA.

Zagré, P. 1992. *Etude des grandes étapes de la croissance et de la relance économique au Burkina Faso: le programme d'ajustement structurel, ses forces, ses faiblesses.* Ouagadougou, Burkina Faso, Coopération Canada/Burkina Faso.

3
Socio-political and economic environment for food security

Contents

Acknowledgements

The preparation of the World Food Summit technical background documents has mobilized, in addition to FAO's own staff contribution, a considerable amount of expertise in the international scientific community, drawn from partner international institutions and governmental or non-governmental circles. The process has been monitored at FAO by an internal Reading Committee, composed of staff selected ad personam, *and established to ensure that the whole collection meets appropriate quality and consistency criteria.*

The present document has been prepared by FAO's G.E. Rossmiller. After initial review within FAO by all technical departments, invited colleagues and the Reading Committee, and by selected external reviewers, a first version was published and circulated for comments to governments, intergovernmental organizations (IGOs) and non-governmental organizations (NGOs), as well as further peer reviewers. Much appreciated comments and advice have been received from Prof. Sartaj Aziz, Pakistan; Prof. Carl Eicher, Michigan State University, USA; Mr Gerard Viatte, the Organisation for Economic Co-operation and Development (OECD); Mr Alex McCalla, the World Bank, Washington, DC; and Mr Robert Paarlberg, Harvard University, United States.

While grateful for the contributions received from all reviewers, the FAO Secretariat bears the responsibility for the content of the document.

Executive summary

Much that affects food security has changed in the two decades since the World Food Conference of 1974. Perhaps the most important event has been the advent of the global economy. Similarly influential in reshaping history have been the breakup of centrally planned institutions in Central and Eastern Europe and the former Union of Soviet Socialist Republics (USSR) and the resultant transition towards a liberal economy; the effort to disarm and not proliferate weapons; the end of apartheid in South Africa; the rapid economic growth in China and in other countries of East Asia; and the conclusion of civil wars in such countries as Angola, Mozambique, Cambodia, El Salvador and Nicaragua.

The last several years have also seen the appearance of more ethnic conflict, sometimes coupled with long-hidden nationalism, as has occurred in Chechnya, the former Yugoslavia, Rwanda and Somalia. Indeed, most current conflicts are within and not between countries, but they compromise food security just the same. Drug consumption and the criminal and corruptive activities of drug trafficking emerge as another major problem for contemporary societies that hurts food security at individual and collective levels.

Some ideas that were put forth at the 1974 conference continue to be important, and issues such as population growth, health, urbanization and poverty still need to be adequately addressed. In addition, more emphasis is now being given to environmental problems, such as deforestation, water and air quality, climate change and overfishing, and their relation to food security.

The reality of global interdependence was called to the attention of policy-makers by the oil crises of 1973 and 1979 and the debt crises of the 1980s. The debt problem, not yet resolved despite numerous debt relief and reduction initiatives, has deleterious implications for food security. Debt-servicing obligations reduce the ability to import food, as well as other items that could increase domestic food production and consumption, and constrain resources for development and social welfare. The most recommended cure consisted of macroeconomic stabilization, enacting structural reforms (liberalization and privatization) and an increasing emphasis on international trade. A combination of policies, *inter alia*, reforming exchange rates, privatizing state-owned enterprises, reducing the public payroll and public spending generally, dampening inflation and cutting subsidies, was employed.

In the process of adjustment, the inward-oriented industrialization strategies of the 1960s and 1970s were replaced by more outward-looking ones. A market-oriented approach has replaced development strategies emphasizing direct government participation in commercial and economic affairs, and targeted subsidies have replaced generalized subsidies. Prices for agricultural products tend to rise with these structural changes, but this development benefits commercial producers and peasants who have clear access to land, not rural and urban wage-earners who are usually net buyers of farm products. Market liberalization and macroeconomic adjustment can create in the initial phase sectoral unemployment and poverty, unless effective social safety nets are put in place simultaneously.

At the same time, a new institutional structure for trade was being constructed. The Uruguay Round of the General Agreement on Tariffs and Trade (GATT) negotiations, dedicated to reducing protection according to a predefined schedule, was concluded and the World Trade Organization (WTO) was founded. Regional trading organizations have also been emerging. Financial markets have become almost completely integrated and globalized. These developments have resulted in the limiting of the ability of countries to manage their own monetary and fiscal policies. It is too early to assess fully the importance of this more liberal and integrated economic environment for food security but, given time, it is likely to be substantial.

External assistance flows have been declining in recent years, and agriculture was hit more than propotionally by the reduction. As a result, total commitments to agriculture in 1994 were 23 percent below those of 1990. External private capital flows into the developing countries increased dramatically from 1990 to 1993, then stabilized subsequent to the Mexican crisis. However, since they mainly accrue to a limited number of countries, these inputs cannot be expected to compensate for the reduced official aid to low-income countries. Futher, experience underlined the potential risk of excessive foreign liability in the face of volatile financial markets.

The accentuation of demographic and economic imbalances between countries caused by political events, most notably in the early 1990s, has strongly affected international labour mobility and migration patterns. Apart from refugees, over 80 million people are living outside their own country at present, and transboundary migrations have reached unprecedented levels for economic and political reasons, while rural-urban migration within borders is of great concern in many countries. Migrations have direct implications for food security in both originating and recipient areas and for migrants. The extensive resources devoted to controlling migrations and combating their consequences could be reduced if more efforts were aimed at enhancing the living conditions and employment opportunities for people where they are.

A socio-political and economic environment most conducive to eliminating food insecurity and undernutrition, or, in other words, to ensuring food for all, would include:

- the adoption by countries of broadly participatory and pluralistic political systems under which governments would be responsive and responsible to the people;
- the use by governments of peaceful means of resolving both internal conflicts and those with other governments;
- government allocation of limited resources to do those things that markets do not do well and that are necessary for the efficient and effective functioning of the economy and society;
- the liberalization of domestic and international markets to allow for resources to be employed globally to maximize the sustainable level and rate of growth of economic activity;
- the focusing of national and international attention on finding the means to assist the poor in increasing their productivity and improving their access to food, thereby narrowing the gap between the rich and the poor.

In the final analysis, food security in any country must be under the responsibility and the authority of the national government in conjunction with local authorities and working with concerned groups and individuals in the society. International coordination and liaison is necessary. The global community and international organizations can be helpful, but they cannot substitute the actions and political will to achieve food security within the country itself.

1. Introduction

1.1 The world is developing in remarkable ways, unforeseen even a decade ago, and these changes have important implications for food security. New states, new issues and new institutions are reshaping international political, economic and environmental relations even as the old ones remain, albeit in some attenuated form. Nevertheless, the new trends are clear: most countries are seeking economic policies that are more market-oriented and desire broader international cooperation and sustainable development together with the political structures to promote and support them.

1.2 The changes in the socio-political and economic environments can be characterized by the following:
- First, many developing countries had come into the 1980s with very high levels of external debt taken on during the 1970s at low and often negative real interest rates. By the early 1980s, their economic fortunes had been reversed with slowed growth rates, rising real interest rates and an appreciating United States dollar in which virtually all external debt was denominated. Their heavy debt burdens could no longer be sustained; indeed, many could not even meet debt service payments. Belt-tightening and policy reform became absolutely necessary with conditionality terms imposed by the World Bank and the International Monetary Fund (IMF) calling for reduced government spending, a reduction of government intervention in markets, the privatization of former parastatals and the correction of overvalued exchange rates, i.e. getting the prices right.
- Second, many countries, particularly in the developed world, found that the budgetary cost of farm support had become untenable. The process of policy reform was begun in order to limit budget exposure by more precise targeting of policy benefits, lower support levels, the decoupling of support payments from current production and generally reduced government presence.
- Third, with the breakdown of the command and control economies of Central and Eastern Europe and the former Union of Soviet Socialist Republics (USSR) came a difficult and painful process of transition towards more open, market-oriented economies. This transition process disrupted traditional trading patterns, drastically decreased real per caput incomes, reduced demand and disrupted production, processing and distribution from which a recovery has not yet been effected. Even the most basic legal and economic institutions have had to be created to allow and encourage the private sector to operate as part of a functioning market economy.
- Fourth, even countries not falling into any of the above three categories have been caught up in the general move to reduce the presence of government and to liberalize markets and trade.

1.3 The quest for new policies to shape contemporary institutions is taking place alongside a wider examination of the basic role of government in forms that are scaled down from those of the past. It has been prompted in part by governments' own need to optimize resource efficiency in the face of growing deficits and in part by the demands of tax-weary citizens who find themselves with stagnating real incomes and who blame government for unsatisfactory economic performance.[1] Shifting international relations and a sharply altered global economic situation result in new challenges to national and global stability; meanwhile, local problems and conflicts go unresolved. Together, these issues shape food security.

1.4 Essentially, food security means that all people at all times have access to safe and nutritious food to maintain a healthy and active life. This definition implies three dimensions to food security, namely, availability, access and stability at various levels of aggregation, i.e. global, national, household and individual. Given this multidimensional framework, it becomes obvious that achievement of universal food security at the individual level, which implies achievement at the more aggregate levels, is constrained or facilitated by a combination of social, political and economic conditions. And, it is clear that the relevance of these conditions to food security at one level of aggregation is not restricted to the state of conditions at the same level of aggregation. That is, for example, the ability to achieve food security in one country can be affected by conditions (economic, political, and social, etc.) in other countries; as the world economy becomes more integrated, it becomes more difficult for a country to insulate itself from the decisions and actions of others. At the same time, this same integration offers the potential for spreading the effects of production shortfalls in one country over the world and thus greatly reduces the negative impact on food security in any one country.

1.5 Because they affect agriculture, global, national and local shifts in national political and economic relations and structures have implications for food security. First, how food is to be produced and distributed are fundamental concerns of national economies and contribute to ongoing policy debates about how to restructure economic and political systems.

1.6 Second, agriculture's technological transformation increasingly links the input market to other sectors of the economy, while international trade joins producers in the national economy to consumers throughout the world.

1.7 Third, no other sector has such wide-reaching effects on the sustainability of the environment and natural resources: farming affects the world's forests, soils, fresh water and fisheries.

1.8 Finally, war and peace, hostility and *détente*, confrontation and cooperation in political relations temper the global environment and influence food security. A principal benefit of the ending of the Cold War should have been disarmament from which a peace dividend might have been realized, as the high-income countries could have reduced to some extent their military expenditures with economic development and food security gains reasonably expected. Unfortunately, there is little evidence that any of the elusive peace dividend has been used to promote sustainable and equitable development. And the proliferation of regional and civil conflicts makes an increase in military spending more likely than a decrease

[1] For a review of the United States case, see Cassidy (1995).

among concerned regions. In addition, the end of the Cold War has reduced the incentive for developed countries to use economic assistance to win the hearts and minds of the developing world over to a particular ideology.

1.9 The global political environment influences the level and destination of resource flows, including international trade in food and assistance for agriculture and food production.

1.10 At the national level, politics govern policy priorities. Final decisions on the sometimes conflicting objectives of development, stabilization, national security and social equity reflect the relative power of a country's various political factions and how national consensus is reached. The primary responsibility for the level of food security in any country depends on the political choices it makes. Bad government begets food insecurity, as was aptly remarked by the representative of Uganda at the FAO Council in November 1994.

1.11 This paper examines how international relations, economic structures, political systems and global issues are related to food security. After a review of the global political environment since the 1974 World Food Conference, discussion turns to the contemporary economic environment and how trends in market liberalization in the transitional economies and structural adjustment in the developing and industrialized countries are affecting national-level food production and consumption. Also explored are the food security implications of the recently concluded Uruguay Round of the General Agreement on Tariffs and Trade and the global trend towards regional trade blocs, as well as issues of natural resources and the environment. Finally, the policy implications for achieving food security are drawn, along with a blueprint for the future.

2. The political environment in historical perspective

2.1 The two decades since the 1974 World Food Conference have brought about enormous changes on the world's political stage. In the mid-1970s, the end of the Viet Nam war helped to ease political tensions worldwide, especially among the superpowers, and a flurry of treaties in the 1970s greatly relaxed East-West tensions in Europe.

2.2 While there was wide divergence among countries and regions, the 1960s and 1970s marked a period of overall positive economic growth for many developing countries. Between 1965 and 1973, economic growth in the developing world reached 3.9 percent annually, an all-time record. This figure declined to 2.9 percent from 1973 to 1980, largely because of the oil crises. In the period from 1980 to 1990, which was characterized by high debt problems, there was a rapid drop-off to an economic growth rate of 1.2 percent.

2.3 The 1970s also witnessed a period of reaffirmation of the developing countries' role in the global economic and political scene. In the wake of the oil embargo in 1973 by the Organization of Petroleum Exporting Countries (OPEC) and subsequent pricing policies, many developing nations, especially those with oil resources, renewed efforts to reduce their political and economic dependence on industrialized countries and to become more articulate and exert more power in the conduct of world affairs. The oil-rich countries also attempted to utilize their newly found economic power to set the terms and write the rules affecting trade, the transfer of technology and foreign assistance. The ideas of a united Third World, which Indian prime minister Nehru and other legendary leaders had fostered, gained ground, as did the concepts of a more just New International Economic Order (NIEO), non-alignment and self-reliance.

2.4 A number of initiatives for common action emerged from developing-country meetings in Algieria in 1973 and Sri Lanka in 1976, resulting in Technical Cooperation among Developing Countries (TCDC) and Economic Cooperation among Developing Countries (ECDC). But the achievement of food security in most developing countries and now in the transitional economies implies the need for major social transformations. The elimination of hunger requires the eradication of poverty through equitable and sustainable growth, which in turn requires significant changes in social relations, production structures and technologies. Economic decisions, both macro and micro, affecting accumulation, production and consumption are needed that are responsive to the objective of food security. This can only happen if the political will is present to make the difficult economic choices and to modify existing institutions or create new ones to support that end.

2.5 Before the 1980s, when economic growth was almost universal and rapid, development strategy focused on the redistribution of growth benefits to include those who were deprived. The mid-1970s marked the emergence of a new policy approach to development that was based on empirical studies that showed it was possible for economies to have rapid growth *and* attain a more equitable distribution of income simultaneously. For a while, equity considerations were placed high on the agenda as was the achievement of basic needs in developing economies. But, in the 1980s, negative growth in many countries, particularly in Latin America and Africa, left little to redistribute. Thus the recent emphasis on free markets, trade liberalization and minimal government intervention carries with it the hope that these approaches will somehow also revive and stimulate economic growth. Unfortunately, the evidence that might confirm this hope, and with it enhanced food security, is not yet available and, in the meantime, the emphasis on redistribution seems to have waned.

2.6 The idea of an assertive and united developing world capable of resisting external intervention by both of the dominant political blocs of the time was frustrated by developments that led to growing diversity among the developing countries and by the ideological and political confrontations among them. Often, while professing solidarity, countries moved to uncoordinated initiatives, sometimes in tune with varying outside patrons and sometimes not. Meanwhile, it became increasingly obvious that there were no short cuts to successful nationhood and self-reliant development and no recipe for a successful developing-country bloc.

2.7 The 1980s saw a return to Cold War tensions. The conflict in Afghanistan, regional conflicts in the Near East and Central America, extended civil wars in Angola and Mozambique, the prolonged Iraq-Islamic Republic of Iran war and internal conflicts in Cambodia are examples. The tensions resulted in a renewed and extravagant armaments race. To this day, the developing countries continue to increase their military spending. The United Nations Development Programme (UNDP) reports that the developing economies have increased their defence expenditures by 8 percent annually since 1960, and sub-Saharan Africa, the region that can least afford it, has increased the portion of its regional gross domestic product (GDP) devoted to the military from about 0.7 percent in 1960 to approximately 3 percent today. Most of these funds are not used in guarding the country from outside attack, but in fighting factions of their own citizens. Every dollar spent for the military is one less for the provision of economic development and food security. Ideological confrontations and open conflict form the basis for much food insecurity.

2.8 In Central and Eastern Europe and the USSR of the 1980s, the twin objectives of military strength and socio-economic progress proved increasingly difficult to achieve simultaneously. The resulting strains on centrally planned economic systems precipitated the major transformations that began in the late 1980s.

2.9 Meanwhile, in many of the developed countries, the global recession of the early 1980s was followed by an unusually long period of sustained growth, stability and integration that strengthened their position in world affairs.

2.10 Events of the latter part of the 1980s and early 1990s were among the most momentous of the century. In a short period, radical political and economic transformations swept across Eastern Europe and the republics of the former USSR. The principles of centrally planned economic management were abandoned in favour of a more market-oriented approach. The political complexities of the transition were compounded by the revolutionary and unprecedented character of the institutional change and the absence of a supporting political and economic conceptual framework. For most of these former centrally planned economies, the initial phase of the reform translated into profound and polarizing dislocations.

2.11 Some feel that the nadir has now been reached. To date, privatization has been accompanied by unemployment, reduced production, lack of credit and consumer and producer subsidies, political instability and growing inequality in income and resource distribution. These phenomena challenge food security in the region. Problems associated with transition, especially in the former USSR, have required the mobilization of human and financial resources and have become a predominant concern of the international community. In addition, they have tended to divert funds from sub-Saharan Africa, where development programmes have done poorly, where population growth has consistently outrun economic growth and where food security is most in jeopardy.

2.12 Experiences in Central and Eastern Europe and in Central Asia contrasted sharply with changes in China, where economic reforms began in 1978. While land remained in the hands of the state, the Household Responsibility System (HRS) broke communes into individual farms and, in a major ideological shift, encouraged profit maximization. The HRS (together with some supplementary measures that were introduced at the same time) contributed to the lifting of millions of families out of poverty during the 1980s when people realized that they could consume and invest the products of their labour rather than ceding them to the state. Farm production rose rapidly as a result, ultimately helping to fuel the economic boom of the mid- and late 1980s and the 1990s.

2.13 For most of Africa and Latin America and the Caribbean, the 1980s represented a decade of economic and financial crisis. Indeed, a long period of recession and adjustment followed Mexico's admission that it had overborrowed and underinvested in the 1970s; in 1982 it could not continue to make payments on its debt. The debt crisis spread quickly to other countries, revealing that much of Latin America was in similar financial straits; political fragility accompanied the economic problems. Many governments lost the capacity to resist external political and economic pressure, and room for domestic-policy manoeuvring was severely circumscribed. Pressing day-to-day financial concerns forced many countries to postpone the long-term development, equity and poverty-alleviation objectives that afforded such bright hope in the 1970s. Concomitantly, the process of regional cooperation and integration slowed or came to a complete standstill.

3. Global relations and food security issues in the 1990s

3.1 As the 1990s unfolded, a new pattern of international relations began to emerge. While the end of the Cold War reduced political tensions among the superpowers and prompted some cutting of military expenditures by both the developed countries and the former centrally planned economies, saved resources were not added to developing-country growth efforts.

3.2 An increasing number of governments espouse democratic principles, popular participation in governance and economic liberalization. Popular participation is often implied to be the equivalent of participatory democracy, with no groups or classes excluded. This, unfortunately, is often not the case. Nevertheless, the United Nations reports that, in 1993, elections were held in 45 countries, and nearly 75 percent of the world's population now lives in countries with democratic and relatively pluralistic regimes. The end of apartheid and the introduction of majority rule in South Africa is the most outstanding recent event in this process.

3.3 The first half of the 1990s has also seen the emergence or aggravation of other trends and influences. More and more small states are emerging, requiring new forms of extranational arrangements and development assistance. Conflicts such as those in Bosnia-Herzegovina and Chechnya are recent and dramatic manifestations of an emergent nationalism that has created new, as well as exacerbated old, political, economic, religious and ethnic problems. Violence and war have continued unabated in various parts of the developing world. Of the 82 armed conflicts recorded between 1989 and 1992, only three were between former sovereign states; the remainder involved civil disturbances of one type or another in which food production, distribution, commerce and consumption were disrupted.

3.4 While violent conflicts often cause severe food insecurity, social hardship has in turn been at the heart of many domestic armed conflicts. The tragedies of civil war in Rwanda and Somalia with their dramatic sequel of human suffering, refugee problems and famine are examples. In 1994, some 14 African countries were in a state of war and another 18 were experiencing systemic violence (Smith, 1994). Emergency food shipments are frequently needed in the wake of these armed conflicts to maintain some level of food security.

3.5 These upheavals will continue to challenge global stability and strain donors' capacity – and resolve, since donor fatigue is a real phenomenon – to deliver needed relief. In some cases, ethnic and political tensions run deep; when analysed, many even find their roots in problems of income and resource inequality, lack of access to land and a shortage of employment opportunities. Events that began publicly in Chiapas, Mexico, after 1 January 1994 provide an example, as does increasing pressure for justice on the part of indigenous peoples in Bolivia and Ecuador.

3.6 External-assistance flows have been falling. Official development assistance, which accounts for two-thirds of the resource flows to low-income countries, declined from 0.35 percent of donors' GDP in 1983 to 0.29 percent in 1994, the lowest level in more than 20 years. This unfortunate trend, which will most likely continue in the coming years, reflects pressure for fiscal consolidation in donor countries, a reduced political rationale for official assistance after the fall of the Berlin wall and changing views on the developmental role of aid *vis-à-vis* private financing in the current era of economic liberalization.

3.7 Agriculture has been particularly hard hit by the reduction in assistance flows. Total commitments to agriculture in 1994 were 11 percent below the previous year's levels and no less than 23 percent below those of 1990. The share of agriculture in total official development financing declined from 13 percent in 1990 to around 10 percent in recent years.

3.8 The consumption of illegal drugs, together with the criminal and corruptive influence of the organizations and individuals involved in drug trafficking, has emerged as another major contemporary problem with negative implications for individual and collective food security. The spread of illegal drug consumption is accelerating, with the number of addicts now reaching millions in several countries. Their own physical and mental health, their capacity to contribute to society and their families' chances for a better life are endangered if not annihilated. Illegal drug trade, involving billions of dollars, diverts resources, empowers corrupters and destabilizes entire regions or segments of societies. The production of drug crops generates relatively high returns to producers, which poses a major constraint to national actions and international cooperation aimed at constructively containing and reducing drug production.

3.9 It has been documented time and again that both the resources and technologies are at hand to eliminate dire poverty and eradicate hunger. The only element lacking is the political will to do so. Until governments are willing and politically able to give the highest priority to the elimination of hunger and the poverty that is its root cause, the hungry will remain in developed and developing countries alike. This means winning widespread support among the interest groups that currently exert power and influence and also empowering those groups that, for lack of control over resources or of access to effective political participation, are on the margins of the political and social economy.

4. Population changes and food security

4.1 Population growth[2] is probably the single most important global trend influencing food security. It took nearly 1 million years for the earth's human population to reach 1 billion people. During the next ten years, another 1 billion persons will be added. The relationship between population growth rates and economic development is a chicken-and-egg phenomenon. Rapid population growth rates most certainly make economic development and per caput income growth more difficult. But the factors that have been shown to slow the rate of population growth are those associated with broad-based economic development: increasing per caput incomes; rising educational levels; growing employment opportunities, especially for women; and an increase in secure access to food, health services and other basic needs.

4.2 Structural characteristics of the world's population are also changing in ways that affect food security. At present, over 800 million people are chronically undernourished because they lack food. Twenty years ago, 80 percent of the population in developing countries lived in rural areas. In the early 1970s, only one city in sub-Saharan Africa had more than 500 000 inhabitants; by 1990, 10 percent of the region's population lived in cities of more than 1 million people. By the year 2000, nearly 40 percent of the population is expected to live in urban areas.

4.3 In the next 30 years, the number of people living in cities in developing countries will quadruple from 1 billion to 4 billion individuals. This imposing shift towards a more urban world calls for a different set of institutions, markets, infrastructure and food policies. These structural changes also modify farm labour supplies and pose important challenges for food security. For example, in sub-Saharan Africa, the steady migration of males to cities and other areas to look for wages or a job in the informal sector makes women responsible for farm work. Women produce 75 percent of the region's food (Saito, 1994). Raising agricultural productivity and output and improving household food security demands a greater emphasis on women farmers by donors and governments alike, including policy reforms to improve women's access to land and credit, their ability to contract labour and their willingness to adopt technology and utilize technical assistance.

---

[2] See also WFS companion paper 4, *Food requirements and population growth.*

5. Food security in a changing world: the economic environment

5.1 The period since the 1974 World Food Conference has seen three different economic performance scenarios for the developing countries: high growth in the mid-1970s; crisis in the late 1970s and most of the 1980s, with the exception of Asia; and spotty recovery in the 1990s.

5.2 The first scenario, a high-growth period during the 1970s, began at the end of the Second World War and was primarily attributed to the locomotive effect of developed-country growth on developing countries through international trade links. This long period was also marked by relatively stable commodity prices and increasing import substitution, while official development assistance to developing countries was also on the rise.

5.3 The global economy underwent a drastic change following the 1973 and 1979 oil shocks, the first of which coincided with the failure of monsoons in South Asia; cereal crop shortfalls in the United States, Europe and the former USSR; and a sharp increase in feed imports by the latter. The developed countries attempted to inflate away the effects of the oil and commodity price shocks by increasing their money supplies. World liquidity increased further as the major commercial banks recycled the petrodollars deposited by OPEC countries. As a result, real interest rates fell markedly.

5.4 Many oil-importing developing countries managed to reduce the potential negative effects of the oil shocks and maintain their overall public and private consumption and investment levels by borrowing heavily at favourable terms. This enabled them to grow at relatively high rates despite the adverse international environment.

5.5 However, some expenditures that were undertaken with borrowed funds were not bankable; others, such as those for infrastructure, were not designed to reach a positive cash flow in the short term. In fact, a significant portion of them were undertaken so injudiciously that they yielded small returns, and the cash flow that they generated could not meet the debt service. Meanwhile, loans continued apace, while both developing and developed countries avoided (or postponed) adjustment to the first oil shock.

5.6 Following the second oil shock in 1979, the OECD countries, led by the United States, altered their macroeconomic stance dramatically, opting for strict monetary policies (with a much more permissive fiscal policy) in order to control inflation. Interest rates rose and the United States dollar appreciated. As a result, many developing countries found themselves caught between a serious and unexpected contraction of capital inflows and a simultaneously large increase in external payments that had to be made with an appreciating dollar. Since the recently expanded foreign debt was primarily to private lenders on a short-term, floating-rate basis (as opposed to previous periods when lenders were largely official and lent on a concessional longer-term basis), the hike in interest rates precipitated the debt crisis. By 1982, many developing countries were paying more in debt service than they received in capital inflows.

5.7 In addition, inappropriate policies in a large number of developing countries, including unsustainable fiscal and monetary policies and severe economic rigidities arising from past inward-oriented development strategies, prevented their economies from adjusting to the external shocks of the late 1970s and early 1980s.

5.8 Inward-oriented policies, which came largely from import-substituting industrialization (ISI), the predominant development strategy of the time, were losing momentum prior to the crisis. A major characteristic of ISI was the relative neglect and, in some cases, discrimination against agriculture, both in terms of price incentives relative to other sectors and in the allocation of public investment. Macroeconomic policies (overvalued exchange rates) and trade policies (border protection of industry) discriminated against agricultural producers by shifting the internal terms of trade away from the farm sector. Sectoral policies that aimed at subsidizing agricultural producers were usually unable to compensate for the negative effects of unfavourable macroeconomic and trade policies.[3]

5.9 The economic crisis had detrimental effects on the food-insecure. The economic recession associated with the crisis deprived the most food-insecure of employment opportunities. Meanwhile, an already overextended public sector could not meet its development and social safety-net objectives in the face of decreased domestic savings and constant cash outflows to meet debt service and repayments.

5.10 For many countries, especially in sub-Saharan Africa and Latin America, poverty increased during the 1980s, reversing the trend of the previous 20 years. Although most indicators of social performance (literacy rates, disease eradication or at least suppression, longevity, secondary-school attendance, infant and childhood mortality and population growth rates) continued to improve for the developing countries as a whole, for some, especially in sub-Saharan Africa, they deteriorated.

5.11 Poverty, on the other hand, continued to have its greatest incidence in rural areas of developing countries with the landless and the near-landless constituting the largest single group of those afflicted by poverty. Some 30 million people in developing countries are landless and an additional 138 million are near-landless, and numbers in this category are growing throughout the developing world, especially in South Asia. Landlessness and near-landlessness are prime determinants of food insecurity in rural areas. Resources to accommodate the poor are shrinking with the expansion of arable land growing at an inferior rate to that of the rural populations.

5.12 It was thought by some Latin American policy-makers in the 1960s and 1970s that if governments were responsive to peasant demands for land reform, food security in the various countries might be enhanced. In East Asia, the late 1940s and the 1950s brought sweeping land reforms in Japan, the Republic of

[3] See also Krueger, Schiff and Valdés (1991) and Schiff and Valdés (1992).

Korea and Taiwan (Province of China) which helped to stimulate production (rental units became ownership units resulting in peasants having more interest in producing) and equity. It was averred that, in Latin America, the effect might be similar. Earlier reforms in Latin America had occurred in Mexico, Bolivia and Guatemala, but the example of Cuba and certain foreign-aid policies of the United States, which conditioned foreign aid on land and tax reforms, returned the issue to centre stage where it remained for the next few decades. By the 1990s, issues of a *dirigiste* land reform were displaced by the idea that the land market could supply the peasantry with the property needed, and there was some effort (led by Mexico in 1992) to *marketize* land reform. Currently, international agencies, worried that very little land is actually going into peasant ownership, are realizing that some direct subsidies for land purchase may be necessary.

Box
LAND REFORM IN LATIN AMERICA

The land reforms of the latter part of the twentieth century in Latin America were usually limited efforts that infrequently challenged the rural élite. They occurred often where peasant land-hunger complaints were most vociferous and to a large amount of publicity and fanfare. But after land was distributed, other inputs were generally not provided on terms the new landowners could afford and production credit loans tended to dry up. While some studies showed that production on the areas turned over to the peasants was at the same level, if not a superior one, as that which had existed prior to reform, most production gains tended to occur on the smaller reserves of landlords who engaged in intensification of their farming programmes in an effort at income maintenance. Alternatively, they occurred in the commercial sector where farmers were usually not expropriated from if they were good producers.

Thus, the new peasant landholders were not afforded, by the institutions of the time, a very propitious beginning to their farming careers. Furthermore, resident farm labourers, the highest-status workers in Latin American agriculture, were usually apportioned the land while the *campesinos* (farmers) who had no land access infrequently obtained property, thereby dampening the income-distribution effect of land reform. Moreover, these new landowners were less willing than the former landlords to hire landless *campesinos* at the going wage.

5.13 Furthermore, governments often compromised the income effects of land reform by turning the domestic terms of trade against agriculture or by spending for the reform in a profligate manner without the needed government savings to back up the land purchases and administrative and technical support for land reform. This economic populism tended to instigate inflation, which lowered the incomes of the rural and urban poor. In general, recent land reforms in developing countries have increased food security, but most increases have not come from the peasant sector that received the land (Thiesenhusen, 1995).

6. Changing the economic paradigm

6.1 The economic development paradigm that dominated developing-country thinking from the end of the Second World War until the late 1980s emphasized the shortcomings of markets in allocating resources and the role of an active government in planning and controlling most aspects of economic life. Several interrelated forces contributed to the abandonment of this paradigm.[4] First, in the industrialized countries, the failure of activist demand management policies to counter the negative effects of the oil shock on growth and employment raised serious questions about government effectiveness in generating sustainable growth. Second, the disappointing performance of most developing countries during the late 1970s and early 1980s revealed the susceptibility of their economies to external shocks and the weakness of the policies meant to manage them.

6.2 The pressing need to overcome the economic and financial crisis prompted a reassessment of the comparative ability of governments and markets to allocate resources efficiently and to create the conditions for sustainable growth. It was overwhelmingly decided that freer markets promote more efficiency and provide for better growth prospects. At the same time, fiscal pressures associated with the crisis and international lending institutions forced many governments to reduce or reorient the public sector's role in economic activity. Today, the widely accepted development paradigm emphasizes macroeconomic equilibrium and market-determined resource allocation.

6.3 In 1974, when the World Food Conference took place, the economic and social environment following the first oil price shock and the recession was such that a global dialogue was seen as necessary and desirable and that government intervention, individually and collectively, was fundamental to confronting what was perceived as the world food problem. Now, in the environment of economic liberalization, reduced government intervention and market-led policy orientation, the utility of a dialogue between governments appears more circumscribed. This is particularly true for problems that, while common to many countries, do not transcend national borders and therefore do not require international cooperation and coordination for their solution.

6.4 In this environment, the role of governments has been greatly restricted, even as global interdependence increases. Governments today can legitimately negotiate international codes of conduct, behaviour protocols, market regulatory agreements, multilateral assistance levels and the like in cases of international market failure. They can agree to cooperative action against international threats such as crime and terrorism. They can agree on the rules of the game and the use of dispute settlement processes in such existing fora as the World Trade Organization (WTO) or the international court. But when it comes to basic resource allocation, accumulation, production and consumption within the

[4] For a more detailed discussion, see FAO (1993). See also FAO (1995b), Chapter 7.

framework thus set, governments have, in principle, abrogated the major responsibility to market mechanisms while retaining the responsibility and authority for ensuring that the formal and informal institutions needed to allow those mechanisms to operate freely and fairly are in place and functioning. Further economic, trade and political liberalization, and, equally as important, institutional development, will need to take place before this transformation is complete.

6.5 What does all of this mean for food security? First and foremost it means that food security is a national, local and individual responsibility. Only national governments have the ability to create the stable political, macroeconomic, legal and regulatory environment within which private-sector activities can flourish. It is governments that have the responsibility, albeit with assistance from international agencies and non-governmental bodies, to provide the safety nets needed to protect those vulnerable groups in society that have no recourse to the resources needed for their own support.

7. Dealing with the crisis: policy adjustments and food security

7.1 Pressure from the major financial lending institutions, including the World Bank and the International Monetary Fund (IMF), forced many recalcitrant countries to adopt economic liberalization policies. Organizations lending to debtor countries conditioned their loans on such policies as macroeconomic austerity and currency devaluation. In addition, a series of structural measures to remove supply-side economic bottlenecks was imposed, including the removal of administered input and output prices and drastic reductions or elimination of subsidies for various sectors including agriculture. A large number of developing countries continue to implement stabilization and structural adjustment programmes that were begun in the 1980s.

7.2 During the mid- and late 1980s, the conditionality required by the IMF and the World Bank on stabilization and structural and sectoral adjustment loans was perceived as stringent, rigid and unbending. The resultant belt-tightening and austerity were often associated with wrenching drops in real incomes and levels of living, primarily hurting those least able to adjust. Some countries rebelled at the severity of the adjustment measures imposed by both the IMF and the World Bank, often in the face of civil unrest in opposition to the imposed austerity. By the early 1990s, the World Bank and the IMF began to show more flexibility in their approach to stabilization and structural and sectoral adjustment, recognizing that unless reforms were both appropriate for the specific conditions and could receive the political support of the people, through proper attention to the social dimension, they were unlikely to be implemented for long enough to work.

7.3 The debt issue continues to plague countries in all regions and, indeed, is becoming more intense, despite all efforts towards debt rationalization. Most disturbing is the situation in sub-Saharan Africa, where, although its absolute external-debt level is the lowest of the developing regions, it is the highest as a proportion of regional GDP (110 percent in 1993), and increasing. The debt problem, not yet resolved despite numerous debt relief and reduction initiatives, has many deleterious implications for food security. Debt-servicing obligations reduce the ability of countries to import food and non-food items that could increase domestic food production and consumption and constrain resources that might otherwise be available for financing development and social welfare schemes. The debt problem has evolved in nature and characteristics. The crisis of the 1980s, mostly in middle-income countries, initially concerned commercial debt and, as such, was perceived as a threat to the stability of the global financial system. Private financing virtually stopped for several years before rebounding forcefully, but much more selectively, in the 1990s. The Brady Plan, among other initiatives, contributed towards alleviating the debt burden in a number of countries. The 1990s have seen a different type of debt problem, which also had its roots in the 1980s, that of low-income countries borrowing from developed-country governments and multilateral creditors. Much of this lending took place to help poor countries cope with falling export commodity prices, rising world interest rates and escalating repayment schedules to commercial banks. Of particular concern is the continuing aggravation of the debt burden in many countries in Africa – 25 of the 32 severely indebted low-income countries are in sub-Saharan Africa. While Latin America and the Caribbean and Asia have seen an improvement overall, serious difficulties are also being faced by a number of countries in these regions as well.

7.4 The structural adjustment policies have an impact on domestic food security in several ways:
- the policies focus on economic efficiency and fiscal prudence entailing a preference for targeted non-distorting interventions as opposed to economy-wide price-distorting policies;
- the policies reduce public-sector involvement in food production, storage and distribution (e.g. parastatals and other state distribution channels) and increase the role of markets and non-governmental organizations (NGOs) in the implementation of food security interventions;
- the surrogate role of the state (mainly in terms of encouraging public investment) is concentrated on actions having the highest potential for promoting overall growth.

7.5 The effects of policy reforms on the poor and the food-insecure are most likely to be different in the short term and in the long term. Who benefits and who loses depends on the income, resource and education profile. In the short term, the stabilization effects dominate. Reductions in the social safety nets (including cuts in the public payroll and welfare-type programmes that benefit the poor) and higher prices for imported items (including basic goods such as food, medicines and fuel) because of devaluation have, at least, short-term detrimental effects on the weakest segments of the population. This shift may also transfer resources from the domestic agricultural sector and leave poor farmers without production credit. In many countries, of course, farmers are net consumers of purchased foodstuffs, and they and city consumers alike are affected by rising retail prices for necessities.

7.6 Important determinants of who loses from stabilization and to what extent depends on whether both poor people and those better off own or at least have clear access to productive resources, whether they can take advantage of opportunities in the formal and informal labour markets and whether they have access to government subsidies or other programmes. For instance, low-income urban residents who depend directly or indirectly on public-sector employment may become food-insecure as a result of reductions in government public-works programmes and cuts in subsidies for food and other goods and services (such as fuel, electricity and health services).

7.7 For the rural poor the situation is often even more complex than for the poor living in cities. While the effects of reform programmes on the agricultural sector are expected to be positive overall, mainly through higher prices to agricultural producers, the distribution of gains and losses among rural people depends on whether they are net food sellers or buyers, whether they are producers of export or subsistence crops and whether they have access to land, labour, credit, input and product markets (Binswanger, 1989).[5]

7.8 In the medium and long terms, the effects of policy reforms are determined by the extent to which they contribute to growth resumption.

7.9 The impact of external conditions, institutional and political factors and pressures and the degree of economic crisis and pre-reform distortions brought about by inappropriate monetary and fiscal policies vary from country to country. Likewise, there are differences in the commitment to change and the political will to carry out often unpopular policy reforms that counter well-entrenched interests. Sometimes nationalistic pressures prevent governments from appearing to have yielded under the pressure of an international organization.

7.10 Countries are at different stages in the adjustment and policy reform process. Several have graduated from the stabilization phase and are implementing structural reforms. Some countries have built credible macroeconomic policies and have managed to attract foreign loans and private investment. Some have succeeded in generating overall growth, although substantial segments of the population are not yet participating in its benefits.

7.11 The package of policy reforms involved in structural adjustment programmes has evolved over time. Experience demonstrates what works and the amount of time required to achieve change. Today, more emphasis is given to social impacts of reforms and to assistance in creating the necessary conditions for growth (including financing infrastructure, education, extension and training, and the creation of market institutions such as market information systems and communications networks). The basic orientation of those programmes continues, nevertheless, to be towards a stable macroeconomic environment, more reliance on market activity and more open trade regimes.

7.12 The effect of structural adjustment on food security, both nationally and at the household level, depends on the stage of the reforms and the impact on various groups within the society. In the initial implementation stages, the impact on food security is likely to be adverse since the correction of economic distortions will tend to cause prices to rise and real incomes to fall. As reforms take hold and growth resumes on a more sustainable basis, the food security situation will improve in general, although some of the more vulnerable groups may be left behind.

7.13 To the extent that policy reform moves the economy towards market liberalization and openness, resources will be allocated more efficiently, jobs will eventually be created, economic growth will be facilitated and food security will be enhanced, in most cases, at least, at the national level. To ensure enhanced food security at the household level, additional policies and programmes will often be required that promote a more equitable distribution of incomes and access to productive resources and employment.

[5] See also Bond (1983).

8. Crisis and adjustment in developed countries and the implications for developing countries

8.1 The adoption of market principles and the pursuance of sustainable macroeconomic balances are not confined to the developing countries. Developed-country policies have also been increasingly oriented towards reducing fiscal imbalances, privatizing public enterprises and exposing their markets to foreign competition.

8.2 As in the developing countries, policy reforms are aimed at improving resource efficiency and reducing the risk of a financial crisis. Reforms are often undertaken with pressure from an increasingly aware electorate that is dissatisfied with heavy taxation and the distribution of the tax burden and with public-sector performance, which they define as overly bureaucratic at best and hopelessly unresponsive and inefficient at worst. There is also growing concern in the developed countries about intertemporal allocation of financial and natural capital and intergenerational equity. Since raising taxes is politically risky and discourages investment, governments are more apt to attempt to reduce budget deficits by curtailing government spending by means of privatizing public enterprises, selling other government assets and curbing public assistance (and sometimes education, health and infrastructure) programmes. Severe structural reforms have taken place in some industrialized countries in the last few years, while, in others, reforms and/or reductions have been planned but not yet implemented.

8.3 The ending of the Cold War, the increasing integration of the world economic system and the reduction in macroeconomic disequilibria and public spending in industrialized countries will continue to have significant economic and social repercussions on matters of food security. Reductions in both trade protection and subsidization have seen the decline of several industries previously categorized as strategic. In addition to agriculture, energy, defence, aviation and natural resources have felt the consequences of the new political and economic realities. Some have become the focus of trade disputes among industrialized countries themselves.

8.4 As in the case of reform programmes in developing countries, industrialized nations are at different stages of stabilization and structural adjustment. Some countries have not yet succeeded in achieving the political consensus needed to carry out the necessary adjustments. Others are beginning to see the growth dividends of previous restructuring efforts, often won at some social cost, especially unemployment. Whether job loss is a short-term phenomenon or will develop into a chronic problem is not yet known.[6]

---

[6] The need for restructuring in developed countries has not always been the result of changes in policy. Rapid technological changes and the concomitant obsolescence in some industries have often been at the root of the decline of certain industries. Such changes may also cause structural unemployment as industries move from low- to high-skilled jobs.

8.5 Policy changes in industrialized countries may entail negative effects for the developing countries in the short term (for example, fiscal restraint in developed countries will probably affect the level of foreign aid). In the long term, however, developing countries stand to gain from the economic boom in high-income countries that is forecast to result, mainly as trade increases and the resultant development instigates a higher level of food security.

8.6 The most radical movement towards market-oriented economic reform has been that undertaken in the last few years in the former centrally planned economies of Central and Eastern Europe and the former USSR. In the initial stages of reform, local food-insecurity situations emerged, caused by declining real earnings combined with both the removal of most internal subsidies and price controls for food and the loss of social safety nets that were an integral part of socialized industry. Problems for those countries were exacerbated by the decline in regional trade following the demise and eventual dismantling of the Council for Mutual Economic Assistance.

8.7 The medium- to longer-term economic prospects in these countries are uncertain; they will also be uneven. A number of countries in Eastern and Central Europe are more advanced than others in the scope of their reforms. These countries have laid the foundations for economic recovery and resumed economic growth. Overall, prospects appear more uncertain for the countries of the former USSR, where the complexities of economic transition have been compounded by political problems and the persistence of collective forms of economic organization.

8.8 Another important constraint to the transition process, especially in agriculture, is the inadequacy of the legal and institutional infrastructure necessary to support the functioning of competitive markets. Markets cannot function in a vacuum. They require information, rules that govern the behaviour of market participants, and the establishment and enforcement of grades and standards. Most transitional economies have invested great effort in the privatization and distribution/restitution of land. In some cases, the process chosen has resulted in landownership structures inconsistent with efficient agricultural production. In a number of cases, land markets have not evolved because of institutional or legal deficiencies (such as titles not being issued or boundaries of parcels not established and registered). Commodity markets have often been slow to evolve beyond local markets because the absence of uniform and enforced grades and standards makes it impossible to buy or sell without both parties and the commodity being present in the same location. Market information is still limited by the need for government agencies to complete the transformation from performing the market function themselves to providing the services necessary for private firms to perform these functions.

8.9 In the countries with economies in transition, the prospects for recovery of domestic food production in the mid- and long term depend on how complete and effective the reforms are and when the turnaround in the overall economy occurs. The resulting changes in domestic demand and supply will influence both agricultural output and participation in world food markets.

9. Changes in global economic relations: international finance and trade aspects

9.1 The trend towards globalization, liberalization and integration has extended to the world's financial markets, as well as to markets for goods and services, both of which play an important role in food security. There has been an unprecedented expansion in the number and volume of financial transactions across borders, much greater in fact than the liquidity needed for trade balancing. The Bank for International Settlements estimates that the daily turnover in foreign-exchange transactions now approaches US$1.3 trillion (The Economist, 1995). At the national level, such flows are an important indication of how macroeconomic policy performance and political stability are judged by markets and domestic and international investors.

9.2 Short-term movements of capital across borders (portfolio investment) respond to differences in the expected rates of return of debt and equity instruments in different countries and to the risk associated with such instruments. Thus, at the national level, capital movements depend on real interest rates, actual and expected exchange rates and the confidence of investors in the ability of the government to maintain a stable macroeconomic environment. Recent experience demonstrates the inability of governments acting individually (or even in tandem) to fend off movements in exchange rates; even massive interventions in the financial markets have little effect. Thus, the credibility of governments and their policies (of which political stability is an important determinant) is a key factor in financial market stability. There is little governments can do to stem the outflow of short-term capital if investor confidence is shaken.

9.3 The amount of direct, private, foreign and domestic investment, on the other hand, reflects the confidence in the expected long-term overall performance of economies and of government policies. Foreign direct investment is far less volatile than short-term portfolio investment, which can literally be withdrawn overnight, leading to a financial crisis.

9.4 When short-term capital flows in large volumes across borders, while at the same time the economy is undergoing a programme of liberalization, the freedom of individual governments to use monetary and fiscal instruments to pursue domestic objectives may be compromised. But this lack of independence is not necessarily a negative phenomenon. Markets tend to reward liberal and prudent economic policies and political and economic stability. Countries that achieve stability frequently benefit from increased financial flows, which helps them alleviate balance-of-payments constraints.

9.5 Capital mobility (including the possibility of capital flight) underscores the need for prudent fiscal, monetary and exchange-rate policies. The "margin" that governments have in committing macroeconomic policy errors is very narrow, especially when private capital that flows into those countries is mainly invested in liquid, short-term instruments that can quickly reverse direction. On the other hand, economies may gain significantly from these capital inflows if consistent interest and exchange-rate policies are followed and investors believe that a country's financial situation is predictable and stable.

9.6 External private capital flows to the developing countries increased dramatically from 1990 to 1993, then stabilized following the Mexican crisis and the rise in interest rates in the United States, before resuming their upward trend. These flows have eased the financial constraint and created growth and developmental opportunities in the recipient countries. However, having accrued mainly to a limited number of Asian and middle-income countries in Latin America and the Caribbean, they cannot be expected to compensate for the reduced official aid to low-income countries. Further, the Mexican crisis and the experience of several recipient countries underlined the potential risk of accumulating excessive foreign liability in the face of volatile financial markets; and the undesirable side-effects of large capital inflows in the form of inflationary pressure and losses in external competitiveness linked to currency overvaluation.

9.7 The present system of floating exchange rates, combined with free capital movements, has resulted in periods of extreme exchange-rate instability (in addition to the short-term "noise" in the movement of nominal exchange rates) such as that from 1980 to 1987. Discussions regarding a "central" exchange-rate control system are still in progress. For such a system to succeed, a central authority with the power to impose macroeconomic coordination is needed. It is unlikely, however, that nation-states will be willing to compromise policy independence by accepting a central authority (International Monetary Fund, 1994).

10. Liberalizing international trade: significant steps forward

10.1 The trend towards market liberalization has manifested itself in international trade[7] through a number of bilateral and multilateral agreements culminating in the conclusion of the Uruguay Round of Multilateral Trade Negotiations. Two of the provisions included in the Uruguay Round of GATT have a direct effect on food security: the Agreement on Agriculture (AOA) and the Decision on Measures Concerning the Possible Negative Effects of the Reform Programme on Least-Developed and Net Food-Importing Developing Countries.

10.2 The AOA prescribes rules concerning policies that directly or indirectly affect food production and consumption and international agricultural trade.[8] These rules fit within three broad categories:
- rules having an impact on market access by foreign suppliers, including tariffication of non-tariff barriers (such as quotas, variable levies, minimum import prices, state trading measures, etc.), reduction of the resulting tariff equivalents and the provision of minimum access for imports where there are no significant imports at present;
- rules affecting policies that provide domestic support to agriculture. (A wide range of policies deemed to be non-distortionary are exempt from this set of rules and there are no limits to increasing such support. Examples include general services to agriculture, food security stocks, domestic food aid and "decoupled" payments to producers);
- rules that determine the limits (in both monetary and quantity terms) to which exports may be subsidized (export competition rules).

10.3 Under the AOA, developing countries receive "special and differential treatment", including smaller required reductions of tariffs as well as trade-distorting domestic support and export subsidies and longer implementation periods. (Fewer restrictive measures apply to very poor countries.) Whenever countries implement trade liberalization policies under structural adjustment programmes, the provisions of such programmes are usually more stringent than those of the GATT agreement.[9]

10.4 While the AOA represents movement towards freer trade in agricultural commodities, it is only a partial liberalization agreement; protection continues. Reductions in agricultural supports are modest and spread over several years, but the AOA begins a process towards more transparent and somewhat less-sheltered agricultural trade.

10.5 One of ways in which the AOA will affect developing countries will be through changes in prices of temperate-zone products relative to those of tropical products. A strengthening of the world prices of temperate-zone products is expected compared with smaller increases or even reductions in the prices of tropical commodities. Increases in prices of temperate-zone foods and export-

[7] See also WFS companion paper 12, *Food and international trade.*
[8] For a more detailed analysis, see Chapter 8 of *World agriculture: towards 2010* (FAO, 1995b). For a discussion of the possible effects on developing regions and on major commodities, see FAO (1995c) and WFS companion paper 12.
[9] For a comparison of specific provisions of the AOA to those of structural adjustment programmes, see Konandreas (1994).

subsidy reductions imply increases in food import bills paid by net food importers (the majority of developing countries) accentuated in low-income countries accustomed to importing food at subsidized prices.

10.6 The Decision on Measures Concerning the Possible Negative Effects of the Reform Programme on Least-Developed and Net Food-Importing Developing Countries is aimed at alleviating possible problems arising from higher import prices of food during the implementation of the trade-liberalizing reform programme on agriculture. While the provisions of the decision are potentially of great significance to developing countries that may be adversely affected by the Uruguay Round Agreement, the modalities under which it will be implemented are not clear and need to be further elaborated.[10]

10.7 The move towards liberalization and lower price-support activities may result in a reduction in government-held food stocks, and whether they will be replaced by private-sector stocks is an open question. However, support to food-security stocks undertaken in a prescribed fashion has been exempted in the AOA. While industrialized countries can afford to build large public stocks, this action is often too expensive for developing countries. The probable reduction in government stocks in industrialized countries will influence food aid availabilities. While other factors are reducing the amounts of grain available for food aid, there is no reason to believe a priori that bona fide food aid will be adversely affected by the agreement.

10.8 The overall impact of the AOA on developing countries depends on their net trade position, the implementation of compensating measures to counter higher world food prices and the long-term effects of possible overall higher growth following trade liberalization. Estimates of overall income growth attributable to the Uruguay Round range from US$109 billion to $510 billion from GATT estimates, to $213 billion according to the World Bank/OECD estimates.

10.9 Countries receiving preferential treatment for their agricultural exports can expect a reduction in the preferential margins as a result of lower most-favoured nation (MFN) tariff rates, assuming that tariffs under the existing preferential schemes, the Generalized System of Preferences (GSP), Lomé, and the Caribbean Basin Initiative, remain unchanged. FAO calculates that the potential value of preferences granted by the European Union, the United States and Japan attributable to the agricultural sector in 1992 was US$1.9 billion. This value is expected to decline by US$0.8 billion as a result of the Uruguay Round reduction of MFN tariff rates.[11]

10.10 Another effect of the AOA on food production in developing countries is related to the risk faced by producers caused by international market price variability. With a reduction in policy stocks as a result of domestic policy reforms, the price effect of a market shock initially is likely to be larger. However, with more countries opening their markets to world price signals through tariffication as a result of the Uruguay Round, shocks arising from unexpected production shortfalls or bumper harvests would be absorbed by the greater number of country markets, thus cushioning the after-effects of such shocks on

[10] See also WFS companion paper 12.
[11] For more details on declines in the value of preferences by region and commodity, see FAO (1995c).

world prices. A reduction in risk caused by the attenuation of erratic and unpredictable price movements may be an incentive to increase food production in developing countries where farmers have very few, if any, instruments to hedge against risk.[12]

[12] Whether a reduction in price variability as a result of supply shocks will occur or not remains an open question. Simulations using FAO's World Food Model did not demonstrate reductions in price variability as a result of the Uruguay Round. What was found was that "...in the absence of adequate stocks, a shortfall in production will push up prices rapidly ..." and that "...The continuing problem of international food price instability will need to be carefully monitored in the future and the role of private versus public stockholding will need to be assessed". For more information on the simulation results, see FAO (1995a).

11. Perspectives on regional economic integration[13]

11.1 A major new characteristic of the world trading system is the expansion of regional trading agreements (RTAs). Examples are the completion of the Single European Market in January 1993, the protocol between the European Economic Community (EEC) and the European Free Trade Association (EFTA) to form the European Economic Area (EAE), and the launching in January 1994 of the North American Free Trade Agreement (NAFTA), which extended the United States-Canada Free Trade Agreement to Mexico. Other Latin American countries are negotiating free trade with NAFTA members and/or are strengthening and expanding trade agreements among themselves. The United States is proposing the creation of an Enterprise for the Americas Initiative, wich would liberalize trade and investment flows in North, Central and South America.

11.2 In part, the revival of trading blocs reflects an adjustment to the end of the Cold War and the declining importance of superpower rivalry and security considerations in trade. The resurgence of RTAs represents a means of competing for investment funds and is also a reflection of the continuing globalization of industry, manufacturing and service operations. For a time RTAs represented a response by countries that desired free trade and were of the opinion that the GATT talks were proceeding too slowly. Thus far, the most successful arrangements have been among the developed countries, but there have also been promising developments in RTAs between developed and developing countries.

11.3 An important question that arises from the proliferation of RTAs is their role in enhancing or undoing some of the discipline imposed on country policies by the Uruguay Round Agreement. While, in principle, RTAs (especially free-trade associations) could establish and maintain open trading arrangements with other countries or blocs (open regionalism), the danger exists that rules will be written to serve the narrower interests of countries belonging to the arrangement at the expense of the outsiders. In such cases, within-bloc liberalization diverts more trade than it creates. Such practices are not allowed by the GATT disciplines, which rule that RTAs should not create or raise trade barriers against other GATT members. Therefore, the question boils down to the ability of the newly formed World Trade Organization (WTO) to enforce such rules.

11.4 For developing countries, participation in RTAs may be a mixed blessing. Small and economically weak developing countries that form trading blocs with developed ones are unlikely to carry much weight in establishing rules. On the other hand, experience with RTAs involving only developing countries has not been very encouraging because of their generally weak economic structure and their lack of countervailing power.

[13] See Josling (1994) and FAO (1995b).

11.5 There are wide differences among RTAs in the way they treat agriculture. In Europe, a common agricultural policy and a free regional market includes 15 countries and accounts for a large part of world agricultural trade. For its part, NAFTA promises a tariff-free zone in ten years. Agriculture is currently only partially treated in many RTAs,[14] since trade concessions often clash with domestic policy objectives. Despite this problem, trade diversion on a large scale seems unlikely. There is scope for increasing intraregional trade in the Southern Common Market (MERCOSUR) and the Association of Southeast Asian Nations (ASEAN) by removing internal trade barriers, while in other continents substitution away from interregional supplies is limited.

11.6 In general, the direct effects of the organization of RTAs on food security through their impact on agriculture will depend on the extent to which those agreements will dominate world agricultural trade and the way in which they will behave towards other regions or countries. If the trend towards proliferation of RTAs continues, pressures will be created to define more acceptable policy frameworks (domestic and trade-related) to deal with agriculture within the RTAs. This development will have implications for the behaviour of individual bloc members towards non-members (in the case of a free-trade area) or of the bloc as a whole (in the case of customs unions). If RTAs become more liberal as a result, then the overall outcome will be welfare-enhancing on a global level.

11.7 The effect of RTAs on food security will depend, at least in part, on whether they behave so as to enhance (liberalize) trade and thus contribute to global resource use efficiency and income. If they do, their existence at the very least increases the potential for increasing access. Should they become a means of circumventing reforms agreed to multilaterally in the GATT/WTO, they will have the opposite effect on food security. Beyond this, it is not possible to generalize about the effects of RTAs on food security.

---

[14] The Closer Economic Relations Treaty (CER) between Australia and New Zealand constitutes an exception in that it fully includes agriculture.

12. Issues of natural resources and the environment

12.1 During the period since the 1974 World Food Conference, international attention has been directed towards issues concerning natural resources and the environment at both the national and international levels. For developing countries, natural-resource pressures (such as land degradation, erosion, water scarcity, deforestation and irresponsible fishing) have the potential to compromise agricultural growth and food security seriously. There is increasing awareness about global environmental issues. For instance, the conservation of biological diversity or the depletion of the ozone layer are global environmental problems, while transboundary fluxes of rivers may be of concern to only a few countries. Nations increasingly understand that most of these problems cannot be resolved by one country or group; they transcend national borders, spreading instability and suffering throughout the region and around the world. Too often, the concerted action needed has not been forthcoming.

12.2 The transboundary and global nature of numerous natural-resource and environmental problems has created the need for coordinated action at various levels to address them. As a result, a number of agreements have been signed by countries involving sharing of environmental goods and conserving global resources, in which, through a system of bargaining, compensation and punishment for non-participants, countries agree to follow policies that address concerns shared by all of the signatories.

12.3 The 1992 United Nations Conference on Environment and Development (UNCED) represents an important expression of the international community's recognition of these matters. In many parts of the developing world, expanding populations and shortages of fertile land, water and forests are already contributing to the expulsion of farmers from agriculture, thereby creating a class of environmental refugees.[15]

12.4 International agreements negotiated to improve environmental problems and trade matters ultimately affect production decisions at the producer level and purchase decisions at the household level. For example, the overwhelming majority of world fish trade is from developing to developed countries. The 1995 United Nations Conference on Straddling Fish Stocks and Highly Migratory Fish Stocks represents a determined effort by countries to reconcile global interests concerned with fishing on the high seas.

12.5 Some international conventions such as those on biological diversity, forestry and climate change, however important, may have negative implications for the world's food supply, at least in the short term. For example, the climate change convention raises the possibility of establishing carbon taxes and would result in higher energy costs, new input mixes and changing technologies. The combination would imply higher production costs for food

---

[15] See Homer-Dixon, Boutwell and Rathjens (1993).

producers and higher prices for consumers, resulting in losses in food security. Furthermore, since the transformation of forest land into agricultural land accounted for the majority of deforestation over the past ten years, international agreements that constrain forest conversion will alter future food production possibilities.

12.6 Food security is also very dependent upon water supply,[16] and water resources are frequently an underlying cause of disputes, especially when they are scarce. The increasing value of water, concern over its quality and problems of access have made hydropolitics a matter of international concern. In Africa, Asia and Latin America, shared river and lake basins make up at least 60 percent of the total land area (Barrett, 1994). Water conflicts are only expected to intensify as the number of users burgeons.

12.7 Contemporary development also includes concepts of intergenerational equity and justice. For the first time in human history, the global community is collectively attempting to understand how today's actions may affect the planet's ecosystems 100 years into the new millennium. Incorporating this broad range of values into sustainable food production is appealing and necessary, but difficult in practice. The question frequently posed is: how can resources be used today to enhance food security considerably, but in such a way that their capacity to generate production for future generations at the same level is not diminished?

12.8 At the national level, governments are under pressure to structure incentives so that natural and environmental resources are managed in a sustainable manner. Policy measures vary among countries depending on the nature of the problems they face.

12.9 Both national and international aspects of environmental and natural-resource issues have significant bearing on the implementation of development policies in general and for food security in particular. National-level resource and environmental problems can present governments with difficult trade-offs between present and future growth and food security. The trade-offs can be particularly acute in the agricultural sector (including forestry and fisheries) where many resource problems of the developing countries are concentrated. In addition, international agreements constrain the range of actions taken by governments to influence natural-resource use.

12.10 In the long term there is no conflict between the sustainable use of the natural-resource base and food security since, for the foreseeable future, food production will be dependent on land and water resources. If these resources are degraded, future productive capacity will be reduced and global food security, and possibly national as well as local food security, will also be reduced.

12.11 In the shorter term, approaches, including policies, chosen to meet present food and income needs can have negative effects both on the resource base and on the environment in general. Conversely, actions to protect the resource base and the environment can reduce production and incomes and, therefore, near-term food security.

[16] See WFS companion paper 7, *Food production: the critical role of water.*

12.12 In the end, the focus of policy needs to recognize that resource degradation has different consequences for different countries and population groups. For the poor countries the consequences can be very serious, as their welfare depends heavily on the productive potential of their agricultural resources. At the same time, it must be recognized that resource degradation anywhere on the planet, particularly in the major food-exporting developing countries, can make the solution of the food security problems of the poor more difficult if it reduces global food production potential.

13. Employment problems and labour markets

13.1 Unemployment and underemployment have been characteristic of (or at least economists have usually assumed so) developing economies and especially of their agricultural sectors since the beginning of the post-colonial era. At least one early development model was based on the assumption of surplus labour in the agricultural sector. What is new in the 1990s is the emergence of relatively high rates of unemployment in a number of highly industrialized countries and in all of the transitional economies.

13.2 The presence of jobless and underemployed people has negative effects on food security. In an aggregate sense, they represent potentially productive resources, but they are not contributing to aggregate output. This waste of resources reduces aggregate income and, of course, leaves the affected individuals and their dependants without earnings, thus reducing access to food at the national and household levels. To the extent that the comparative advantage of these jobless and underemployed people is in agriculture, the aggregate availability of food is reduced. Of course a reduction in the national income reduces the ability to import food. Consequently, underutilization of labour (or any other resource) may reduce food availability regardless of the sector in which the comparative advantage rests.

13.3 There is not a total consensus on the causes of and cures for unemployment, but there are some areas of general agreement. In the developed countries, policies and institutions established over many years to protect the interests of workers have introduced rigidities into the labour market and increased the cost of labour. As the world's markets have become more integrated and competitive and as structural changes occur, the labour markets are not flexible and efficient enough to reallocate labour and structural unemployment is the result. Changing policies and institutions is proving to be a slow and politically painful process in most countries, and safety-net approaches are being relied on to mitigate the food-insecurity problems in the interim.

13.4 The countries with economies in transition have undergone unprecedented economic and political restructuring with, in most cases, very inadequate policies or institutions to facilitate the functioning of an efficient labour market. Thus, it is no wonder that massive unemployment has resulted. This in turn has led to serious food insecurity and undernutrition in many of these countries.

13.5 The employment problems of the developing countries, especially in sub-Saharan Africa and South Asia, are in many ways more complicated and intractable and the food security consequences more direct and serious. Much more of the unemployment as well as underemployment is rural and agricultural and, thus, the negative impact on both availability and access dimensions of food security is direct. While agricultural labourers are without work or underemployed for much of the year, labour is a serious constraint to agricultural production because of the high seasonal requirements of the technologies employed. Labour markets are not well developed, but, at the same time, in the industrial and formal service sectors, some of the same policies and institutions that cause labour markets in the developed countries to be rigid and labour to be expensive have been adopted. This limits opportunities for seasonal or full-time off-farm employment for rural people.

13.6 Many countries' macroeconomic policies (such as overvalued exchange rates and subsidized credit and inputs) have, in some cases, provided incentives for the adoption of labour-substituting technologies. Finally, most of these countries have invested very little in education or health services to increase the productive value and mobility of their human resources. Most have also failed to recognize that ensuring adequate nutrition is an investment in human capital as well as a current consumption expenditure.

14. A changing world economic environment: policy implications

14.1 The impact of the world's changing economic environment on food security in developing countries depends on the constraints it places on the policy options of these same countries. In the global economy, national policies and the instruments to implement them will be increasingly conditioned directly or indirectly by outside events or pressures of globalization, economic integration, environmental and natural-resource treaties and the process of economic liberalization.

14.2 For example, loan conditionality requiring policy reforms directly constrains policy options in many developing countries. Even in the absence of explicit conditionality advanced by the donor countries, the threat of economic and financial crisis forces the governments of developing economies to take steps to reduce budget deficits and the public debt through public-spending reductions and/or tax increases. This is when governments have to make politically difficult choices as to how reductions in spending are to be shared among various segments of the population. To a large extent, the allocations depend on the relative power that various social groups can exercise on the government.

14.3 To combat poverty and food insecurity, governments are constrained according to the types of interventions that they can undertake. Budget austerity and efficiency considerations imply that general subsidies and assistance programmes that distort market incentives will be either severely limited or abandoned altogether. Since those policies have been found to be counterproductive in the past, other more targeted policies and instruments will be used in support of food security. The implementation of such acceptable policies will require removing institutional bottlenecks and upgrading the efficiency of the managerial capacities of the public sector.

14.4 In addition, the role of NGOs and the private sector to carry out food security programmes will be enhanced in the face of shrinking government budgets and services. Indeed, NGOs have proliferated in recent years and many have assumed important roles in the delivery of services and in the implementation of policy and programmes formerly reserved as the purview of government. While most NGOs are serious and responsible entities, they should not always be taken as reliable substitutes for the state.

14.5 As the global economy ushers in increasing economic cooperation and integration, domestic policies will be constrained by their obligations to adhere to the disciplines of regional or international agreements (including those relevant to natural resources and the environment) of which they form a part. In turn, a more limited range of domestic policies less susceptibile to political manipulation and considerations can be utilized. For agriculture, such agreements require discipline with respect to any domestic agricultural policies attempting to manage the price structure in favour of agriculture. The challenge for countries is to find low-cost, decoupled methods that give a boost to the productivity of the agricultural sector. Such interventions may include improving infrastructure and research and extension or assisting in the creation of market and credit institutions in the rural areas.

14.6 The accentuation of demographic and economic imbalances within and between countries, civil strife and natural disasters, the loss of jobs caused by transitions to alternative economic and political systems and the emergence and strengthening of economic cooperation and integration schemes have strongly affected international labour mobility and migration patterns. At present, over 80 million people are living permanently outside their own country and a further 18 million people are migrants as a result of political problems or natural catastrophes. Each year about 1 million people emigrate definitively and another 1 million seek political asylum. The accentuation of economic imbalances between rural and urban areas has also given rise to rural/urban migration within borders, which has assumed disquieting proportions in many countries.

14.7 Migrations have major food security implications for the migrants themselves and, through the impact of these, whether they are positive or negative, on the economies and agricultural sectors of both the recipient and the donor areas. In many cases, migration has been an important contributor to agricultural as well as overall growth in the recipient countries, remittances from migrant workers have represented sizeable sources of income, foreign exchange and rural capital formation and returning migrants have brought back skills and savings acquired abroad. On the other hand, despite the apparent paradox, in many cases migration has also created labour shortages and reduced agricultural activity in the countries or areas of origin. This has occurred in part because those who migrate are often more educated, skilled and dynamic than those who remain. Increasing migration has posed difficult problems of economic and social integration in many recipient countries.

14.8 The mounting gravity of these problems points to the urgent need to shift the policy balance towards tackling their root causes rather than reacting to the events. Actions to accelerate progress towards universal food security – adequate food supplies, stability in food production and access to food – including those designed to create sustainable business and employment opportunities, can help reduce the developing countries' heavy losses of human resources. They can also help to contain the massive outlays being made in recipient countries to reduce the flows of migrants.

15. Looking back and ahead

15.1 What prospective lessons can be derived from the experience of the past two decades? The world is profoundly different from what it was at the time of the World Food Conference in 1974. However, several features of the old political order, and the ideologies behind it, are appropriate to be reviewed because of their contemporary relevance. Calls for developing-country solidarity, self-reliance and a new and more just economic order now manifest themselves in different ways. The solidarity principle has broadened to a global dimension as awareness of the interdependence of economic interests has increased. Solidarity and self-reliance may be seen as having evolved into a broader perspective of intraregional collaboration and integration. A more just economic order, at least concerning trade, was the purpose of the recently concluded Uruguay Round of GATT negotiations and the founding of the WTO. At the same time, however, official development assistance has lagged behind growing needs. Official commitments of external assistance to agriculture and, hence, to food security have declined in real terms in recent years.

15.2 Some political developments have also imposed perspectives radically different from those that existed in 1974. The principle of non-alignment has lost relevance in the current context of both East-West and North-South relations. No longer are there two big superpowers vying for hegemony in the developing countries. Developing-country solidarity has given way to a more pragmatic approach, in which self-interest plays a greater role in alliances and agreements. This new approach is exemplified by the Cairns Group, in which developed and developing country members worked together to pursue common objectives of trade liberalization.

15.3 The North-South *rapprochement* was also evident in the emergence of free-trade arrangements involving countries with markedly different levels of economic development and income. Most striking in this process is NAFTA; negotiations are now under way to broaden its scope and create other forms of North-South economic and trade agreements. North-South disagreements have also been moderated by the fact that a number of rapidly industrializing developing countries can now claim a developed-country status in some important respects.

15.4 The overall political balance has shifted towards a less polarized pattern of dominating influences, which reflects the growing relative weight of a highly industrialized Japan, a more integrated Europe and a dynamic East and Southeast Asia, with China playing an increasingly important role in the global political and economic scene.

15.5 These developments generally suggest better intercountry relationships overall and better prospects for global food security. The possibilities for improved food security at both country and household levels are, however, more problematic in this global context. Improvement in food security at the country level depends heavily on the ability of a given country to integrate its economy into the international community and compete in an interdependent world. Improved food security at the household level depends on the ability of individual household members to gain greater access to food. This, in turn requires access to employment opportunities and participation in the rewards of a growing and dynamic economy. For poor households without prospects, safety-net programmes are necessary to assure food security.

15.6 At the same time, the world faces extremely complex problems associated with the nationalistic tendencies of the countries with economies in transition and the upheavals caused by political, religious and ethnic conflicts. This process accentuates problems of food insecurity, specifically, and security, generally. Dismantling a nuclear arsenal of a destructive power that defies comprehension, doing it safely and avoiding proliferation in the newly created states and elsewhere are but one aspect of the problem; realizing and utilizing peace dividend resources in productive ways that *inter alia* help countries improve their food security situation is another. Helping new states stabilize and consolidate their political and economic situation is a further challenge. It is fundamental that the past 50 years of peace through fear give way to a new period of peace through shared wealth.

15.7 The international environment is now more favourable to economic growth than it was in 1974. Trade and capital market liberalization combined with capital mobility motivates developed and developing countries alike to improve their position by creating credible investment opportunities. But the prerequisites are political stability, stable institutions and macroeconomic policies that avoid large and protracted disequilibria. Creating such an environment is a challenge that each country must face.

15.8 There are special opportunities for profitable investment in developing countries that have a comparative advantage in low-skilled labour-intensive activities. Barring increased protectionist tendencies by the developed countries under the pressure of labour market adjustment problems, these opportunities should continue as more and more countries present themselves as credible and stable investment locations. Increased employment and income-earning opportunities, especially for low-skilled workers, cannot but help developing countries' efforts to combat food insecurity.

15.9 Taking advantage of increased opportunities in the global economy will be a challenge that not all developing countries will be able to meet, at least not in the near future. Some countries are searching for the political consensus necessary to undertake economic reforms that may harm some domestic interests in the short term; others are struggling to rebuild their economies and to create proper institutions and infrastructure. Some countries will have to rely more on their own efforts, internally generated resources (savings) and official assistance for several years to come.

15.10 National-level policies to address domestic problems will continue to be restricted by international obligations assumed by international treaties and by the increasing influence on domestic policies of events in the international markets. Although countries could, in principle, isolate themselves from such influences, it is unlikely that they will do so, given the catastrophic consequences of such policies in the past.

15.11 In an ideal world, what would constitute the socio-political and economic environment most conducive to the elimination of food insecurity and undernutrition, that is, to ensuring food for all? It may be difficult to achieve agreement on all elements of such an ideal environment, but it would surely include most of the following:

- countries would adopt broadly participatory and pluralistic political systems under which governments would be responsive and responsible to the people;
- governments would find peaceful means of resolving internal conflicts and, with the assistance of an effective United Nations or other legitimate peacekeeping organizations, conflicts with other governments;
- governments would devote their limited resources to doing those things that markets do not do well and that are necessary for the efficient and effective functioning of the economy and society (these would include, but not be limited to, providing safety nets, such as food stamps, for those with only limited or no access to the market, assuring socially optimal levels of investment in public goods and providing appropriate incentives for the sustainable use of natural resources and the environment as well as the legal, regulatory and institutional structure to assure conditions for a competitive market);
- domestic and international markets would be liberalized to allow resources to be employed globally to maximize the sustainable level and rate of growth of economic activity;
- national and international means would have been found to assist the poor effectively to increase their capacity to be productive, thereby closing the gap between the rich and the poor without unduly reducing the incentive of the rich to be productive.

15.12 In the final analysis, food security in any country must be under the responsibility and the authority of the national government in conjunction with local authorities and working with concerned groups and individuals in the society. International coordination and liaison is necessary. The global community and international organizations can be helpful, but they are no substitute for the actions and political will to achieve food security within the country itself.

Bibliography

Barraclough, S.L. 1991. *An end to hunger?* London, Zed Books Ltd for the United Nations Research Institute for Social Development (UNRISD) and the South Centre, Geneva, Switzerland.

Barrett, S. 1994. *Conflict and cooperation in managing international water resources.* Policy Research Working Paper No. 1303. Washington, DC, World Bank.

Binswanger, H.P. 1989. The policy response of agriculture. In *Proc. World Bank Conference on Development Economics.* Washington, DC, World Bank.

Binswanger, H.P. & von Braun, J. 1991. Technological change and commercialization in agriculture: the effect on the poor. *World Bank Res. Observer*, 6(1): 57-80.

Binswanger, H.P. & Khandker, S. 1994. *The impact of formal finance on the rural economy of India.* World Bank Working Paper Series No. 949. Washington, DC, World Bank.

Bomfim, A. & Shah, A. 1991. *Macroeconomic management and the division of powers in Brazil: perspectives for the nineties.* Washington, DC, World Bank.

Bond, M.E. 1983. Agricultural responses to prices in sub-Saharan Africa. *IMF Staff Papers*, 30(4): 703-726.

Boserup, E. 1965. *Conditions of agricultural growth: the economics of agrarian change under population pessure.* New York, NY, USA, Adeline Publishing Co.

Boserup, E. 1970. *Women's role in economic development.* London, Allen & Unwin.

Cassidy, J. 1995. Who killed the middle class? *The New Yorker*, (16 October): 113.

Crook, R. & Manor, J. 1994. *Enhancing participation and institutional performance: democratic decentralization in South Asia and West Africa.* Report to Advisory Committee for Economic and Social Research Overseas (ESCOR), Overseas Development Administration, UK.

De Janvry, A. 1981. *The agrarian question and reformism in Latin America.* Baltimore, MD, USA, Johns Hopkins University Press.

Donovan, G. & Cleaver, K. 1995. *Agriculture, poverty and policy reform in sub-Saharan Africa.* Washington, DC, World Bank.

FAO. 1993. *Perspectives on agricultural development and adjustment in developing countries.* Rome.

FAO. 1994. *The State of Food and Agriculture 1994.* Rome.

FAO. 1995a. *The Uruguay Round Agreement on Agriculture: implications for food security in the Asia and the Pacific Region.* Paper presented to the Expert Consultative Meeting on Benefits and Challenges facing Asia-Pacific Agricultural Trading Countries in the Post-Uruguay Round Period of the Economic and Social Commission for Asia and the Pacific, Bangkok, Thailand, February 1995.

FAO. 1995b. *World agriculture: towards 2010.* N. Alexandratos, ed. Rome, FAO, and Chichester, UK, John Wiley.

FAO. 1995c. *Impact of the Uruguay Round on agriculture.* Report to the Committee on Commodity Problems, 16th session, Rome, 3-7 April. Rome.

Gardner, B. 1989. Recent studies of agricultural trade liberalization in agriculture and governments in an interdependent world. *In* A. Maunder & A. Valdés, eds. *Proc. 20th International Conference of Agricultural Economists*, Buenos Aires, Argentina, 24-31 August 1988. Aldershot, UK, Dartmouth.

Homer-Dixon, T.F., Boutwell, J.H. & Rathjens, G.W. 1993. Environmental change and violent conflict. *Sci. Am.*, 268(2): 38-45.

International Agricultural Trade Research Consortium. 1994. *The Uruguay Round Agreement on Agriculture: an evaluation.* Commissioned Paper No. 9. Minneapolis, MN, USA,Department of Agricultural and Applied Economics, University of Minnesota.

International Monetary Fund (IMF). 1994. *The IMF at 50 entering a new era?* IMF Survey, 8 August 1994. Washington, DC, IMF.

Josling, T. 1994. *Implications of regional trade arrangements for agricultural trade.* Rome, FAO.

Konandreas, P. 1994. *Uruguay Round Agreement on Agriculture: implications for developing country policies.* Paper presented at the American Agricultural Economics Association Meeting, San Diego, CA, USA.

Krueger, A.O. 1992. A synthesis of the political economy in developing countries. *In* A.O. Krueger, M. Schiff & A. Valdés, eds. *The political economy of agricultural pricing policy,* Vol. 5. Baltimore, MD, USA, Johns Hopkins University Press.

Krueger, A.O., Schiff, M. & Valdés, A., eds. 1991. *The political economy of agricultural pricing policy.* Baltimore, MD, USA, Johns Hopkins University Press.

Lipton, M. 1977. *Why poor people stay poor: a study of urban bias in world development.* Canberra, Australia, Australian National University Press.

Lipton, M. & Ravallion, M. 1995. Poverty and policy. *In* J. Behrman & T.N. Srinivasan, eds. *Handbook of development economics,* Vol. 3B, p. 2551-2657. Amsterdam, the Netherlands, Elsevier/North-Holland.

Maxwell, D. 1995. *Land access, tenure security resource conservation and food security.* Land Tenure Centre Paper (May). Madison, WI, USA, University of Wisconsin.

Meenakshisundaram, S.S. 1991. *Decentralisation in developing countries.* New Delhi, India, Concept Publishing Company.

Mellor, J. 1961. The role of agriculture in economic development. *Am. Econ. Rev.,* 51:566-593.

Mellor, J. 1966. *The economics of agricultural development.* Ithaca, NY, USA, Cornell University Press.

Parikh, K.S., Fischer, G., Frohberg, K. & Gulbrandsen, O. 1986. *Towards free trade in agriculture.* Luxembourg, International Institute for Applied Systems Analysis (IIASA).

Ravallion, M. & Datt, G. 1994. *How important to India's poor is the urban-rural composition of growth?* Washington, DC, World Bank.

Saito, K. 1994. *Raising productivity of women farmers in sub-Saharan Africa.* World Bank Discussion Paper No. 230. Washington, DC, World Bank.

Schiff, M. & Valdés, A. 1992. *The plundering of agriculture in developing countries.* Washington, DC, World Bank.

Schultz, T.W. 1964. *Transforming traditional agriculture.* New Haven, CT, USA, Yale University Press.

Smith, D. 1994. *War, peace and Third World development.* Occasional Paper No. 16. New York, NY, USA, United Nations Development Programme (UNDP).

The Economist. 1995. Survey. *The Economist,* (7-13 October): 12.

Thiesenhusen, W.C. 1995. *Broken promises: land reform and the Latin American campesino.* Boulder, CO, USA, Westview Press.

Timmer, P.C. 1993. *Why markets and politics undervalue the role of agriculture in economic development.* Benjamin H. Hibbard Memorial Lecture Series.

Tyers, R. & Anderson, K. 1988. Liberalizing OECD agricultural policies in the Uruguay Round: effects on trade and welfare. *J. Agric. Econ.,* 30: 197-216.

World Bank. 1993. *Poverty education handbook.* Washington, DC, International Bank for Reconstruction and Development (IBRD).

4
Food requirements
and population growth

Contents

Acknowledgements

The preparation of the World Food Summit technical background documents has mobilized, in addition to FAO's own staff contributions, a considerable amount of expertise in the international scientific community, drawn from partner international institutions and governmental or non-governmental circles. The process has been monitored at FAO by an internal Reading Committee, composed of staff selected ad personam and established to ensure that the whole collection meets appropriate quality and consistency criteria.

The present document has been prepared jointly by P. Collomb, Director of the Committee for International Coordination of National Research in Demography (CICRED) in Paris, and FAO's J. du Guerny. After initial review within FAO by all technical departments, invited colleagues and the Reading Committee, and by selected external reviewers, a first version was published and circulated for comments to governments, intergovernmental organizations (IGOs) and non-governmental organizations (NGOs), as well as further peer reviewers. Much appreciated comments and advice have been received from Prof. A. Palloni, University of Wisconsin, United States; Prof. B. Popkin, Carolina Population Center, United States; W.G. Sombroek, International Soil Reference and Information Centre, the Netherlands; Dr E. Boserup; J. Chamie, Director, United Nations Population Division. Further comments and advice were received from participants at the FAO/UNFPA Expert Consultation on Food Production and Population Growth, held in Rome from 3 to 5 July 1996, namely: Drs S. Rao, A. Khalifa and A. Jorgensen-Dahl for the United Nations Population Fund (UNFPA), United States; Prof. A. Adepoju, African Institute for Economic Development and Planning (IDEP), Senegal; Dr J. Bongaarts, Population Council; Prof. T. Dyson, London School of Economics and Political Science, United Kingdom; F. Gendreau, President, CICRED; Dr A. Khan, International Labour Organisation (ILO); Dr R. Leemans, National Institute of Public Health and the Environment, the Netherlands; Dr L. Marovatsanga, University of Zimbabwe; Dr S. Nasser, University of Cairo, Egypt; D. Ouedraogo; Dr T. Preston, University of Agriculture and Forestry, Thu Doc, Viet Nam; Dr M. Rai, Indian Council of Agricultural Research; Dr V. Smil, University of Manitoba, Canada; Dr R. Tuirán, National Population Council, Mexico; Dr F. Vio, University of Chile; M.B. Weinberger, United Nations Population Division; Prof. P.A. Yotopoulos, Stanford University, United States; and J. Zaini, Consumers International, Malaysia.

This document has been prepared with the support of, and in collaboration with, the United Nations Population Fund (UNFPA), whose contribution is gratefully acknowledged.

While grateful for the contributions received from all reviewers, the FAO Secretariat bears responsibility for the content of the document.

Executive summary

The world will inherit a very diversified food situation at the end of the second millennium. This paper highlights the regional contrasts and specificities within the global situation and trends. Its long-term analysis is based on the concept of food requirements, thereby taking a normative perspective to the extent that actual and projected food consumption and demand do not meet, or at times exceed, requirements.

Emerging from an acute food deficit in 1962, Asia has continually improved the proportion of its population's energy requirements met by available food supplies, and is catching up with the situation of Latin America where, after a period of increases in the requirement/supplies ratio, stabilization has been observed. In contrast, Africa did not manage to improve the average food situation, and some countries, namely those mainly consuming cassava, yams or taro, have experienced a severe decline in this respect.

In the decades leading to 2050, by which time most of the increase before stabilization will have taken place, world population growth will dominate over other demographic factors as the primary cause of increasing global food demand. Food production is expected to increase broadly in line with this rise in demand, but not without further stress on agricultural, economic and environmental resources. The situation in parts of Africa is of particular concern. However, strategies do exist to slow down future population growth – especially in the longer term. They include programmes to raise levels of education (particularly of women) and improving access to methods of contraception, which also facilitate the achievement of food security and food production objectives.

It is useful to illustrate the challenge of demographic factors as given by the United Nations population projections to the year 2050 by evaluating the associated food energy requirements and plausible dietary patterns. The scenarios presented need be considered more as food for thought than as projections. The focus is placed on the demographic challenges at the regional level and for certain classes of countries identified by their dietary patterns which, for countries dependent on agriculture, correspond roughly to agrometeorological zones.

The increase in food energy requirements, expressed in terms of the total plant-derived energy incorporated into human food, of developing countries until 2050 results from the growth of population numbers and, to a lesser degree, of the changing age structure of the population. The ageing of the population and the increase in physical height as a consequence of better nutrition are factors that increase energy requirements, whereas declining fertility and increasing urbanization are factors reducing energy requirements. As a result, by 2050, energy requirements will be double what they are today in developing countries as a group (and more than triple current requirements in sub-Saharan Africa).

Many developing countries will have to graduate to more nutritious average diets in order to eliminate chronic undernutrition. Partly because of uneven food availabilities among the population inside countries, this process could require a 30 percent increase in food energy availabilities in Africa (but 40 percent south of the Sahara), 15 percent in Asia and less than 10 percent in Latin America.

In order to reach a well-balanced diet, people will have to diversify their food intake. Adopting for the year 2050 a level of diversification similar to that projected by FAO for the world in 2010, Africa would have to improve its plant-derived energy by another 25 percent (46 percent for countries consuming mainly roots and tubers) and Asia by 21 percent.

As a result of the combined effects of the preceding three factors, developing countries would have to increase their plant-derived energy by 174 percent. This means that, while the countries of Latin America and Asia would roughly have to double their plant-derived energy, Africa would have to multiply it by five (multiplying it by seven for the root- and tuber-consuming countries).

For Asia or Latin America, such a perspective requires further productivity growth, but at a rate lower than that seen in the last 15 years. In contrast, Africa would have to accelerate drastically the growth of its productivity. The demographic transition in Africa would facilitate the process of achieving food security: the annual growth rate in available plant-derived energy would be 2.6 percent in the low variant instead of 3.3 percent in the high variant of the United Nations' population projections.

Where land and water become scarce, increases in yields will be achieved mostly through an increase in productivity sustained by the development of human capacities. In light of the level of education already achieved, many countries in Asia seem well prepared for the change in the nature of development. On the other hand, Africa's lower level of development of economic infrastructures and of human resources will constitute a serious handicap for this region. By overcoming the challenge of simultaneously improving its human resources and infrastructure while facing a very difficult food situation, Africa would provide the groundwork for solving its food security problem in the long term.

The reduction of poverty and eradication of undernutrition, principally present in rural areas among food producers, will lead to an increase in food demand, a large part of which can be met through imports, notably cereals, particularly in Asia. Meeting this demand and the associated requirements for inputs and infrastructure will generate an increase of output in the global economy that must take place under sustainable conditions.

1. Introduction

WILL HUMANKIND BE ABLE TO COPE WITH THE CONTINUING GROWTH OF ITS POPULATION?

1.1 According to United Nations projections (medium variant), the world's population will increase by 72 percent between 1995 and 2050. It is hoped that by that time food deficits will be reduced, per caput food consumption in countries suffering from shortages will increase and the diets of populations will be diversified in order to eliminate specific deficiencies. All these changes will weigh heavily on food production systems, natural resources and the environment.

1.2 The main question is whether the required improvements in food production and available natural resources will be enough to cope with this population growth in a sustainable manner until 2050, when the world's population is projected to stabilize. The distribution of natural resources needed for agricultural production does not correspond to the geographical distribution of population, and migration does not necessarily compensate for this difference in distribution, which can cause additional difficulty. This issue is relevant at the local, national, regional and international levels.

SCOPE OF THE PAPER

1.3 This paper focuses on the relative importance in the trends of three factors: the demographic factors determining food energy requirements,[1] the closing of existing gaps in energy requirements and the diversification of dietary patterns to meet nutritional needs better. From this perspective, a population is seen not only as a sum of people with demographic or socio-economic characteristics, but as a collection of individuals with differing nutritional requirements because of variables such as gender, height, age, degree of physical activity and dietary pattern.

1.4 This paper, therefore, uses mainly minimum energy requirements as a basis to estimate the plant-derived energy needed to meet them. These energy requirements are evaluated for 2050 according to several demographic and nutritional scenarios and their interplay.

1.5 Obviously, the relative importance of the three demographic and nutritional factors of change (identified above) depends on the assumptions adopted. Changing assumptions would modify the results. The United Nations population projections present three highly different scenarios which show the importance of demographic factors. In contrast, nutritional assumptions adopted in terms of closing the gap in energy requirements and diversifying diets are conservative: the food energy level expected to be reached by developing countries in 2050 would be that projected by FAO for East Asia for 2010 and the level of diversification of diet adopted does not differ markedly from that projected by FAO for the whole world in 2010.

---

[1] In the title of the paper, the term "food requirements" has been used. Strictly speaking, it should be replaced by the term "food demand". However, in view of the economic meaning of the term "demand", the expression "food requirements" was preferred. It covers the nutrient requirements, which include energy, protein requirements and micronutrients.

1.6 Such scenarios make it easier to assess the consequences of different assumptions for population and nutritional changes in 2050 and have been adopted for the following reasons.

- The United Nations population projections are available up to 2050 and cover a period that is long enough for the role of population factors to be revealed fully.
- Population growth is generally expected to stabilize after 2050. Therefore, from a population and food balance perspective, the problem of achieving sustainable development needs to be resolved by 2050 or preferably earlier.

1.7 These results will give an idea of the magnitude of population challenges for food production to meet nutritional requirements by 2050, without consideration of the calendar during that period. Consequently, the paper expands the population projections of the United Nations to include the nutrition field.

1.8 It should be clear that the paper cannot be seen as an extension of population projections into the field of economics.

1.9 It should also be taken into account that focusing on sustainable development over a period roughly corresponding to two generations highlights the importance of human capital development and policies that cover more than one generation.

CLASSIFICATIONS USED

1.10 Besides using the common distinctions between developed and developing countries (i.e. socio-economic) and by continent (i.e. geographic), it is also useful to attempt to classify countries according to the main sources of energy in the diets of their populations. The three modes of classification should be seen as complementary.

1.11 In determining the number of dietary pattern classes, there is a trade-off between the precision that comes with defining a large number of classes and the stability of the classification over the long term. Of course, by choosing the stability option as far as possible, and thus reducing the number of classes, some anomalies can occur, which will be discussed where appropriate.

1.12 Owing to the small number of classes adopted here, there will probably be few changes in diet class. Even though some countries will have to import cereals to augment their food supplies and may have to buy wheat in spite of their diet being structured differently, these imports would have to be on a very large scale at the national level to change a country's diet class.

1.13 The following important assumption is adopted implicitly: populations that consume mainly roots or tubers (cassava, yams, taro, etc.) will not change this pattern radically. The assumption can be explained by three observations: the countries concerned can intensify cultivation of those crops without damaging soils; they still have considerable land reserves for rain-fed agriculture; and, as a result of their great poverty, they might not be able to import enough cereals to generate a change in their dietary class for a number of decades.

STRENGTHS AND LIMITATIONS

1.14 The predictability of the various aspects of the food/population question varies considerably.

1.15 Of these aspects, population changes are probably the least difficult to project. Soon after the Second World War the United Nations was able to project world population for the year 2000, and it has produced subsequent projections without any substantial changes in the results (Table 1).

1.16 Because of internal and international migration flows, often caused by economic changes, the observation made on the projections is better verified for larger geographical areas than for smaller ones.

1.17 It is difficult to project changes in farming practices such as technological changes, the development of new cultivars, the selection of new animal species, the success of research on adapting farming to the environment or the environment to farming (irrigation, etc.) and the dissemination of expertise and innovations.

1.18 Adopting a time frame of 50 years, or even 20 years, presents difficulties because of the unpredictable nature of certain exogenous variables such as: public investments in infrastructures that may influence the development of agriculture; the supply of agricultural inputs; the regulation of agricultural markets; and the effectiveness of structural adjustment policies that affect factors such as farmers' income or debt. But, by focusing on relatively robust population projections and nutritional aspects, these difficulties, to a certain extent, can be avoided.

Projections based on those of international organizations

1.19 The projections in this paper draw from a series of projections produced by international organizations.

Table 1 UNITED NATIONS POPULATION PROJECTIONS FOR THE YEAR 2000		
Year of reference	Date of publication	Projected population for the year 2000 *(million)*
1950-55	1958	6 280
1982	1985	6 127
1994	1995	6 158

1.20 The three United Nations scenarios for population projections up to 2050 have been examined to estimate the relative or absolute impact of certain demographic factors on energy requirements and of dietary changes on food demand. Even stopping at this level, it is apparent that the magnitude of the challenges for food production is unprecedented and raises fundamental questions regarding possible improvements in productivity, sustainability and environmental costs.

1.21 FAO projections for food and agriculture until 2010 have served as a framework for this study. Thus this document draws on *World agriculture: towards 2010* (*WAT2010*) (FAO, 1995a) for its country-level results and its assumptions for trends up to the year 2025.

1.22 The procedures for evaluating energy requirements have been elaborated by FAO.

1.23 The combined use of these sources has permitted a long-term projection of energy requirements and of the demographic and nutritional factors that determine these requirements.

1.24 The scenarios presented in this paper imply that meeting challenges of the magnitude described will require:
- holistic strategies that combine national and international efforts and mobilize human, technical and financial resources;
- a major and unprecedented change in the scale of food security and human capital development, including resolution of those population and gender issues that have an impact on food security.

1.25 In Chapter 2, the historical balance between population and food production is examined and the countries are classified according to level of development, continent and dietary patterns. The factors affecting the balance between energy requirements and food supplies are discussed and some lessons are drawn from the observed trends.

1.26 In the third chapter, some future scenarios are examined in order to illustrate the relative impact on energy requirements of population growth and other demographic factors such as urbanization. The importance of closing existing gaps in energy requirements is then shown, as well as the additional requirements made necessary by changing dietary habits. Finally, the aggregate impact of the previously mentioned factors is discussed and some conclusions are drawn. It should be noted that each factor is presented as a multiplying coefficient of plant-derived energy. The aggregate effects are obtained by multiplying each specific coefficient.

2. The balance between population and food production since 1950

2.1 The first consideration is an examination of population trends that may have influenced the energy requirements of populations and thus affected the food supply needed to satisfy those requirements. Changes in food supply are described below. Finally, the paper examines whether food supply has covered these requirements.

POPULATION CHANGES

2.2 Population changes that have affected food supplies since the Second World War can be summarized as follows:
- Mortality has decreased on all continents.
- Fertility has declined or is declining, with exceptions in certain regions.
- As a consequence of these trends, a demographic transition has taken place or is ongoing:
  - world population doubled between 1950 and 1990;
  - the maximum increase, as measured in growth rates, occurred in the 1960s;
  - the maximum increase in population numbers is occurring now in the 1990s;
  - world population will continue to grow for several decades;
  - ageing in population structures has started, although in a staggered manner.
- There is a massive concentration of populations in cities. Fifteen mega-cities with populations of more than 10 million have emerged.
- The growth of rural populations in all developing regions except Latin America is expected to continue but at a slower pace until 2015. In the least-developed countries, the growth of the rural population is expected to continue beyond 2025 (United Nations, 1995a). Densities of rural populations have increased.
- Migration is a particularly complex issue and is difficult to project. Certain issues in this area need to be highlighted.
- Although food insecurity is often an important factor in migration, as was evident during the Irish potato famine, for example, it is often a combination of factors that triggers a move. This is why, more generally, the unequal distribution of resources and opportunities inside countries and between countries has played a major role in human mobility throughout history.
- Migration can have positive and negative consequences for sending and receiving areas (e.g. introduction of new ideas and knowledge or labour shortages) and for the migrants and their families (e.g. remittances), which

can change the development of communities, depending on the circumstances.

- As mentioned above, the absence of food security, especially when linked with natural-resource depletion, is an important factor in triggering migration flows. Natural disasters, drought, civil disturbance and war also lead to migration.
- The volume of migration has generally increased over the last few decades, and the recent revolutions in communication and transport are creating the conditions for both rapid and large-scale population movements: rural-rural (to clear and settle whatever land is still available), rural-urban, urban-urban and country-to-country.
- International migration is no longer confined to South-North movements. It has also taken on a South-South dimension, as increasing differentiation has appeared within the development levels of the developing countries themselves.

On the basis of these remarks, population movements can therefore be expected to increase in volume and diversify in destination. Appropriate national and international policies will be necessary to ensure that the impact of migration is positive. In this respect, policies designed purely to stem migration flows, whether internally or internationally, cannot be successful and will often be counterproductive without effective development policies in sending areas.

THE IMPACT OF QUANTITATIVE OR STRUCTURAL POPULATION CHANGES ON ENERGY REQUIREMENTS

2.3 In addition to the obvious role played by population growth itself, all the structural changes mentioned above have influenced the energy requirements of populations to varying degrees.

2.4 The increase in life expectancy contributes to the increase in population of all ages. Furthermore, improving the diet of children contributes to increasing their size and weight, thus increasing their average energy requirements as adults.

2.5 The decline in fertility has two opposite effects. On the one hand, it tends to reduce the average energy requirements, because the requirements of pregnant and nursing women are somewhat higher than those of other women of the same age. On the other hand, it tends to increase energy requirements through a reduction of the proportion of children, whose requirements are less than those of adults. On balance the latter effect dominates, but the net effect is a weak one.

2.6 Physical activity increases requirements, and levels of physical activity tend to be greater in rural areas than in urban ones. Inversely, urban populations change their diet and adopt eating habits that generally require more plant energy (Calories).

2.7 This document describes the specific effects of these demographic factors on energy requirements.

CHANGES IN FOOD SUPPLIES

2.8 Since 1971, FAO has been developing an integrated and computerized system for compiling and maintaining, in the form of supply/utilization accounts (SUAs), current agricultural statistics for 300 primary food, agricultural and fishery commodities and 310 processed products derived from those commodities for about 200 countries and territories with data series from 1961 to 1990.

2.9 The total quantity of foodstuffs produced in a country added to the total quantity imported and adjusted for any change in stocks that may have occurred since the beginning of the reference period gives the supply available during that period. On the utilization side, a distinction is made between quantities exported, fed to livestock, used for seed, put to industrial and other non-food uses or lost during storage and transportation and those food supplies available for human consumption at the retail level, i.e. the form is noted in which the food leaves or otherwise enters the food supply for consumption (FAO, 1993a).

2.10 It is important to note that the quantity of food available indicates the quantity of food reaching the consumer but not necessarily the amounts of food actually consumed. Amounts consumed may be lower than the quantity shown because of the losses of edible food and nutrients in the household during storage, preparation and cooking (which affect vitamin and mineral content more than they affect energy, protein or fat), plate-waste, quantities fed to domestic animals and pets or food thrown away (FAO, 1993a).

2.11 FAO has thus evaluated food supply for 1992 at an average (after losses) of 2 718 Calories per person per day, of which 2 290 Calories were from plant products and 428 Calories from livestock products.

A considerable increase in food supplies

2.12 Globally, food supplies have more than doubled in the last 40 years. This has resulted in global food supplies increasing faster than the population, which has led to a substantial increase in average per caput food supplies in Calories. The data available show that between 1962 and 1991 average daily per caput food supplies increased by more than 15 percent, but these global averages conceal important regional variations.

2.13 In developing countries the increase in per caput food supplies was substantial, rising from almost 1 990 Calories in 1962 to 2 500 Calories in 1991, while in the same period the total population almost doubled, growing from 2.2 billion to more than 4.2 billion people. At the same time food supplies in developed countries rose from 3 000 Calories in 1962 to a maximum of about 3 300 in 1982, then diminished to about 3 150 Calories in 1991. The increase was especially significant in Asia, which fully exploited the advantages of the green revolution, and in Latin America, which benefited greatly from technological progress in the form of hybrid varieties of maize.

2.14 Three categories of countries are not included in these trends. The European countries, first of all, reduced their supplies between 1982 and 1992, while North American countries greatly increased theirs. African countries, especially those whose populations consume cassava, yams or taro, underwent a reduction in food supplies during the same period. This African evolution needs to be seen particularly as a consequence of the failure to carry out a green revolution on that continent. It should be noted that during the same period (1982 to 1992), those populations that obtain most of their energy requirements from maize also underwent a decrease in their supplies.

Diversion of cereal production from human consumption

2.15 Only half the cereals produced are destined for human consumption: 48 percent in 1969-1971 and 50 percent in 1988-1990 (FAO, 1995a).

2.16 Most of the cereals put to other uses are destined to feed livestock. Just over 20 percent of the world's cereal production was used to feed livestock in 1988-1990 (15 percent in 1969-1971). Developing countries used a little less than 20 percent for livestock in 1988-1990 (a little more than 10 percent in 1969-1971) (FAO, 1995a). The rest is used for seed reserves (seed requirements are estimated at around 5 percent) (James and Schofield, 1990) or is lost between harvesting and retailing. (The proportions are difficult to evaluate except by looking at the leftover balance.)

Food losses

2.17 No one knows exactly the harvest losses between production and retailing. There are existing case-studies that focus on losses in yields caused by pests, but it is difficult to generalize (FAO, 1993b). The FAO evaluation of food supplies takes into account various losses. The loss of food during storage may be considerable. Important losses have been observed in Latin America (SOLAGRAL, 1995). Some authors estimate losses at 10 to 20 percent. Others estimate losses to be as high as one-third of the quantities produced (Erlich and Erlich, 1991). At any rate, losses of 10 to 15 percent in commercial warehouses are not infrequent (James and Schofield, 1990) (see Paragraph 3.61).

2.18 To compare national requirements and per caput food supplies, a percentage representing food losses occurring between retailing and domestic consumption (at the stage of preparation or consumption) must be added to the evaluation of requirements. A figure of 5 to 10 percent is frequently quoted (James and Schofield, 1990). These losses are greater in developed countries than in developing countries, and in the latter losses are greater in urban areas than in rural ones.

2.19 Losses from household security stocks, usually made in rural areas by the farmers themselves, must also be considered. Rural societies often experience crop failures. The stocks are exposed to deterioration or destruction by pests, mould, etc. Losses are greater when reserves are larger and when they are made for periods exceeding one year. Stocks are small in developed countries and larger in developing countries. In the latter, they are larger in rural areas than in urban areas. Stocks are smaller in rural societies with higher living standards.

2.20 Available figures cannot be used as statistics because they are so imprecise and specific to certain cases. However, in the absence of more precise figures, losses resulting from stock constitution and the losses sustained between retailing and domestic consumption are estimated to amount to between 10 and 40 percent of the total food supplies of a family (Uvin, 1995).

COVERING ENERGY REQUIREMENTS

2.21 The evaluations of per caput food supplies cannot be considered evaluations of energy requirements. Nutritionists have evaluated human energy requirements. A manual for planners and nutritionists details current knowledge and suggests methods for evaluation at the country level (James and Schofield, 1990).[2]

2.22 It should be recalled that there is a difference between energy requirements and food demand. All people consume food to satisfy their requirements for energy and nutrients, which vary according to age, sex, height, weight, etc. However, the demand for food to satisfy these requirements varies according to food supplies as well as such factors as consumers' tastes, income and relative prices. A population increase and a change in its structure, notably by age and sex, will lead to changes in requirements, especially in energy, according to the parameters previously mentioned, but these requirements may be satisfied by a great variety of combinations of food products.

2.23 What are the factors that most affect energy requirements? With a constant population, height and weight account for 49 percent, the age structure for 35 percent and urbanization for 15 percent in the national average allocation of energy (James and Schofield, 1990). The main factors to consider are the following:
- age structure of the population;
- weight, which greatly depends on age, height and sex (all things being equal, the level of requirements does not appear to vary according to gender);
- emaciation (an indicator would have to be defined);
- desirable growth, which corresponds to children's requirements according to age, including requirements linked to weight, emaciation and growth (it would therefore be enough to take the energy requirements of a model population as a reference) (James and Schofield, 1990);
- level of physical activity.

Trends in energy requirements

2.24 Retrospective evaluation of energy requirements shows that they vary greatly in different countries. Those of developed countries are greater than those of developing countries.

[2] See also WFS companion paper 5, *Food security and nutrition.*

2.25 The energy requirements of North American countries average almost 2 400 Calories per person per day, which is a little more than the requirements for European populations. At the other end of the scale, the lowest energy requirements are those of African populations (less than 2 150 Calories), which are slightly below those of Asian or Latin American populations (almost 2 150 Calories) (see Figure 1). For a definition of dietary classes, see Paragraphs 2.42 to 2.48.

2.26 In general, populations whose diets are based on rice, maize, wheat, millets or cassava (Figure 2, Classes 1, 2, 3, 5 and 6, respectively), for the most part in developing countries, have energy requirements that are almost 10 percent lower than those of developed countries, where the diet is richer in animal products.

2.27 The energy requirements of populations have generally increased since 1970 (after having decreased during the previous decade), reaching a level of 2 220 Calories per caput per day. The requirements in developed countries have been increasing more rapidly since 1970 after slow growth during the preceding decade. The requirements in developing countries have increased even more rapidly than in developed countries. This is because the energy requirements of Asian countries, especially those consuming mainly rice, and of Latin American countries have increased very rapidly, much more so than those of developed countries (Figure 1).

2.28 The trends in Africa are different (Figure 1). Average per caput energy requirements have decreased very slightly since 1960 because of the slight reduction in the requirements of populations consuming mainly millets or sorghum and of populations consuming cassava, yams, taro or plantain (Figure 2, Classes 5 and 6, respectively). This is also the case for the energy requirements of populations consuming maize. The changes observed in average energy requirements are mainly caused by changes in population structures by age.

Trends in food supplies

2.29 Coverage of human energy requirements, i.e. the ratio of food energy supplies to the value of requirements, improved rapidly during the 1960s, but this progression slowed considerably during the 1970s. The average rate of coverage even diminished during the 1980s. This does not mean that the food situation of developing countries worsened during the same period. It is in the developed countries that consumption has diminished in relation to constant energy requirements. Even though progress is now slower, the food situation in developing countries has, on average, improved.

2.30 Food supplies in developed countries increasingly surpass their energy requirements. With a rate of coverage already exceeding 1.35 in 1980 and approaching 1.5 in 1990, the populations of North America seem assured of almost total security of their food supply, even in the advent of massive losses at the production level or before or after retailing. Their supplies now exceed their requirements by almost 50 percent (Figure 3). European countries, on the contrary, are reducing their supplies. The rate of coverage of their requirements

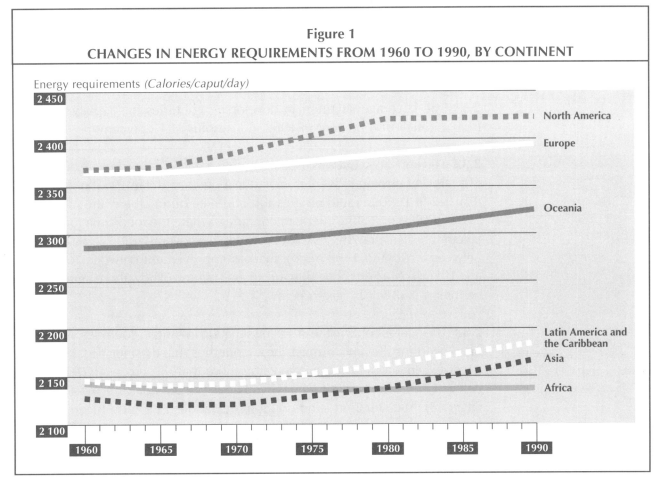

Figure 1
CHANGES IN ENERGY REQUIREMENTS FROM 1960 TO 1990, BY CONTINENT

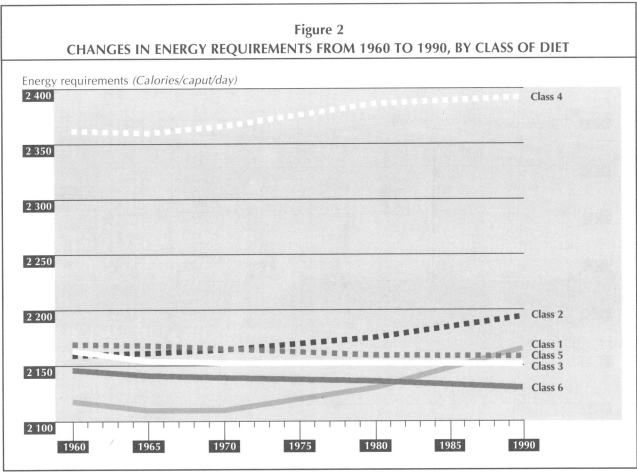

Figure 2
CHANGES IN ENERGY REQUIREMENTS FROM 1960 TO 1990, BY CLASS OF DIET

has gone from 1.4 in 1980 to 1.36 in 1990 (Figure 3). Given the moderate losses that probably occur between the production and domestic consumption of food products, the food situation undoubtedly remains at a surplus level for most of the population.

2.31 The coverage situation in developing countries has greatly improved from a deficit of 6 percent in 1962 to a surplus of 17 percent in 1990.

2.32 The improvement was especially noticeable in Asia. The rate of coverage of energy requirements went from a little more than 0.9 in 1962 to slightly less than 1.2 in 1990, a rapid progression observed during the entire period from 1962 to 1990. In Latin American countries, where the food situation is not as favourable on average as in Asian countries, the coverage rate regressed slightly between 1980 and 1990 after a marked improvement between 1962 (1.10) and 1980 (1.25). Further details and an explanation of how these figures should be interpreted will be given below.

2.33 The figures confirm the alarming situation in African countries. As supplies have been insufficient to meet these countries' needs since 1962 and have never exceeded their requirements by more than 8 percent (coverage rates below 1.06), the food situation is obviously inadequate in most of Africa (Figure 3). The situation is no doubt more serious in some African countries

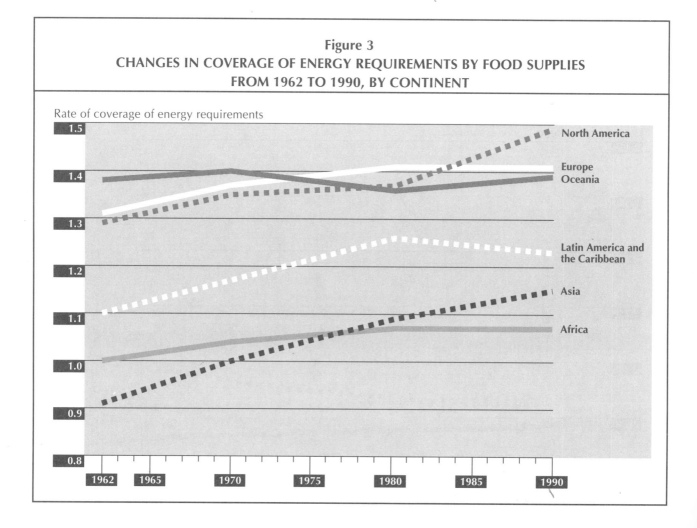

Figure 3
CHANGES IN COVERAGE OF ENERGY REQUIREMENTS BY FOOD SUPPLIES FROM 1962 TO 1990, BY CONTINENT

Rate of coverage of energy requirements

1.5
1.4
1.3
1.2
1.1
1.0
0.9
0.8

North America
Europe
Oceania
Latin America and the Caribbean
Asia
Africa

1962   1965   1970   1975   1980   1985   1990

than the average figures indicate. North African countries, where wheat is an important part of the diet, are able to import grain to satisfy their needs. Conversely, because North Africa is part of the average, the situation has to be worse than average in parts of sub-Saharan Africa.

Critical areas

2.34 Despite an improvement in the ratio between supply and requirements for populations that obtain most of their food energy from millets and sorghum, their food supplies did not cover their needs, even in 1990 (coverage rates below 1.00) (Figure 4, Class 5).

2.35 Even allowing for the poor quality of data, the trends for populations that consume mainly roots or tubers, cassava, yams or taro differ from those of other diet classes. Their food situation is deteriorating and their food supplies were below their requirements in 1980 and in 1990 (Figure 4, Class 6).

2.36 The food situation of sub-Saharan African populations is completely different from that of rice-growing populations. From 1962 to 1990 the coverage rates for Classes 5 and 6 went from 0.89 and 1.02, respectively, to 1.00 and 0.98, while that of Class 1 (rice) rose from 0.88 to 1.18 (Figure 4). Taking into

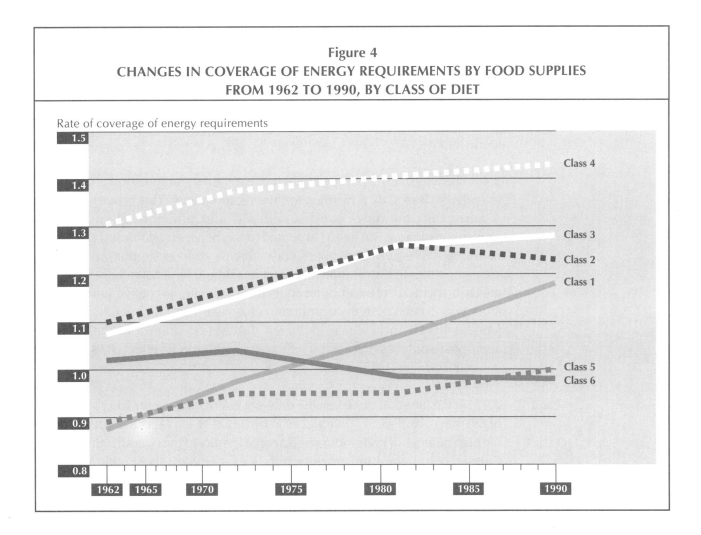

Figure 4
CHANGES IN COVERAGE OF ENERGY REQUIREMENTS BY FOOD SUPPLIES
FROM 1962 TO 1990, BY CLASS OF DIET

account food losses after retailing, which are usually considerable in poor countries, the situation of these populations is often critical.

2.37 In the developing countries, the classes include a large number of countries (with the exception of Class 5, which is small). They thus represent averages and mask local situations. It should be stressed that Africa is not the only continent facing serious food shortages at the national level. Countries such as Ethiopia, Mozambique, Central African Republic, Sierra Leone and Somalia (FAO, 1995b) are effectively in this situation, but so are some Asian countries such as Afghanistan or even Mongolia and Nepal. World Health Organization (WHO) bulletins show that other countries such as Bangladesh, Cambodia and Myanmar also suffer from chronic undernourishment (Erlich and Erlich, 1991). There also exist chronic deficits at the subnational level in India and China. This is why chronic undernutrition continues to be an important problem in East Asia and South Asia (FAO, 1992).

2.38 Large numbers of people still suffer from chronic undernourishment. Figures show that 918 million people suffered from undernourishment in 1969-1971, 906 million in 1979-1981 and 841 million in 1988-1990 (FAO/WHO, 1992).

2.39 The unequal distribution of food supplies occurs at both the micro and macro levels. Until now, no mention has been made of the widespread inequality of people's access to food which occurs regardless of the degree of coverage for the entire population. Women do not always have the same access to food as men, which not only affects their health, but also the future development and growth of their children. It is also known that children's diets can be up to 20 or 30 percent inferior to their needs (FAO, 1987) and that, in the case of food shortages, men sometimes have preferential access to food. It is also true that economic inequalities can generate unequal distribution of food supplies.

2.40 The approach developed here has assumed so far that food is distributed to individuals exactly according to their requirements. This is rarely the case. A fairer distribution of food supplies would probably eliminate most undernourishment. But just as accepted losses between retailing and domestic consumption require a compensatory increase of food supplies, when there are inequalities in distribution food supplies should be substantially larger than needs if there is to be enough food to satisfy the energy requirements of those who come last in the distribution chain (see Paragraph 3.62). Increasing food supplies can facilitate improved distribution only if accompanied by appropriate policies (Paragraph 3.58). The trickle-down effect does not occur automatically.

2.41 At the intercountry level, the differences are increasing. The combination of the macro and micro differences in distribution explains the persistence of the high number of undernourished people in spite of the overall improvement. Current population and poverty trends exacerbate this situation in many developing countries.

DIETS OF THE POPULATIONS OF THE WORLD:
CLASSIFICATION OF COUNTRIES

2.42 The major eating patterns of the world and their socio-cultural dimensions have been classified using the same national information that was used for the analysis of the principal components of daily per caput consumption. Six classes have been defined using an ascending hierarchical classification of 151 countries for which FAO had information. Another 32 countries have been excluded because of insufficient information. However, since these 32 countries together represent only 0.4 percent of the world's population, their exclusion has minimal impact.

2.43 The six classifications include 16, 25, 25, 27, 5 and 21 countries, respectively (Table 2). The inclusion of a category with only five countries may be questioned. But even in a typology programmed with five classes instead of six, the small category would remain because, as will be seen, its characteristics are very important. As explained in the following paragraph, a typology reduced to five classes would group Classes 1 and 2 together, although they are composed of populations consuming mainly rice and maize, respectively.

2.44 To simplify this typology, each class has been named according to the food product that best characterizes its diet. Thus, Class 1 is rice, Class 2 is maize, Class 3 is wheat, etc. But this simplification should not be taken literally. Each class contains countries with similar diet structures according to the FAO food balance sheets. Here it is important to keep in mind that this classification process considers only the energy aspects of each element of the diet in order to compare the structures. It does not consider qualitative aspects such as proteins from fish origin or glucides from wheat. Because each food is recognized only for its energy value in the diet structure, a country will be grouped with a specific class if it has a similar diet structure, even if it differs in an important food. The few anomalies that have emerged in the classification process are of considerable interest, such as the case of Japan, which is explained below in some detail. The differences between some structures can be relatively small. For example, the structure of the Class 1 diet (consumers of rice) is closer to that of Class 2 (consumers of maize) than to any other class. So, if only five classes were defined, countries consuming mainly rice would be grouped with those consuming mainly maize. The diet of this combined group is substantially different from the diet of those countries that consume mainly wheat, because a diet of wheat also includes other sources of energy. On the contrary, if more than six classes were programmed, it would mean separating some countries, such as Japan, into independent classes. With the division of six classes, Japan is grouped with the countries that consume mainly maize, despite the fact that its population does not eat maize. This can be explained by three facts: Japan is not classified within the group of high-revenue countries (Class 4) because its level of energy intake is lower than that of high-revenue countries; its consumption of meat is low; and its consumption of rice is low compared with that of other countries of the rice class. Thus the consumption of plant products other than rice places Japan in a different category from the countries that

Table 2

ASCENDING HIERARCHICAL CLASSIFICATION OF COUNTRIES ACCORDING TO AVERAGE NATIONAL CONSUMPTION FOR EACH COMMODITY[1]

Class 1 Rice (16 countries)	Class 2 Maize (25 countries)	Class 3 Wheat (25 countries)	Class 4 Milk, meat, wheat (27 countries)	Class 5 Millets, sorghum (5 countries)	Class 6 Cassava, yams, taro, plantains (21 countries)
Bangladesh	Bolivia	Afghanistan	Australia	Burkina Faso	Angola
Cambodia	Brazil	Albania	Austria	Mali	Benin
China	Colombia	Algeria	Belgium	Namibia	Burundi
DPR Korea	Costa Rica	Argentina	Canada	Niger	Cameroon
India	Cuba	Botswana	Denmark	Sudan	Central African
Indonesia	Dominican	Bulgaria	Finland		Republic
Laos	Republic	Chile	Former		Chad
Myanmar	Ecuador	Egypt	Czechoslovakia		Congo
Nepal	El Salvador	Ethiopia	Former USSR		Côte d'Ivoire
Philippines	Guatemala	(including	France		Gabon
Republic of	Honduras	Eritrea)	Germany		Ghana
Korea	Jamaica	Former	Greece		Guinea
Senegal	Japan[2]	Yugoslavia	Hungary		Haiti
Sierra Leone	Kenya	Iran	Ireland		Liberia
Sri Lanka	Lesotho	Iraq	Israel		Madagascar
Thailand	Malawi	Jordan	Italy		Mozambique
Viet Nam	Malaysia[2]	Libyan Arab	Lebanon		Nigeria
	Mauritius	Jamahiriya	Netherlands		Rwanda
	Mexico	Mauritania	New Zealand		Togo
	Nicaragua	Morocco	Norway		Tanzania,
	Panama	Pakistan	Poland		United
	Peru	Paraguay	Portugal		Republic of
	South Africa	Romania	Saudi Arabia		Uganda
	Trinidad and	Somalia	Spain		Zaire
	Tobago	Syrian Arab	Sweden		
	Venezuela	Republic	Switzerland		
	Zimbabwe	Tunisia	United		
		Turkey	Kingdom		
		Uruguay	United States		
		Yemen			

[1] Based on three-year average consumption for 1989-1991, in Calories.
[2] See Paragraph 2.44 for an explanation of the appearance of these countries in this group.
Note: 32 countries not classified because of insufficient data: Bahamas, Barbados, Belize, Brunei, Cape Verde, Comoros, Cyprus, Djibouti, Dutch West Indies, Fiji, French Polynesia, the Gambia, Guadeloupe, Guinea-Bissau, Guyana, Hong Kong, Iceland, Kuwait, Maldives, Malta, Martinique, Mongolia, New Caledonia, Papua New Guinea, Réunion, Samoa, Solomon Islands, Suriname, Swaziland, United Arab Emirates, Vanuatu, Zambia.

consume mainly rice (Class 1), and the low consumption of meat, especially beef or mutton, places Japan in a different category from the countries that consume mainly wheat (Class 3). A similar explanation could be given for Malaysia.

2.45 This typology distinguishes six major types of diets (Table 3).
   • The first three classes include countries consuming mainly rice, maize and wheat, respectively.
   • The fourth class includes countries where the diet includes a high content of livestock products, mainly dairy products and porcine meat products, as well as wheat. This class corresponds to developed countries.
   • The last two classes include almost all countries in sub-Saharan Africa. Class 5 populations consume mainly millets or sorghum. Class 6 groups populations that consume mainly roots and tubers (potatoes not included).

Table 3
MAIN CHARACTERISTICS DIFFERENTIATING THE DIETARY CLASSES (ratio to average [1.00])

Characteristics	Class 1 Rice	Class 2 Maize	Class 3 Wheat	Class 4 Milk, meat, wheat	Class 5 Millets and sorghum	Class 6 Cassava, yams, taro, plantains
Active variables						
Rice	3.93	0.94	0.39	0.20	0.33	0.75
Maize	0.65	2.37	0.70	0.14	0.86	1.14
Wheat	0.38	0.62	2.13	1.44	0.25	0.19
Potatoes	0.35	0.62	0.94	2.64	0.00	0.15
Barley	0.28	0.61	1.11	2.42	0.03	0.28
Millet	1.03	0.13	0.11	0.02	13.32	1.40
Sorghum	0.33	0.34	0.98	0.07	8.35	1.78
Cassava	0.35	0.35	0.19	0.00	0.21	4.70
Sweet potato	0.81	0.43	0.15	0.03	0.33	4.26
Sugar (cane, beet, derived)	0.46	1.46	1.02	1.51	0.53	0.29
Veal and beef	0.22	0.96	1.16	1.90	0.51	0.41
Milk	0.20	0.77	1.13	2.30	0.59	0.15
Pork	0.70	0.35	0.43	3.12	0.07	0.17
Surplus of food supplies compared with energy requirements	0.66	0.77	1.18	2.15	0.07	-0.11
Other variables						
Population growth rate (1990-95)	1.00	1.05	1.13	0.38	1.45	1.48
Life expectancy (1990-95)	0.94	1.05	1.00	1.18	0.79	0.80
Infant mortality rate (1990-95)	1.23	0.79	1.06	0.19	1.98	1.81
Total fertility rate (1990-95)	0.97	0.91	1.08	0.49	1.56	1.55
Population density, inhabitants per km² (1990-95)	2.02	1.09	0.49	1.23	0.13	0.65
Requirements for energy of plant origin (1990)	0.91	0.95	1.02	1.28	0.83	0.79
Food supplies (1990)	0.60	0.86	1.07	1.73	0.69	0.52
Requirements (1990)	0.96	0.98	0.99	1.08	0.98	0.96

2.46 The classes in this typology closely correspond to the principal plants of the different civilizations in the world, rice, wheat, maize, millets (to which can be added sorghum) and cassava (to which can be added yams and taro). The effects of diet diversification can be observed only in developed countries which have introduced many livestock products into their diets (Class 4).

2.47 Three developing countries are in Class 4 alongside developed ones. However, these developing countries, Saudi Arabia, Israel and Lebanon, are on or near the Mediterranean rim and are considered high-revenue countries by the World Bank. Their economic situations have enabled their populations to diversify their diets (World Bank, 1994).

2.48 This classification is not very different from that obtained using earlier data. Similar results would probably have been obtained if even older data had been taken into account. The differences would probably have concerned the three countries mentioned above and some developed countries, such as France, which until recently consumed much greater proportions of cereals. There is therefore a certain stability of diets in developing countries, although some changes in dietary patterns can be observed as countries develop.

Relationships between socio-demographic characteristics of populations and their classification according to diet

2.49 Classifying countries according to dietary patterns also organizes them according to important demographic characteristics regarding the energy requirements of their populations. These relations are associative, not causal. In addition, these classifications correspond to different food situations (see Table 3):

- Rice countries (Class 1) are characterized by high population densities. On average, their mortality rates, especially infant mortality, have remained substantially higher than the world average. Increases in life expectancy are anticipated and will lead, with a constant number of births, to an increase in population size. The energy value of food supplies is the number of Calories actually consumed. The amount of livestock products in this diet requires many more plant Calories than there are on the plate. The conversion of these food supplies from plant products confirms, in this case, that there is still little diet diversification in these countries.

- The maize countries (Class 2) should not, on the whole, experience the same type of land scarcity as in rice-growing societies, although there are large disparities in the distribution of their arable land. The potential population-supporting capacities of lands (and waters) of South American countries should be substantially higher than present population densities, especially in a hypothesis using average levels of agricultural inputs (as defined in FAO, 1982). However, six of these 25 countries, mainly in Central America, are probably experiencing serious overpopulation (FAO, 1982). In general, the fertility of these populations is close to the world average, and mortality, especially infant mortality, is substantially lower than the global figure.

- In the wheat countries, on average, the demographic transition is well advanced. The relatively low average population density of Class 3 countries conceals serious water and land shortages, affecting 15 of its 25 countries.

- In Class 4, which includes the most developed countries in the world, the only observations are that its fertility, mortality and population growth rates remain very much below global averages.

- The countries with diets of mainly millets or sorghum (Class 5) are characterized by high population growth, high fertility, low life expectancy and food surpluses very close to the world average. In 1980, FAO identified almost all of these countries as having precarious land resources in spite of their low population densities (FAO, 1982).

- Almost all the populations whose food situations are most critical and continue to worsen can be found among the Class 6 countries, which consume mainly roots and tubers such as cassava, yams and taro. However, these populations have the greater part of the world's reserves of unexploited arable land. The great poverty of these populations, the weakness of their infrastructures, their high fertility and mortality rates and their rapid population growth are not encouraging for the future.

Countries without food security

2.50 Even though improvements in the coverage of energy requirements in developing countries may have been remarkable, they have been too slow. As mentioned earlier, the increase in per caput daily food supplies in developing countries has been substantial, increasing from almost 1 990 Calories in 1962 to more than 2 500 Calories in 1991, which exceeds these countries' requirements (2 160 Calories in 1990). In many countries these gains have not benefited the poor.

2.51 However, the losses of food that occur between retail sale and household consumption have played an important role in increasing the gap between supply and needs. Such losses can be considerable, especially in the case of cereals or vegetables. Losses of roots and tubers are low because they are consumed in countries with relatively small markets (so there are few transport and storage losses) and because they can be left in the ground until they are needed without too much damage occurring. The losses are greater when households are forced to make reserves as a guarantee against crop failure or catastrophes caused by weather, flooding or supply problems. The longer these reserves are kept, the more vulnerable they are. Average annual losses of 10 percent would increase the average food supplies needed to 2 380 Calories, which is not far below the available food supplies of developing countries in 1988-1990 (2 470 Calories).

2.52 The inequality of food distribution within countries also increases the gap between average requirements and the food supplies needed by populations. It has already been pointed out that in countries with the greatest inequalities in distribution, food supplies per caput would have to be 20 to 30 percent above the average requirements to overcome malnutrition (FAO, 1995a). However, such an increase does not automatically solve the problem of distribution, which is why policies in this area are crucial.

2.53 It is understandable, therefore, that the food supplies of countries that consume mainly rice (about 2 520 Calories) should be inadequate and that, since these countries represent the majority of the world's population, most people suffering from malnutrition in the world live in these countries. But the most acute food shortages are in those countries that consume mainly cassava, yams or taro. Their food supplies, which in 1990 were 2 090 Calories, do not equal their average food energy requirements. This class includes many food-insecure countries which will probably account for the majority of people suffering from undernutrition in 2010 (FAO, 1995a). They are also countries with rapid population growth.

FACTORS AFFECTING THE BALANCE BETWEEN ENERGY REQUIREMENTS AND FOOD SUPPLIES

2.54 It is not within the scope of this study to define the factors that determine increases in food supplies. In fact, not much is known about these factors. But with the above results, past conditions that have led to increased food production can be recognized. They are partly demographic since population growth almost automatically leads to an increase in total food energy requirements. They are also partly economic.

General economic development and decline in poverty

2.55 Since the Second World War, those populations that produce their own food and find employment in and earn their living from agriculture have steadily declined in relation to the total population, but they still remain in the majority. In general, the poorest populations are still to be found in rural areas (World Bank, 1990). It is observed that population growth is greatest among the low food consumption countries. This underscores the importance of studying the interactions between increasing requirements and increasing demand. The damage caused to policy formulation by an insufficient understanding of these linkages should be appreciated. Still, general economic growth and a decline in poverty which leads to an increased demand for food commodities seem to be the main factors for ensuring success in meeting increasing energy requirements in many developing countries. Policies addressing rapid population growth can also make an important contribution to these factors.

Rural development brought about by agricultural intensification

2.56 A considerable increase in food supplies made possible by increased productivity and, to a lesser degree, by an increase in cultivated area has been observed. According to FAO (1995a), 69 percent of the increase in plant production between 1970 and 1990 was due to improved yields and 31 percent to increases in cultivated area.

2.57 The increase in productivity was mainly for wheat (2.8 percent per year), rice (2.3 percent per year) and, to a lesser degree, maize (1.8 percent per year) and sorghum (1.5 percent per year). Barley, millet and cassava yields only progressed by 1 percent per year (FAO,1995a). Intensification was also made possible by irrigation, which, apart from directly increasing yields by allowing the use of high-yielding varieties (HYVs) of cereals (hybrids, etc.), has increased the number of harvests. In developing countries (China not included), 123 million hectares of arable land were irrigated in 1988-1990, of which 35 million hectares were arid or very arid land (FAO, 1995a). Although no detailed studies have been made on the subject, the substitution of high-yielding crops for low-yielding ones and changing plant products also added to the increase in food production.

2.58 Technological changes have made food products less expensive, which has allowed increased consumption by humans. Developing countries have also started to feed their livestock food initially intended for human consumption because of lower costs. Increased demand has generated technological innovations, which in turn have become cheaper to use. The increased concentration of populations has probably stimulated production as a result of mass consumption, although this hypothesis has not yet been proved.

2.59 In spite of the increase, production in developing countries has not been enough to satisfy needs. Apart from a few large rice-producing countries, China in particular, developing countries have had to import cereals. These imports have been especially large since prices were abnormally low as a result of farm subsidies given by some countries.

2.60 The long-term trend has been a decline in food prices, partly because, at a global level, there is probably no obstacle to food production increasing to meet demand. The global decline in per caput cereal production during the last ten years can only be explained by a decline in the production of the major exporters.

2.61 Two incompatible policy objectives are being pursued. The first is to reduce poverty and help the poor have access to food, which leads to increasing demand. The second is to maintain prices at a level sufficiently attractive to encourage production on the part of the big cereal exporters, which leads to land being left fallow and curbs increases in available per caput food supplies.

2.62 Increased food production and increased agricultural productivity are the principal means of reducing poverty and improving the food situation in developing countries. The main cause of chronic undernourishment has been the inability to reduce poverty in these countries. The potential for increasing production, e.g. in Africa, is still considerable, but it requires appropriate and effective policies. These policies need to improve the situation of rural women, who are burdened with the major role of food production but who, in the absence of men, frequently have to reduce the number of tasks or the time allocated to each, which can result, *inter alia*, in land degradation.

Increased food imports in developing countries

2.63 A great many developing countries have, to varying degrees, increased their grain imports over the last few decades. The major grain exporters have easily met the increase in demand. Support given to agriculture in exporting countries partly explains the increase in imports by developing countries. However, this support is beginning to ebb.

2.64 As gaps between national production and energy requirements have increased, poor countries have become increasingly dependent on cereal imports. But the size of the imports depends on the solvency of the country: the impact of population size behind these imports becomes apparent only if the countries are solvent.

2.65 Beyond a certain level of economic progress which may initially encourage a decline in fertility, cereal imports increase as fertility and population growth decline. Essentially, it has been observed that the more countries prosper, the more fertility declines and the more cereal imports increase.

2.66 This is not the case when fertility is high. The situation of countries in sub-Saharan Africa is different for two reasons. First, imports are smaller when population growth is rapid, probably because of the poor solvency of countries with high fertility rates. Second, the higher the population pressure in relation to farming area in countries consuming cassava, yams or taro, the smaller the cereal imports per caput. This reveals how extremely insecure food supplies are in these countries (Collomb, 1988, 1989). They cannot import enough cereals to feed their populations.

2.67 An observation specific to Arab countries is that the higher the fertility rate, or population growth, the higher the cereal imports (and the slopes of the regression curves are steep) (Collomb, 1988, 1989). Oil revenues and tourism probably make such imports possible.

LESSONS LEARNED

2.68 The main lesson learned is that poverty is the major economic factor behind the failure to improve access to food, a situation exacerbated by rapid population growth.

2.69 There has been a general improvement in coverage of energy requirements by food supplies in developing countries. The most illustrative case is that of Asia, with an increasing rate of coverage over the period 1962-1992. More recently, the rate of improvement has slowed in Latin America.

2.70 Africa is the exception to these positive trends, with no improvement in coverage of energy requirements during the period 1962-1992. There was an actual decrease in coverage in Class 6 during the period 1970-1980.

2.71 These trends reveal the consequence of the green revolution in Asia and to a lesser degree in Latin America. The absence of such a green revolution in Africa is clearly apparent. These results will have an impact on future scenarios.

2.72 A related factor is probably the insufficient development of human capital. Health and the fulfilling of energy requirements of populations are obviously the preliminary conditions for rural and agricultural development. Humankind is far from ensuring "health for all" by the year 2000, as set out in 1978 at the International Conference on Primary Health Care in Alma Ata, USSR. High illiteracy and lack of information on new techniques or innovations hinder development. The positive effect of training on production and productivity has been proved, but the effects on gross domestic product vary greatly from one country to the next. The higher the initial level of education, the more productive are the investments in education. It would seem that sub-Saharan Africa is an exception to this rule, probably because of the lack of appropriate infrastructure and institutions (World Bank, 1990).

2.73 Thus ensuring that countries suffering from food deficits are able to make progress in their population and development policies in a sustainable manner, a condition for social order in the world, presents a great challenge for agricultural production. It also presents a great challenge for the general development of countries where demographic factors, isolated from or combined with the effects of dietary patterns, play an important role, as will be shown in the rest of this document. These considerations highlight the time-scale necessary for development, which could amount to two generations.

3. Some future scenarios

THE ROLE OF POPULATION FACTORS IN CHANGING ENERGY REQUIREMENTS BY THE YEAR 2050, WITH A CONSTANT DIET SCENARIO

3.1 Contrary to what is widely believed, per caput energy requirements vary according to populations. They also vary according to changes in population structure, independent of the effects of population growth on global requirements.

3.2 It should also be recalled that nutritionists have continually lowered their assessments of human energy requirements since the Second World War.

3.3 It is useful to examine first the impact of population changes on population energy requirements. Within a context of rapid population growth, the increase in the number of people is obviously the dominating factor. But too much attention placed on the impact of absolute numbers has led to insufficient attention being given to the impact of changes in population structure. It will be seen that this has, in turn, led to a poor evaluation of the process through which the energy requirements change.

Population trends

3.4 According to the latest United Nations projections (medium variant), there will be another large world population increase between 1995 and 2050 (72 percent), with the total growing from 5.7 billion inhabitants in 1995 to 9.8 billion in 2050 (Table 4) (Quesnel, Vimard and Guillaume, 1991).

3.5 This projection allows a variation of roughly 2 billion inhabitants over or under the average estimate for the year 2050 because of possible variations in fertility decline (medium variant: population of 9.8 billion; low variant: 7.9 billion; high variant: 11.9 billion) (United Nations, 1995a).

Table 4
PROJECTIONS OF ANNUAL POPULATION GROWTH RATES FROM 1990 TO 2050

Period	Africa	Latin America	North America	Asia	Europe	Oceania	World total
1990-95	2.81	1.84	1.05	1.64	0.15	1.54	1.57
2000-05	2.56	1.50	0.81	1.38	0.00	1.31	1.37
2010-15	2.37	1.20	0.78	1.15	-0.06	1.18	1.20
2020-25	2.08	0.96	0.66	0.89	-0.12	1.00	1.00
2030-35	1.62	0.77	0.23	0.68	-0.22	0.52	0.78
2040-45	1.19	0.55	0.14	0.49	-0.26	0.39	0.57
2045-50	1.14	0.47	0.15	0.40	-0.26	0.35	0.51

Note: The population numbers used to produce these estimations are based on the medium variant of United Nations projections (United Nations, 1995a).

Figure 5
TOTAL POPULATION OBSERVED FROM 1950 TO 1990 AND PROJECTED FOR 1995 TO 2050,
BY CONTINENT (medium variant)

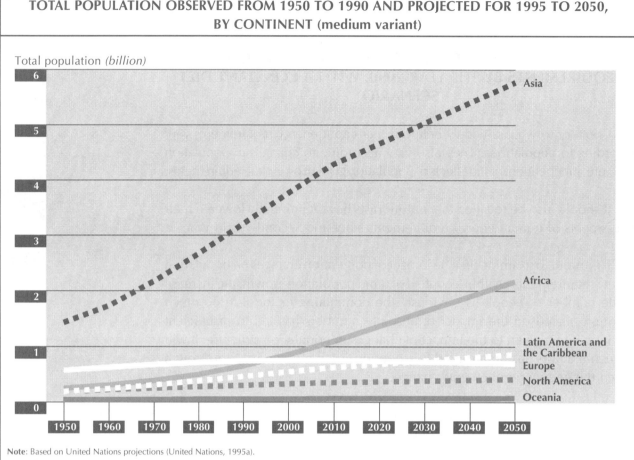

Note: Based on United Nations projections (United Nations, 1995a).

3.6 The two extreme scenarios (high and low variants) are based on the assumption that all countries will simultaneously adopt schedules for reduction in fertility that are slow (high variant) or rapid (low variant). Because it is unlikely that either of these two scenarios will ever occur, the medium variant should be included since some countries will adopt schedules for a slow reduction in fertility, while others will mainly adopt schedules for a rapid decrease.

3.7 Using the medium variant, two continents, Asia and Africa, will represent the great majority of the world population in 2050 (Figure 5). This means that the demographic weight of the population consuming rice will be much greater in 2050 (Figure 6, Class 1). The population consuming mainly wheat will be greatly increased (Figure 6, Class 3). The demographic weight of the population consuming mainly cassava, yams or taro (Figure 6, Class 6) will be close to that of the population consuming maize (Figure 6, Class 2).

Signs of future population growth in the present age pyramid

3.8 The current age structure of world population is the result of fertility rates that have remained high through the last several decades (United Nations, 1995a). Characterized by its youth, the present age structure holds the promise of large population increases in the coming decades, even if fertility were to fall rapidly. A great many of the women born during the first doubling of the world population are now reaching child-bearing age and are ensuring the replacement of their own numbers in daughters who will, by their capacity to procreate, be at the origin of a rapid population increase. Obviously, the number of children will be all the more important given that the fertility of these generations of women will remain high. This will probably be the case for sub-Saharan Africa.

3.9 According to the medium variant of the United Nations projections, the world's population will increase by 4.7 billion between 1990 and 2050 (United Nations, 1992). Almost half of this increase is inescapable. Even if there were a sudden reduction of fertility to the level strictly needed to replace the population, the world population would still increase by more than 2 billion.

Independence of population projections from trends in natural resources

3.10 Changes in available natural resources per caput are not taken into account in the evaluation of population growth rates or in the evaluation of associated factors (mortality or fertility) that are used in population projections.

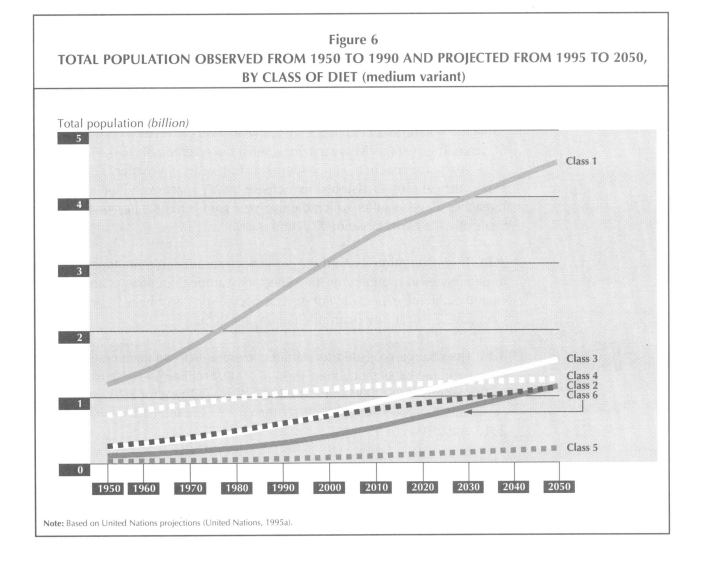

Figure 6
TOTAL POPULATION OBSERVED FROM 1950 TO 1990 AND PROJECTED FROM 1995 TO 2050, BY CLASS OF DIET (medium variant)

Total population *(billion)*

Note: Based on United Nations projections (United Nations, 1995a).

Shortages in arable land or in renewable water supplies may result in some agriculturally dependent countries being unable to fulfil their food energy requirements. Currently used threshold measures of renewable water supplies per inhabitant (the stress level, under 1 700 m^3 of water per inhabitant per year, and the chronic shortage level, under 1 000 m^3 of water per inhabitant per year) should be discussed. They are defined on the basis of work by Malin Falkenmak, a hydrologist, and use norms of the more developed countries. However, there could be lower consumption, as is observed in Israel, especially regarding agricultural use, with the use of adapted technology and equipment as well as the meticulous management of water resources.

United Nations mortality projections

3.11 A more detailed scrutiny of the methodology used to make these projections reveals that they are generally based on the assumption of an increase in life expectancy of 2.5 years every five years when no information points to a stagnation or decline in mortality at the beginning of the 1990s. If there are signs that life expectancy has stopped improving, a stagnation or even a decrease could be projected for the future. Two other models of mortality trends, which assume rapid and slow increases in life expectancy respectively, have been used in certain cases. After 2025, it is assumed that life expectancy at birth will increase according to a model in which the average increase is shared by all countries.

3.12 Based on historical examples, all these models assume slower improvements in life expectancy as mortality is reduced and life expectancy rises. The highest life expectancy at birth allowed in these models is 87.5 years for females and 82.5 for males. The middle model assumes that male life expectancy at birth will increase by 2.5 years every five years until it reaches 60 years. The average five-year gain is then reduced gradually to 0.4 years until 77.5 years are reached and remains at 0.4 years thereafter. Female life expectancy at birth is assumed to increase by 2.5 years every five years until it reaches 65 years, after which the five-year gain is reduced gradually to 0.4 years at a life expectancy of 82.5 and over.

3.13 This assumption is why these projections describe a substantial reduction in differences in mortality or life expectancy among countries (Table 5). For example, the life expectancy of African populations is only eight years lower than that of North American populations for 2050.

3.14 The change projected for Africa corresponds to an acceleration in the increase in life expectancy from 1995 to 2000. From an increase of 1.2 years for the periods 1995-2000 and 2000-2005, Africa will reach a 2.2-year increase between 2000-2005 and 2005-2010, then a 2.5-year increase between 2005-2010 and 2010-2015.

3.15 These mortality projections are based on the assumption of regular economic growth and improvements in the food situation which may occur

Period	Africa	Latin America	North America	Asia	Europe	Oceania	World total
Table 5							
LIFE EXPECTANCIES PROJECTED FOR 1990 TO 2050							
1990-95	53.0	68.5	76.1	64.5	72.9	72.8	64.4
2000-05	55.8	71.0	77.6	67.9	74.3	74.7	67.1
2010-15	60.5	73.2	78.8	70.8	76.1	76.5	69.9
2020-25	65.4	75.1	79.8	73.2	77.5	78.1	72.5
2030-35	69.4	76.6	80.7	75.0	78.7	79.3	74.6
2040-45	72.3	78.0	81.5	76.7	79.9	80.3	76.4
2045-50	73.4	78.6	81.8	77.4	80.4	80.8	77.1

Note: These estimations are based on United Nations projections (United Nations, 1995a).

in Africa in the coming decades. They imply that the energy requirements of the projected populations will be satisfied, which is not guaranteed in countries with high fertility rates or in countries where there may be a shortage of natural resources following high population growth.

3.16 Changes in life expectancy at birth assumed by the United Nations for countries in sub-Saharan Africa, especially countries that consume cassava, yams or taro (Class 6), project an added 20 years of life expectancy, which seems to indicate an elimination of the major food deficits that are typical of these countries. This seems to be in contradiction to economic projections used by FAO that foresee a stagnation in average per caput food supplies by 2010 for the whole African continent.

3.17 These projections take into account the presumed impact of the acquired immune deficiency syndrome (AIDS) pandemic in those countries that are most affected. The impact of AIDS is also related to the fact that it provides an entry point for other diseases such as tuberculosis and malaria. Because of the particular age group affected by AIDS, no models of life tables represent the prevailing mortality structure by age and by sex in these countries.

3.18 One model made by the World Health Organization (WHO) in 1991 makes it possible to evaluate the number of future deaths caused by AIDS. This model uses estimated human immunodeficiency virus (HIV) infection data plus observed and estimated annual progression rates from HIV infection to AIDS and from AIDS to death.

3.19 In applying the model, the United Nations assumed that there would be no new adult HIV infections after 2010 but that mother-to-child infections will continue after this date and AIDS deaths will follow for many years thereafter as a result of the long latency period between HIV infection and AIDS.

3.20 The models used in this case should be discussed further since they account for the evolution of the phenomenon in urban areas but may not give a precise account of the pace of the evolution of the pandemic in rural areas. Another major unknown is the future course of the pandemic in Asia.

United Nations projections of fertility reductions

3.21 Three hypotheses have been used: in the medium variant, fertility is assumed to reach and stabilize at the replacement level of 2.1 children per woman: in the high variant, fertility is assumed to stabilize at about 2.6 children (or will rise to that level if currently below); and in the low variant, it is assumed to stabilize at about 1.6 children, i.e. below the replacement level.

3.22 In all three variants, the assumed target period at which fertility will stabilize is determined through a range of socio-economic factors such as population policies and programmes, adult literacy, school enrolment levels, economic conditions [gross domestic product (GDP) or gross national product (GNP) per caput], infant mortality and marriage, as well as historical, cultural and political factors.

3.23 The fertility schedules are based on the work of experts rather than on mathematical models because of the uneven quality or even the lack of data and because of the qualitative nature of some of the data.

3.24 One remarkable fact revealed by the projections is that fertility rates in African countries will decrease. According to United Nations projections, in the medium variant, the reduction in fertility rates that might be observed in African countries between 1990-1995 and 2045-2050 would be almost as rapid as the one observed and estimated for Latin American countries over a period of the same length, between 1960-1965 and 2015-2020 (Table 6).

3.25 It must be pointed out that it is extremely difficult to forecast fertility levels and changes. The fertility decline in Latin America at the end of the 1960s surprised many experts. Once they observed the phenomenon, they agreed that increased urbanization and literacy, indicators related to fertility reduction, had been determining factors in triggering this decline and could have been used to forecast the trend (Chesnais, 1985). So even though the factors that determine the fertility rates of the social categories in a given country are relatively well known, little is known about the factors that determine reductions in fertility. This has led scientific literature to show the effects of development first, and then the effects of extreme poverty, on fertility

Table 6
TOTAL FERTILITY RATES PROJECTED FOR 1990 TO 2050

Period	Africa	Latin America	North America	Asia	Europe	Oceania	World total
1990-95	5.80	3.09	2.06	3.03	1.58	2.51	3.10
2000-05	4.91	2.62	2.07	2.73	1.59	2.40	2.84
2010-15	4.09	2.31	2.10	2.44	1.73	2.35	2.60
2020-25	3.37	2.18	2.10	2.19	1.86	2.23	2.38
2030-35	2.63	2.12	2.10	2.12	1.97	2.11	2.22
2040-45	2.10	2.10	2.10	2.10	2.04	2.10	2.10
2045-50	2.10	2.10	2.10	2.10	2.06	2.10	2.10

Note: These projections are based on the medium variant of United Nations projections (United Nations, 1995a).

reduction (Cosio-Zavala, 1992; Quesnel, Vimard and Guillaume, 1991), which has gradually changed the original meaning of the term "demographic transition".

3.26 Making projections is difficult because some populations are still reticent to accept family planning programmes. That is why, as the statements presented by the Chinese delegation to the Population Commission in 1994 and 1995 suggest (Peng, 1994, 1995), it is difficult to predict changes in fertility in a country such as China. It is made even more difficult because current fertility is perhaps underestimated, especially fertility in rural China. According to the Chinese Institute of Family Planning, on the basis of a survey of 32 villages, fertility in rural China could be underestimated by as much as 37 percent and urban fertility might, in some cases, be underestimated by 19 percent. If such observations were verified on a large scale, fertility for the whole of China could be underestimated (Zeng, 1995; Wang and Wang, 1995). The United Nations projections already have taken into account this possible underestimation.

3.27 On the other hand, some experts now claim that fertility in developing countries will fall so rapidly that the United Nations low variant projection should be used (Chesnais, 1985); however, there is some question as to the basis for such arguments.

Population growth as the main factor behind increases in food energy requirements

3.28 During the expected period of continued high population growth between 1995 and 2050, as during the last 50 years, increases in energy requirements will mostly be affected by increases in population numbers. This represents a global increase of 72 percent based on the medium variant, 38 percent based on the low variant and 108.4 percent with the high variant (Figure 7).

The impact of other population factors

3.29 Changes in energy requirements since the Second World War have been evaluated retrospectively by following the evaluation method adopted by FAO.

3.30 The results presented in this document were obtained by applying the ENREQ 2 program to population evaluations by age for the three variants used in the United Nations projections (United Nations, 1995a). Calculations of future requirements have taken into account the impact of urbanization described in the United Nations projections (United Nations, 1995b) as well as the possible impact of the increased height of populations.

3.31 Changes in age structure are increasing the energy requirements of developing countries. Energy requirements increase during the first 25 years of a person's life (until 18 or 25 years according to case and source used) and decrease slightly after the age of 60.

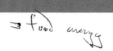

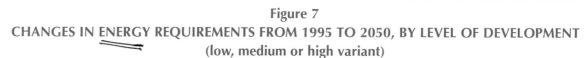

Figure 7
CHANGES IN ENERGY REQUIREMENTS FROM 1995 TO 2050, BY LEVEL OF DEVELOPMENT
(low, medium or high variant)

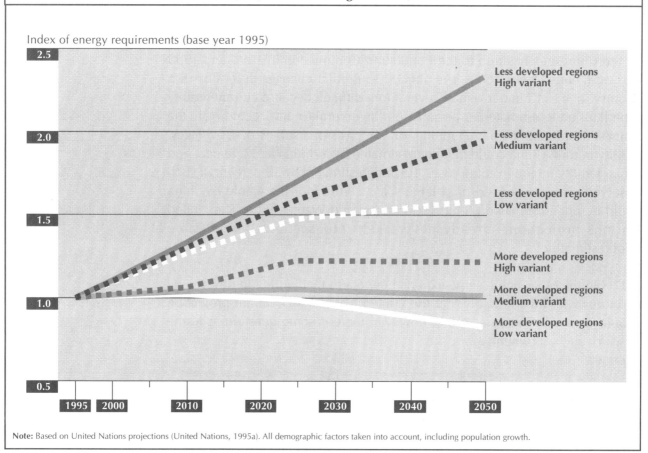

Index of energy requirements (base year 1995)

Note: Based on United Nations projections (United Nations, 1995a). All demographic factors taken into account, including population growth.

3.32 Thus, the ageing of a population is initially driven by the decline in fertility and in the proportion of children; as such, it brings about an increase in per caput energy requirements (see Paragraph 2.5). Later, it is mostly driven by the decline in mortality and the rise in the proportion of older people; this causes a decrease in average energy requirements. Developing countries for the time being are concerned mostly with the former process, and developed countries with the latter (Table 7).

3.33 These influences on average per caput requirements remain moderate at a global level (+2 percent) but hide important regional variations.

3.34 Therefore, the impact of structure by age varies between two extremes: a 7 percent increase is expected in the average energy intake required between 1995 and 2050 for Africa (7.8 percent for populations consuming cassava, yams or taro, 8.1 percent for populations consuming millets or sorghum, 8.2 percent for Central Africa and 8.5 percent for East Africa) and a 1 percent reduction for developed countries.

3.35 The increasing height of individuals increases per caput energy requirements. A better diet at a young age results in an increase in average height. The height of populations, therefore, depends partly on children's diets.

Table 7
ESTIMATED EFFECTS OF DEMOGRAPHIC FACTORS ON THE ENERGY REQUIREMENTS OF THE POPULATION AND THE FOOD SUPPLIES NEEDED TO SATISFY THESE REQUIREMENTS IN 2050
(base year 1995 [1.00])

Variable (multiplying coefficient)	Africa	Asia	Europe	Latin America and the Caribbean	North America	Oceania
Age structure	1.07	1.02	0.99	1.02	1.00	1.00
Change in height	1.02	1.02	1.00	1.02	1.00	1.01
Change in percentage of pregnant women	1.00	0.99	1.00	1.00	1.00	1.00
Change in proportion of urban population	0.97	0.96	0.99	0.98	0.99	0.99
Combined previous effects	1.07	1.02	0.98	1.03	0.99	1.00
Impact of population numbers	2.94	1.66	0.93	1.74	1.33	1.61
ALL DEMOGRAPHIC EFFECTS	3.14	1.69	0.91	1.80	1.31	1.61

Note: The population numbers used to produce these estimations are based on the medium variant of United Nations projections (United Nations, 1995a).

Very rapid responses to diet changes have been observed (Piazza, 1986), such as height increases of substantially more than 1 cm per decade in certain regions of China.

3.36 In the hypothesis of improved diets in developing countries and of the gradual disappearance of malnutrition by the year 2050, the average height of populations could increase by 1 cm per decade. That is the growth assumed in this document, with a limit set at a height of 1.75 m. Such an increase in the average height of populations would bring about an increase in their average energy requirements.

3.37 This increased height could lead to a 1 percent increase in average energy requirements in the world between 1995 and 2050. The needs of developing countries would be increased by 2 percent and the increase could reach as much as 3 percent in southern Africa or in East Asia.

3.38 It would seem that urbanization leads to a reduction in energy requirements. This reduction is expected to be especially perceptible in developing countries where the urbanization process is likely to be rapid (Popkins, 1994). It could then result in a 3 percent fall in requirements between 1995 and 2050. Urbanization is expected to produce the greatest impact in Asia (-4 percent) and Africa (-3 percent). It should also be noted that new technologies and lifestyles can have other effects on food energy requirements; for example, traditional food prescriptions for pregnant women and babies may be modified. However, data on such effects have not been collected on a national scale.

3.39 The potential impact of a smaller number of pregnancies on the energy requirements of populations as a result of fertility declines was found to be negligible (Table 7). It will represent a reduction of about 1 percent for developing countries. In the case of a sharp decrease in fertility, in the Near East for example, the decrease could reach 2 percent. Although all pregnancies are treated equally in this document, the issue of adolescent pregnancies needs to be further explored.

3.40 Overall, the factors increasing energy requirements have a greater impact than those leading to decreases. The cumulative effect of factors determining increases can exceed 10 percent, whereas the cumulative effect of factors determining decreases never reaches 5 percent.

3.41 A remarkable fact is that changes in a population's age composition can lead to reductions in average energy requirements because of the increased percentage of older people. Thus, the combined effect of ageing and urbanization will reduce food energy requirements in Europe by 2 percent.

3.42 The four demographic structural effects examined previously work in opposing directions in developing countries, and this contributes towards reducing their final impact. Trends in age structure always have a greater impact than the others. The positive effect of height increase on energy requirements of populations cancels out the negative effects of both urbanization and the reduction in the proportion of pregnant women in countries with high fertility. Thus, the resulting impact of these factors is equal to that of age structure, for example, +7 percent for Africa. A similar observation can be made, but at a higher level, for the countries with the highest fertility in Africa, for example, countries that consume cassava, yams or taro, for which the impact is also equal to that of age structure, but at the level of +8 percent.

Total effect of population factors on global food energy requirements

3.43 Except for developed countries as a whole, the effect of population growth in numbers on energy requirements is definitely more important than the effect of changes in population structures (Tables 7 and 8).

3.44 For developed countries, the 4 percent increase in population between 1995 and 2050 projected by the United Nations under the medium variant compensates for changes in population structure (-2 percent).

3.45 The outlook changes entirely in the case of developing countries. Requirements resulting from population growth will increase by as much as +95 percent, whereas the combined effect of changes in structure will be hardly more than +3 percent.

3.46 As a result, a 76 percent increase in requirements is projected for the whole world, +74 percent as a result of population growth and +2 percent because of changes in population structures.

3.47 At a global level, the combined effect of population changes means that a 75 percent increase can be expected in energy requirements. This result is

Table 8
EFFECTS OF DEMOGRAPHIC FACTORS ON CHANGES IN THE ENERGY
REQUIREMENTS OF POPULATIONS TO 2050
(base year 1995 [1.00])

Classification	Variant of fertility changes		
	Low	Medium	High
Level of development			
Developed	0.83	1.02	1.22
Developing	1.59	1.95	2.34
World total	1.43	1.76	2.10
Continent and subcontinent			
Africa	2.65	3.14	3.67
Asia	1.36	1.69	3.67
Europe	0.76	0.91	1.07
Latin America and the Caribbean	1.44	1.80	2.23
North America	1.02	1.31	1.60
Oceania	1.28	1.61	1.91
Diet classification of countries			
Rice	1.27	1.60	1.93
Maize	1.46	1.78	2.16
Wheat	2.01	2.42	2.86
Livestock products and wheat	0.92	1.13	1.35
Millets, sorghum	2.99	3.43	3.89
Cassava, yams, taro	2.96	3.51	4.10

Note: The population numbers and structures used to produce these estimated requirements are based on United Nations projections (United Nations, 1995a).

not surprising, nor is it particularly worrying, given that stagnation or even regression of total world agricultural production or agricultural production per caput is caused by big cereal exporters putting the brake on production, which curbs their capacity to expand. But this should not be considered a major finding of this study.

3.48 The average change in food energy requirements masks very strong regional differences (Table 8), (Figure 8). The requirements of European countries will diminish and those of North American countries will increase by only one-third. Asian countries and countries in Latin America and the Caribbean will probably have to cope with increases reaching 69 and 80 percent, respectively, from 1995 to 2050. Africa, on the basis of the medium variant of United Nations projections, will have to deal with a trebling of its food energy requirements (Figure 8).

3.49 Countries that get their energy from wheat, mainly Arab countries and especially those on the Mediterranean rim, will probably see their energy requirements increase by 142 percent (Table 8), (Figure 9, Class 3). This suggests that grain imports in these countries will increase substantially, as long as the countries remain solvent.

3.50 In Africa, the contrast between countries that belong to Class 3 and those that belong to Classes 5 and 6 is expected to increase. Countries in Class 3 will probably be faced with a doubling of their food energy requirements, while the others will have to deal with more than a trebling of their energy requirements

Figure 8
CHANGES IN ENERGY REQUIREMENTS FROM 1995 TO 2050, ACCORDING TO CONTINENT
(medium variant)

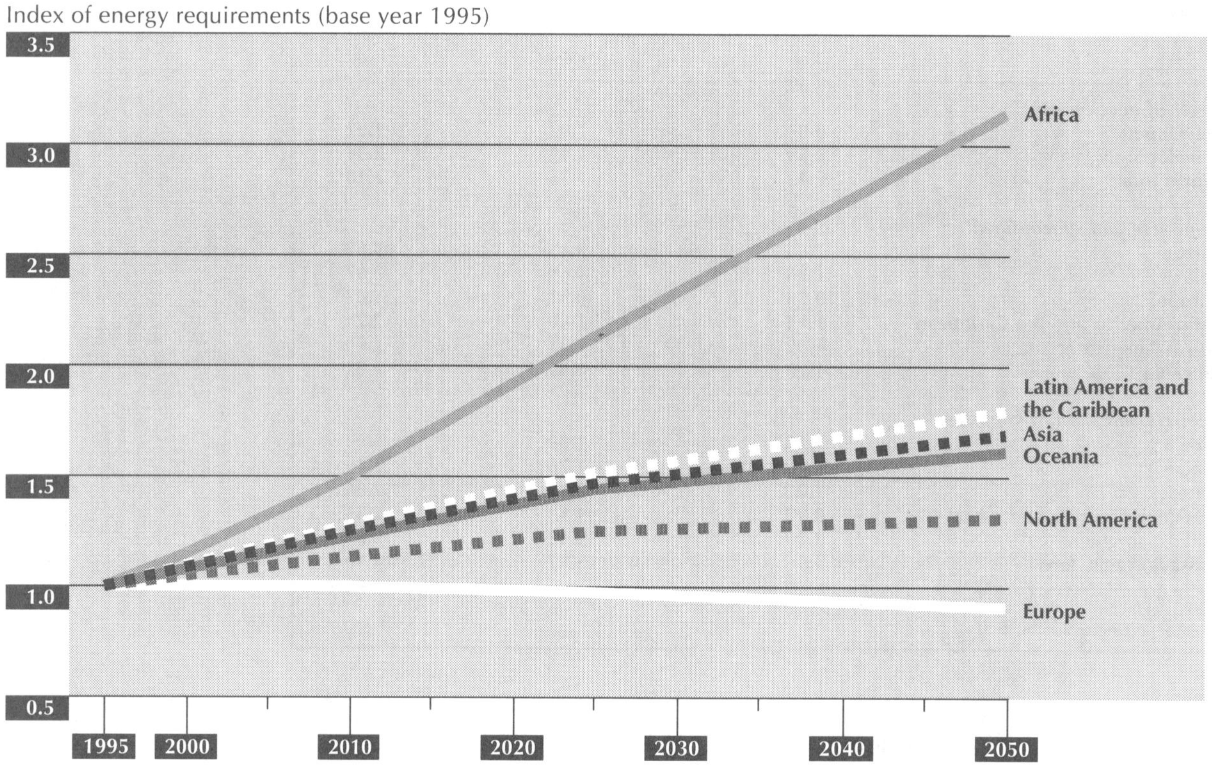

Index of energy requirements (base year 1995)

Note: Based on United Nations projections (United Nations, 1995a). All demographic factors taken into account, including population growth.

because of population changes. Countries that consume mainly millets or sorghum (Figure 9, Class 5) and those that get most of their food energy requirements from cassava, yams, taro or plantains will undergo 243 percent and 251 percent increases in energy requirements, respectively (Figure 9, Class 6).

The crucial importance of a decline in fertility
Uncertainties regarding the assumption of a fertility rate of 2.1 children per woman

3.51 The United Nations projections have made it possible to work until now with a medium variant trend in fertility which assumes that fertility will stabilize at the replacement level, in other words, at 2.1 children per woman. As mentioned earlier, this globally favourable scenario is based on the assumption that a sharp increase in life expectancy resulting from improved living conditions and diets will be combined with a sharp decline in fertility. It is hardly likely that all the countries in the world will follow the projections made for them. Some will change faster than others.

Figure 9
CHANGES IN ENERGY REQUIREMENTS FROM 1995 TO 2050, ACCORDING TO CLASS OF DIET
(medium variant)

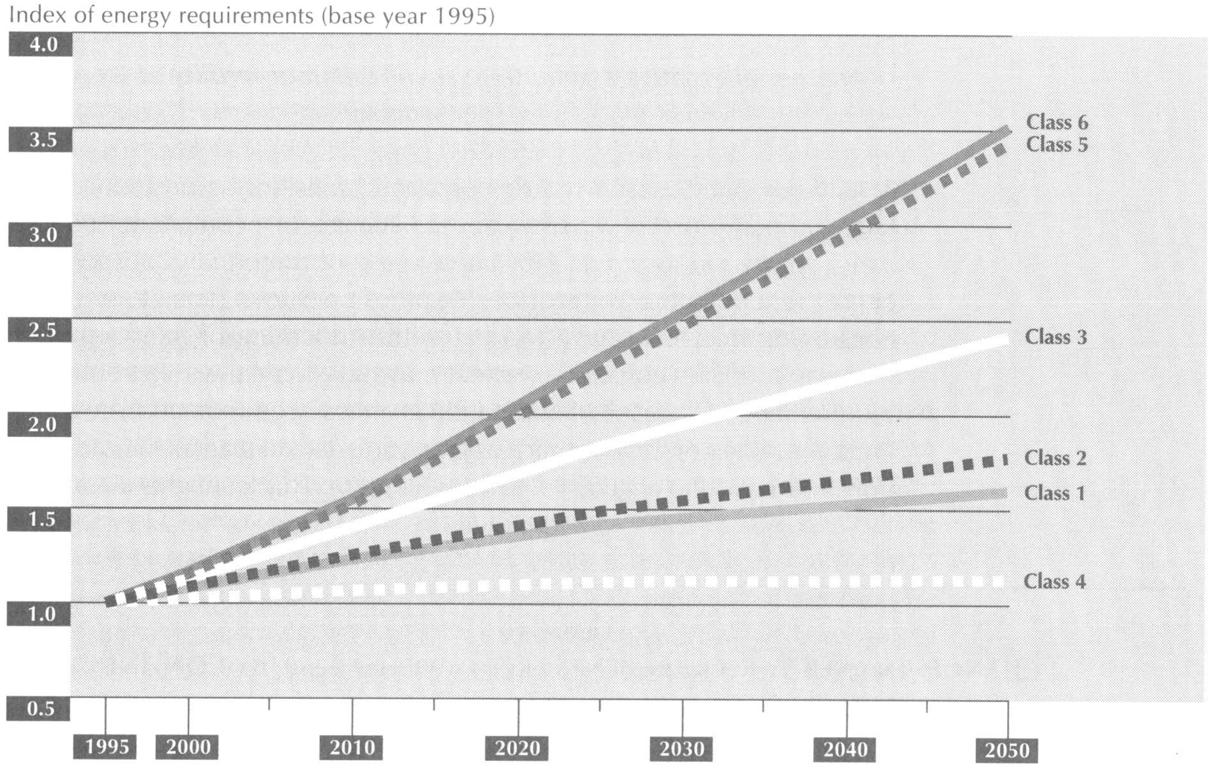

Index of energy requirements (base year 1995)

Note: Based on United Nations projections (United Nations, 1995a). All demographic factors taken into account, including population growth.

An alternative assumption: the stabilizing of fertility at 1.6 children per woman

3.52 Stabilization of the number of children at a much lower level than that of replacement would greatly affect changes in food energy requirements (Figure 7). Instead of doubling their requirements, as in the medium variant projection, developing countries would be faced with an increase of only 59 percent. Energy requirements in Africa would increase by 165 percent instead of doubling as projected using the medium variant (Figure 10), although in extreme situations where there is no demographic transition, or where it is delayed, they would basically not be modified from the earlier scenario. The energy requirements of countries consuming millets or sorghum or of countries consuming cassava, yams, taro or plantains would treble, whereas in medium variant projections they would increase by 250 percent from 1995 to 2050 (Figure 11, Classes 5 and 6). The challenge facing countries with such a pronounced food deficit would remain huge. The issue at stake here is the mode of development. If appropriate action is taken, however, population could increase in line with the United Nations low variant scenario because, as noted in the Programme of Action (Paragraph 1.8) adopted by the

International Conference on Population and Development held in Cairo in 1994 (United Nations, 1995c), strategies do exist to slow future population growth, especially in the longer term. They regard reproductive health, including family planning, which also facilitates the achievement of food security and food projection objectives.

Another alternative assumption: stabilization of fertility at 2.6 children per woman

3.53 If for some reason the demographic transition is postponed, a much larger proportion of the world will face challenges of incomparable dimensions. Africa may have to provide for an increase of more than 250 percent of its energy requirements (Figure 12). Countries consuming maize, or even those consuming rice, may have to deal with a doubling of their requirements, whereas countries consuming wheat may have to deal with a trebling of their requirements. As a result of population changes, requirements in countries that consume millets or sorghum and cassava, yams, taro or plantains could quadruple from 1995 to 2050 (Figure 13, Classes 5 and 6). This highlights the importance

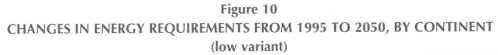

Figure 10
CHANGES IN ENERGY REQUIREMENTS FROM 1995 TO 2050, BY CONTINENT
(low variant)

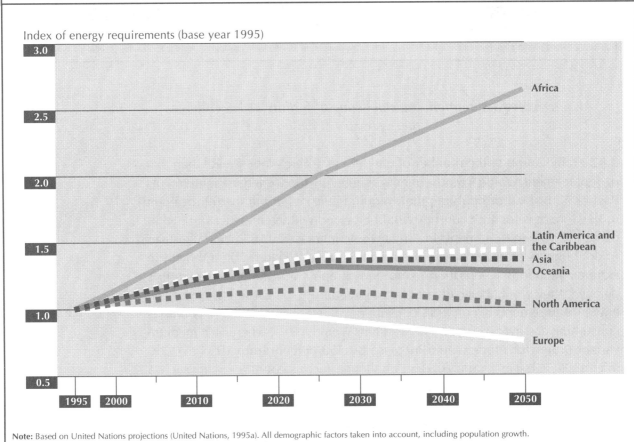

Index of energy requirements (base year 1995)

Note: Based on United Nations projections (United Nations, 1995a). All demographic factors taken into account, including population growth.

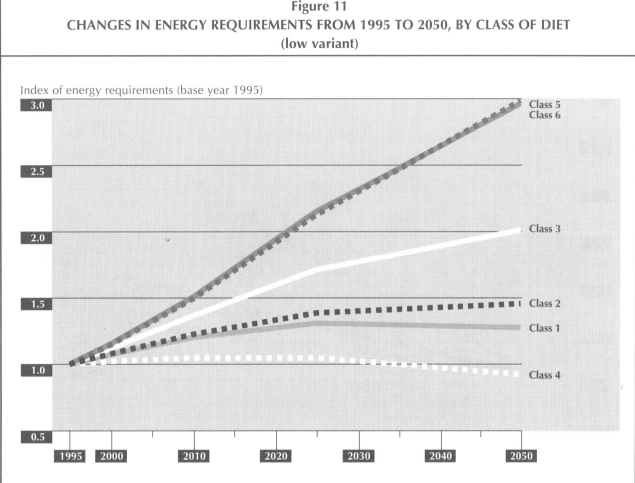

Figure 11
CHANGES IN ENERGY REQUIREMENTS FROM 1995 TO 2050, BY CLASS OF DIET
(low variant)

Index of energy requirements (base year 1995)

Note: Based on United Nations projections (United Nations, 1995a). All demographic factors taken into account, including population growth.

of implementing fully the Programme of Action of the International Conference on Population and Development (United Nations, 1995c; UNFPA, 1995).

3.54 There could also be deviations from the average assumption. For example, estimates of future fertility rates in East Asia are as unsure as those of the current fertility level. A high fertility level in East Asia and the resulting new doubling of its energy requirements would necessitate a new green revolution with even greater challenges, because the preceding green revolution already benefited from the allocation of the best lands, especially irrigated lands.

3.55 It is possible that the demographic transition will be postponed in certain African countries. The consequences would probably be very serious. The solution to the quadrupling of food energy requirements mentioned earlier would require a completely different infrastructure and a completely different macroeconomic context if the countries are not in a position to import cereals.

3.56 While the possibilities are recognized, it seems that the demographic transition is spreading in Africa, and it is encouraging to note the acceptance

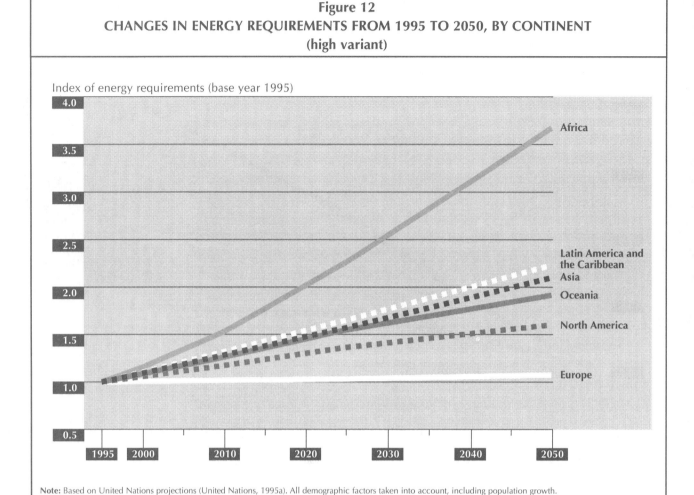

Figure 12
CHANGES IN ENERGY REQUIREMENTS FROM 1995 TO 2050, BY CONTINENT
(high variant)

Index of energy requirements (base year 1995)

Note: Based on United Nations projections (United Nations, 1995a). All demographic factors taken into account, including population growth.

and rapid spread of population programmes there despite the poverty and economic difficulties of many of the countries concerned. A decline in fertility is occurring in poor areas. Urbanization also seems to be a strong factor determining the decrease in fertility.

CLOSING THE ENERGY REQUIREMENTS GAP

3.57 There is no information allowing the reliable forecasting of dietary trends for 2050. This being said, unless there is major environmental degradation and humankind is incapable of providing the development needed to satisfy its food energy requirements, two basic trends could be expected. The first would be a change in available food supplies to satisfy the energy requirements of humanity. This trend is the subject of the present section. The second would be a move towards diversification in the composition of diets. This would lead to changes in patterns partly brought on by urbanization and would help provide populations with important nutritive supplements (vitamins, essential amino acids, etc.). This second trend will be dealt with in the following section.

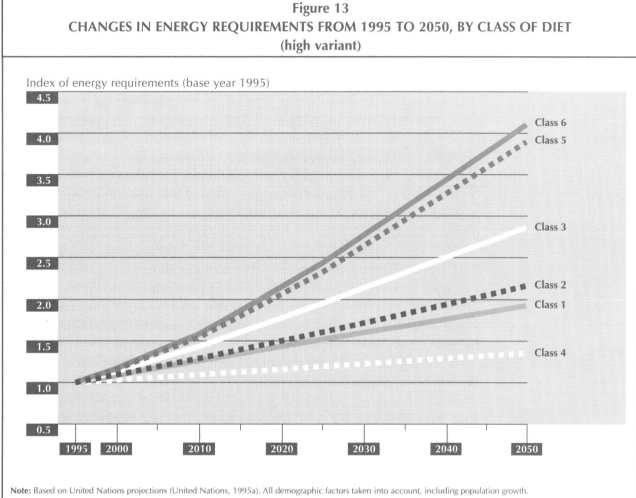

Figure 13
CHANGES IN ENERGY REQUIREMENTS FROM 1995 TO 2050, BY CLASS OF DIET
(high variant)

Index of energy requirements (base year 1995)

Note: Based on United Nations projections (United Nations, 1995a). All demographic factors taken into account, including population growth.

Increases in food supplies: only part of the solution

3.58 An essential point should be stressed: the projections developed in this document in no way imply that the food problem should be solved only by measures intended to increase per caput food supplies. Whatever the projected level of food supplies, these measures must be an integral part of policies aimed directly at the roots of the food problem – poverty and its gender dimensions and the lack of access to food for the poor, both in rural and in urban areas. These policies work in tandem in countries where, at present, most of the poor work in agriculture.

Supplementary food supplies in developing countries by 2050

3.59 In order to cover average energy requirements, food supplies in developing countries will probably have to exceed energy requirements by a great margin in 2050. Food demand will increase even more if equality of internal distribution improves. It will also take into account household losses (resulting from cooking, domestic storage of staple foods, etc.).

3.60 How, then, should the effort required be evaluated? FAO (1992) has estimated the number of people suffering from malnutrition in the world by combining each country's average food supply, a food distribution indicator and an evaluation of minimum requirements. However, this does not give any information concerning the extent of the food deficits of countries where hunger is still rife. It does not indicate what the reduction in the proportion of undernourished people would be if food supplies were increased by 10, 20 or 30 percent. It is necessary, for the purpose of this study, to suggest an order of magnitude. The task is difficult because the two main explanations for the discrepancy between energy requirements of populations and availability of needed food supplies (i.e. losses realized between retailing and consumption of products and losses caused by inequalities in distribution within the countries) probably vary greatly in importance from country to country, according to the degree of poverty.

3.61 It is known that losses sustained between retailing and consumption can vary greatly from one country to another and from one year to the next. Losses in the order of 10 percent have been quoted when reserves have been made to guarantee against insecurity. Food losses at the household level will probably be reduced by 2050. Household appliances can be expected to improve, and market regulation will save households from having to keep food products stocked over long periods of time.

3.62 According to FAO (1992), when there is unequal food distribution, the proportion of the population suffering from malnutrition is 10 percent if average national daily food supply per caput amounts to 2 700 Calories and 15 to 35 percent when this supply is between 2 200 and 2 500 Calories. Therefore, in order to guarantee total security in food supplies the level should be more than 2 800 Calories, or perhaps 2 900 or 2 950 Calories if it is considered that in much improved conditions losses could be substantially reduced (maybe under 5 percent). This should be evaluated only on the basis of reliable technical information which could eliminate any risk of error.

3.63 It is feared that distribution problems will remain in 2050. It is true that these problems have never been totally eliminated in human societies. By the year 2050, however, it is hoped that populations will be coming to grips with these inequalities and reducing them further. The health of a large proportion of the world's population the population's ability to take control of its own future depends on this.

3.64 It is assumed that developing countries will need to increase their food supplies to 30 percent above their food energy requirements, which would create the conditions for malnutrition reduction. With average requirements of developing countries at 2 160 Calories per person per day in 1990, food supplies should reach a minimum of 2 808 Calories. This estimate is above the current estimate of available world per caput food supplies (2 700 Calories, FAO estimate 1988-1990) as well as the average energy requirement projected by FAO for all developing countries for 2010 (2 730 Calories) but less than the average energy requirements projected by FAO for the whole world for 2010 (2 860 Calories). The same 30 percent rule has been retained for 2050.

3.65 These adjustments have been applied even though the countries concerned differ greatly in levels of food losses and in inequality of access to food. This choice can be explained by two reasons, which pertain to the underlying logic of this study. First, these necessary increases in food supplies must be evaluated according to the average requirements of the populations of each country. The method used for estimating these must be the same for all countries and must not be influenced by a lack of information on a given country (especially concerning loss of food and unequal distribution of resources). This procedure does not imply that increasing food supplies will solve the problem of malnutrition. The real challenge is to solve the problem of access to food for the poor. But as most of the poor in the world live in rural areas and make a living in agriculture, the supplement referred to here is a necessary one.

Per caput food supplies for 2050 for developing countries to reach the level projected for 2010 for East Asia

3.66 Fixing a minimum food supply for the poorest countries increases average per caput supplies in the world considerably. This would mean a 14 percent global increase from 1995 to 2050 and an 18 percent increase in developing countries. On average, these countries would fall in line with the energy intake projected by FAO for East Asia for 2010 (FAO, 1995a), that is, 3 040 Calories.

3.67 The amount of catching up (supplementary supplies) needed depends on the current situation and varies considerably according to the region. An increase of one-third is required in food supplies for Africa in general, but only an increase of one-half for East Africa. The required increase in supplies is lower for Asia (+14 percent) and Latin America and the Caribbean (+8 percent).

3.68 The countries that consume mainly millets or sorghum and those that consume mainly cassava, yams, taro or plantains would have to increase available food supplies by 40 percent. This greatly adds to the already considerable task facing countries that are expected to undergo high population growth.

Trends in developed countries

3.69 There is no more information available on the future trends in diets of developed countries than there is for developing countries.

3.70 The populations of some developed countries are still increasing their energy intake to well over 3 500 Calories, resulting in problems of obesity. Other populations are lowering their energy intake to 3 200 or even 2 900 Calories. After increasing over one or two decades, the average energy intake of populations in developed countries may eventually come close to that observed in certain countries of northern Europe (3 000 to 3 200 Calories). FAO (1995a) also projects for 2010 a high average energy intake of 3 470 Calories. In the absence of more detailed information, it is assumed in this study that the energy intake for those countries where supplies observed in 1990 were more than 30 percent over the nutritional requirements projected for them for 2050 (3 400 Calories) will not vary from 1990 to 2050.

CLOSING THE QUALITATIVE DEFICIENCIES GAP
Changes in dietary patterns

3.71 Diet trends are now evolving in opposite directions. Nutritionists have observed significant declines in the quantities of food energy consumed in certain developed countries. By contrast, an important part of the world's population is diversifying and could continue to diversify its diet. This diversification allows populations to introduce dietary components that are indispensable for health, such as amino acids, vitamins and micronutrients. This is the case in certain large countries such as China and India and in some subregions where there is robust and steady economic growth and effective demand is growing. Such populations constitute a large proportion of humanity, and their numbers are increasing. They will probably contribute to this continuing trend and, in turn, affect the level of available food necessary to sustain populations.

Specific changes in dietary habits according to country

3.72 Economic growth brings changes in food habits. With the introduction of meat, seafood, fruits and vegetables, daily food rations become less rich in cereals. Meat consumption does not always increase when there is an increase in food intake. This can be verified by classifying all countries according to available food energy and isolating only the two deciles for which availability has increased most between 1962 and 1990, i.e. the ninth decile, which has experienced an increase of 535 to 789 Calories per inhabitant (average 630 Calories) and the tenth decile, which has seen an increase of 814 to 1 629 Calories per inhabitant (average 995 Calories). It can thus be observed that the contribution of meat to such increases, which varies between 0.79 and 56.56 percent, differs in various countries. Furthermore, the countries where meat contributed the least (between 0.79 percent and 4.89 percent) are those that, in 1962, had less available food than the countries where meat represented a larger share of the diet (contributing between 5 and 56.56 percent). There is a difference of some 350 Calories. The countries where meat contributed least (under 5 percent) are those in which cereals contributed most and oil-producing crops contributed least.

3.73 Evidence shows that the structure of consumption evolved differently in developed and in developing countries where the increase in average energy intake was high. Average energy intake in Egypt, for example, went from 2 290 Calories in 1962 to 3 310 Calories in 1989, whereas meat consumption nearly doubled, from 10 to 18 kg per inhabitant per year. This level is still low compared with that of developed countries, where meat consumption reaches 80 kg. The increase in energy in developing countries was mostly achieved by an increase in cereal consumption.

3.74 Dietary patterns are strongly influenced by history and culture. Modifying diets depends on economic changes and societies' levels of exposure to foreign ideas, goods and people. Long-term forecasting has always been risky. This paper, therefore, does not develop any food consumption scenario for the year 2050.

3.75 It is nonetheless useful to note that urbanization influences dietary patterns considerably. Trends in food consumption will probably be strongly affected by the supplies reaching cities. It is sometimes easier to buy food in import markets than in local markets. The diversity of foods available as well as the constraints placed on women by changing lifestyles could have a major impact on dietary trends because women usually decide on the foods produced, purchased and cooked. Studies of the relationship between evolving gender roles and food security would be very useful for policy-making. Market conditions also have an impact on dietary trends. For example, it can be less expensive to borrow for the brief period between purchasing and selling than for lengthier periods because of long-term agreements made with local producers. This can lead to an increase in imported food supplies in preference to locally produced foods. In addition, changes in the dietary patterns of populations in developing countries will probably be linked to the increasing number of high-yielding poultry- and pork-raising facilities.

Some impacts of modifications in dietary structures

3.76 The energy requirements of populations are obviously not influenced by changes in their dietary structures. The amount of energy necessary to satisfy nutritional needs can be obtained from a diet rich in livestock rather than from one rich in plant-derived energy. However, for similar quantities of energy intake, a livestock-rich diet will require additional plant-derived energy in order to produce the livestock-based foods.

3.77 The consumption of livestock products means greater pressures on natural resources. These pressures increase much faster than the energy consumption of the population itself. This is why it is necessary to push the study further by also assessing the amount of plant-derived energy required to produce food rations. Admittedly, the lack of data hinders such a study, but it is necessary to have some idea of how fast pressures on natural resources increase with dietary diversification.

3.78 As the energy value of the daily rations of populations increases, so does the quality of the products. At the same time, the demands made on natural resources appear to increase faster than consumption. This is a difficult phenomenon to interpret. The problem cannot be addressed directly in this paper. In any event, the available data would be insufficient.

The role of livestock

3.79 Diversification of dietary patterns leads to inclusion of animal products in the diet, and the production of livestock requires great quantities of plant-derived food energy.

3.80 Because of the lack of data concerning the composition of individual countries' livestock herds (species and breeds according to sex, age and weight), the following estimates have been adopted arbitrarily from working documents used by FAO. It takes:

- 11 plant-derived Calories to produce 1 Calorie of beef;
- 11 plant-derived Calories to produce 1 Calorie of mutton;
- 4 plant-derived Calories to produce 1 Calorie of pork;
- 4 plant-derived Calories to produce 1 Calorie of poultry;
- 8 plant-derived Calories to produce 1 Calorie of milk;
- 4 plant-derived Calories to produce 1 Calorie of egg.

3.81 The basis for calculation is debatable and these figures should be considered rough estimates. Such standards vary according to the constitution of the herd and methods used to raise the livestock. A herd of cattle raised without much attention to productivity can have a ratio of 50 or more Calories to 1. It is probable, moreover, that averages have declined, especially for industrially raised herds, which are more and more prevalent. But, as mentioned above, the relevant information with respect to each country is not available. In fact, there are no statistics by country in this field, and scientists at FAO have no country-based assessments from which to work on animal nutrition.

3.82 Considering the implications of diet changes on farm production, a rough estimate is better than none at all. It is therefore in the interest of this study to estimate the amount of food energy necessary to produce a given ration of food and to evaluate the process of transformation of plant-derived energy into consumed energy.

3.83 The results thus obtained should be interpreted by taking the following factors into account:

- grazing livestock generally feed on plants that humans do not consume;
- grazing livestock often have other uses, food-related in particular, and are therefore a security stock;
- monogastric livestock such as pigs or poultry can enhance foodstuffs that humans consume and can help improve the technical performance of those grain crops that contribute to the plant-derived energy intake of human beings;
- industrially raised livestock can also enhance subproducts.

3.84 The difficulty is in assessing the relative importance of such effects and the conditions under which the effects are produced. It should be mentioned here that the extension of grazing for cattle, in some cases by deforestation, can result in environmental costs.

A heavy influence on the level of necessary available food energy

3.85 The figures set out above indicate that any quantity of livestock-derived products added to food rations puts a demand on natural resources that is at least four times the level of energy it can deliver. The remainder of this study is based on this type of observation.

3.86 To be complete, it should be noted that this manner of computing plant-derived energy requirements does not take into account food from ocean or lake fishing or from aquaculture. Food products from hunting are likewise not counted. It would have been difficult to factor in these products.

3.87 It would be possible to count products from aquaculture activity, especially its most intensive forms, which use artificial fish feed. These practices are used particularly in China. Other developing countries do not employ on a large scale the expertise acquired in China. These factors could not be measured, however, with the information available.

Assumptions regarding dietary changes in developing countries
Assumption of changing composition of dietary patterns

3.88 No projection for a date as far into the future as 2050 can be made. Therefore, only an assumption can be ventured. This assumption takes into account the problems of urbanization that contribute both to the diversification of diets and to import of food supplies from other countries. The ratio of the number of plant-derived Calories necessary to produce the Calorie intake in an average food ration to the number of Calories in that ration, i.e. 1.783 in 1990, was taken into account. For the purpose of simplification, it can be assumed that all countries that were below that level in 1990 will have reached it by 2050. According to this assumption, developing countries will require 5 477 plant-derived Calories per person per day to produce the various foods in their diet – a diet richer in livestock products than it was in 1990. This figure is clearly larger than the number of plant-derived Calories necessary to produce the average energy requirements for the world (4 900 Calories in 1995). In 2050, with 5 477 plant-derived Calories necessary to produce 3 040 consumable Calories, populations of developing countries will have a diet close to that reported for Mexico in 1988-1990.

Assumption of stabilization of dietary composition

3.89 The necessary data or reliable analyses are not available that would allow it to be stated that the average diet of a country would provide all of the nutrients required to keep the population in good health. No country can be cited as a model in this respect, so targets cannot be proposed for countries. Therefore, a crude assumption is selected for the purpose of this study. It is assumed that, with the existing levels of energy supplies, the current level of diversification of the global food pattern would ensure the elimination of serious nutritional deficiencies. So, with the average conversion rate of plant-derived Calories to consumed Calories (1.783 in 1990), the composition of each country's diet would be the same in 2050 as it was for the world population in 1990. Beyond the average conversion rate of plant-derived Calories to consumed Calories, the composition of each country's diet is assumed to be constant between 1990 and 2050 unless the energy level of such diets increases (as indicated in Paragraphs 3.59 to 3.65). As was suggested for the energy ration, and for lack of more reliable information, it can be assumed that populations whose ratio of necessary plant-derived Calories to consumed Calories per ration was higher than 1.783 in 1995 will not modify their diets between now and 2050. It is, of course, a different case for those countries whose energy requirements in 1990 were not 30 percent higher than their projected requirements for 2050.

Results
Increased need for plant-derived energy owing to dietary diversification

3.90 Dietary diversification sharply increases the quantity of necessary plant-derived energy. The underlying assumption for 2050 is therefore that all countries of the world will have access to a diet that implies a minimum ratio of necessary plant-derived Calories to consumed Calories per average ration per inhabitant. This minimum ratio is 1.783, obtained on the basis of observations made on a global scale in 1990.

3.91 This leads to the following consequences:
- The amount of plant-derived energy used per developed country remains unchanged. The accuracy of such an assumption is limited because, in the future, this figure will probably first increase and then decrease. Furthermore, the magnitude of the estimated figures involved here is not of the same order as that of the estimates used in the remaining part of this study.
- By contrast, this objective entails a 19 percent increase in available plant-derived energy for developing countries between 1995 and 2050, which implies a 12 percent increase worldwide.

3.92 The needed rate of increase of plant-derived energy varies considerably depending on the region. It is 20 percent in Asia and 23 percent in Africa. Likewise, it varies considerably within the African continent. It reaches 29 percent, for example, in countries whose populations consume mainly rice and 46 percent in those with diets based on cassava, yams or taro.

Aggregate effects of two types of dietary evolution (higher energy content and diversification)

3.93 The impact of the two trends examined above, added to the higher per caput energy requirements and diversification of diets, considerably increases the effects of population changes. Changes in the populations of developing countries could be the cause of a 28 percent average increase in the plant-derived energy necessary to fill global needs and a 40 percent increase in their own requirements.

3.94 The impact of the two possible trends varies considerably by region. They are without effect for North America and Europe and would result in an increase in requirements of only 7 percent for Latin America. However, Asia would have a 38 percent increase and Africa would experience a 64 percent increase. Populations that consume cassava, yams or taro would have to double the plant-derived energy necessary to meet their requirements.

AGGREGATE IMPACT OF POPULATION FACTORS, ENERGY REQUIREMENTS AND DIETARY CHANGES
Greater impact of demographic effects than of dietary changes

3.95 Whatever the country, whatever the region, the consequences of demographic changes for levels of energy requirements are far more significant than those of changes in dietary patterns. This is partly because of the conservative nature of the assumptions made in the preceding section. The impact of population developments on the levels of plant-derived energy requirements is magnified for countries with high fertility rates (in Africa, for example) because the multiplication factors are 2.94 for demographic effects of all types and 1.64 for the effects of dietary changes. In countries with the highest levels of food shortages – populations whose main source of food is roots or tubers – the respective multiplication factors are 3.51 and 2.04. Here again, demographic effects have far more significant consequences than dietary modifications.

3.96 The effects of changes in age structure on energy requirements could appear negligible in comparison with those of changes in population growth. In the case of developing countries, the respective increases of 3 percent for the former and 90 percent for the latter are not of the same magnitude (see Table 7). However, the impact caused by changes in age structure should not be overlooked. For example, the increase in needs generated by the changes in age structure by 2050 would correspond to that created by adding a new country the size of Bangladesh. Furthermore, these effects will vary from country to country; in some cases, they will result in an increase in energy requirements of more than 8 percent.

Ways of balancing food and population

3.97 The combined effects of demographic changes and dietary modifications on the level of plant-derived energy requirements lead to results, whose reliability should be discussed (Tables 9 to 11).

3.98 The plant-derived energy would need to double for Asia and Latin America and the Caribbean. (Plant-derived energy would be multiplied, respectively, by 2.34 and 1.92.) This corresponds to annual growth rates (referring to growth in the production of plant-derived energy necessary for the production of food supply of plant or animal origin) of 1.6 percent in Asia and 1.2 percent in Latin America and the Caribbean during a 55-year period. Such growth rates are lower than those achieved by the green revolution in rice-producing Asia or by the introduction of hybrid maize in Latin America. Faster-moving research into new varieties of cereals will certainly be a basic factor for maintaining present levels for 55 years in regions where infrastructures are more favourable than in Africa. It remains to be seen whether these growth rates are sustainable.

3.99 The fivefold (precisely 5.14) increase in plant-derived energy required in Africa and the sevenfold (7.17 exactly) increase in countries with diets based on cassava, yams, taro or plantains have another meaning. They suppose annual average growth rates of 3.0 and 3.6 percent, respectively, for 55 years. These

Table 9
EFFECTS IN 2050 OF DEMOGRAPHIC FACTORS AND DIVERSIFICATION OF DIETS ON PLANT-DERIVED ENERGY REQUIREMENTS, BY LEVEL OF DEVELOPMENT (base year 1995 [1.00])

Variable (multiplying coefficient)	Developed	Developing	World total
All demographic effects	1.02	1.95	1.76
Supplementary food supplies[1]	1.00	1.18	1.14
All previous effects	1.02	2.30	2.01
Diversification of diets[2]	1.00	1.19	1.12
All diet changes	1.00	1.40	1.28
ALL EFFECTS	1.02	2.74	2.25

[1] Minimum food supplies are set for developing countries at 30 percent above their food energy requirements in 2050. For the developed countries, the level of food supplies in 2050 is assumed to be constant and to have remained at its 1990 level.
[2] The minimum diversification of diets in 2050 is set for developing countries at the level observed for the whole world in 1990. This diversification results in an increase in the required plant energy. For the developed countries, the composition of the diet in 2050 is assumed to be constant between 1990 and 2050, except if their food supplies have not reached the minimum projected level explained in the above footnote.
Note: The population numbers and structures used to produce these estimated requirements are based on medium variant United Nations projections (United Nations, 1995a).

results suggest a complete change in the scale of development. Such a rate of development would be close to the rate evident in East Asia between 1975 and 1990, which was the highest growth rate in East Asia's history: 4.3 percent annually. But the overall economic growth context in Asia at that time created an environment extremely conducive to rural development. The economic backdrop of sub-Saharan Africa is by no means as favourable; the highest growth rate observed in this region during a 15-year period was 2.4 percent between 1971 and 1990 (FAO, 1995a).

3.100 This change of scale implies a need for a very determined effort to increase national potential for constructing basic infrastructure, with agricultural policies and international supply policies adapted to this extreme type of situation. In the face of such an omen, only the ineffectiveness of the national and international struggle against poverty can be highlighted. This ineffectiveness has been responsible for the lag in demographic transition.

3.101 In this regard, certain countries were already identified by FAO in 1980 as facing high risks concerning their food security before the year 2000 (FAO, 1982). Some have already experienced serious ethnic or religious confrontations that were probably caused to some extent by competition for natural resources. These countries are now part of the regions or country groupings mentioned above that face serious long-term risks, but this time on a wider scale. Can the factors of local conflicts be thwarted? Can international migrations be contained? Will it really be possible to continue to ignore the significant risk of extreme social disorders for entire subregions? The logical consequence of the inability to produce or import food would be an absurd solution to agrodemographic problems, namely, an increase in mortality, the opposite of the trend envisioned by the United Nations.

Table 10
EFFECTS IN 2050 OF DEMOGRAPHIC FACTORS AND DIVERSIFICATION
OF DIETS ON PLANT-DERIVED ENERGY REQUIREMENTS,
BY CONTINENT
(base year 1995 [1.00])

Variable (multiplying coefficient)	Africa	Asia	Europe	Latin America and the Caribbean	North America	Oceania
All demographic effects	3.14	1.69	0.91	1.80	1.31	1.61
Supplementary food supplies[1]	1.33	1.14	1.00	1.08	1.00	1.00
All previous effects	4.18	1.93	0.91	1.94	1.31	1.61
Diversification of diets[2]	1.23	1.21	1.00	0.99	1.00	1.00
All diet changes	1.64	1.38	1.00	1.07	1.00	1.00
ALL EFFECTS	5.14	2.34	0.91	1.92	1.31	1.61

Note: See notes to Table 9.

Table 11
EFFECTS IN 2050 OF DEMOGRAPHIC FACTORS AND DIVERSIFICATION
OF DIETS ON PLANT-DERIVED ENERGY REQUIREMENTS,
BY DIET CLASSIFICATION OF COUNTRIES
(base year 1995 [1.00])

Variable (multiplying coefficient)	Rice	Maize	Wheat	Livestock products and wheat	Millet and sorghum	Cassava, yams and taro
All demographic effects	1.60	1.78	2.42	1.13	3.43	3.51
Supplementary food supplies[1]	1.15	1.10	1.15	1.00	1.38	1.40
All previous effects	1.84	1.96	2.78	1.13	4.73	4.91
Diversification of diets[2]	1.29	1.00	1.02	1.00	1.02	1.46
All diet changes	1.48	1.10	1.17	1.00	1.41	2.04
ALL EFFECTS	2.37	1.96	2.84	1.13	4.82	7.17

Note: See notes to Table 9.

The crucial role of fertility rates

3.102 The stabilization of the fertility rate at 1.6 (the United Nations low variant), 2.1 (medium variant) or 2.6 children per mother (high variant) would imply that the African continent must multiply its available plant-derived energy by 4, 5 or 6. The populations that consume mainly cassava or other roots or tubers would have to increase their available plant-derived energy to 6, 7.2 or even 8.4 times their present quantities.

3.103 Such prospects of pressure on resources can lead to the hasty conclusion that whatever the lower level reached by fertility, there is no possible solution. In this paper, it is emphasized that this observation runs counter to reason.

3.104 Admittedly, these results show the inertia of demographic phenomena and their transmission effects over the generations: high fertility of one generation determines the number of women of child-bearing age for the next generation, some 15 or 20 years later, and brings a minimum number of children born to that generation of daughters, even assuming reduced fertility. This is why the consequences of demographic changes on growing demand for food energy in high and low fertility conditions were presented in Table 8, despite the fact that these extreme hypothetical cases, when applied on a global scale, are purely academic.

3.105 Nonetheless, the facts have to be faced: lower fertility rates make the necessary economic changes appear less absurd and closer to the realm of possibility. Thus, in the case of Africa, for each scenario of fertility decline there is a different corresponding development model and rate of growth of production of energy of plant origin required for the production of food supply. This growth rate would be 2.6, 3.0 and 3.3 percent per year over 55 years for the three scenarios, respectively. Each of these rates surpasses the observed maximum rate of agricultural production for sub-Saharan Africa between 1971 and 1990 (2.4 percent), but remains lower than the maximum rate for East Asia for the same period (4.3 percent). Asia, however, is the most densely populated region in the world, with more developed infrastructures, a greater degree of human capital development (in terms of literacy, etc.) and a more dynamic general development context than in Africa. The situation appears more acute in countries whose populations consume cassava, yams, taro or plantains, because the growth of plant-derived energy required would have to reach levels as high as 3.3, 3.6 and 3.9 percent per year in the different scenarios – growth rates approaching the maximum attained in East Asia. These are probably very difficult goals to achieve, perhaps impossible in the current economic and structural context of Africa.

3.106 The lateness of Africa's demographic transition, and thus its development, explains the different results from those obtained for East Asia. East Asia is the most highly populated region in the world, where the food situation will still be a problem in 2010 and where the growth of agricultural production should be maintained at a rate of 2.2 percent per year until 2010. It is therefore obvious that Africa faces a major challenge to the capacity for sustainable development.

3.107 Rationalization of budgetary choices and the priority given to urgent food security problems explain why heavy investments in agricultural research have been centred mainly on highly populated (especially rice-growing) regions. Efforts must now be oriented towards the regions where agriculture has been neglected and investment is urgently needed because of the rapidly growing population. These regions already contain the greatest number of the poor in the world. Such investments should be made in cultivars of roots, tubers and pulses which provide indispensable protein for populations that eat little meat or plantains. Even these technical changes will probably not suffice. It will be necessary to bring together all the required infrastructure-oriented factors for true development in these countries.

BEYOND THE PRESENT STUDY: INFORMATION NEEDS

3.108 This study needs to be taken further. Throughout this document, attention has been drawn to problems of insufficient data, estimates and information.

3.109 The most important development would be the analysis of the effects that limited available resources (in human resources, earth and water) would have on various productivity assumptions of the factors of rural development. This would require each country to have the necessary information to analyse all interacting factors, such as population, basic training, professional training, the food situation, qualitative and quantitative assessments of available renewable natural resources, infrastructure and vegetation.

3.110 The technology useful to the development of such studies is advancing rapidly. Available data have increased greatly, and techniques for gathering data have changed. For example, remote sensing provides a considerable amount of geographical and human information that could be useful for this subject.

3.111 Techniques for analysis have improved. The studies of interrelationships have increased at the local level in the form of pilot studies, especially studies of the links between changes in plant cover and population changes. Such studies could be assisted by using remote sensing.

Insufficient information on the major factors determining food security

3.112 Nonetheless, at present, data and analyses are often incomplete. The determinants of mortality are not well known, particularly the link between undernourishment and mortality. The interactions between water availability and usage and mortality have not been sufficiently studied. The quality of fertility estimates is often insufficient. Moreover, the determinants of fertility decline have not been clearly identified. The data-gathering situation is alarming. The recording and quality of vital statistics are not progressing in many countries. The socio-economic structure of populations is often badly assessed, and the number of persons active in agriculture or fisheries is only roughly estimated.

3.113 From the agrogeographical perspective, the situation is not as good as it was in 1980 when the FAO agrodemographic study was conducted (FAO, 1982), because the geographic data based on soil terrain conditions have been only marginally extended and improved in quality. Global plant cover has still not been established. There are still significant gaps in data relating to agricultural resources, land use by agro-ecological zone (AEZ), the state of deterioration of irrigated lands and erosion damage to land in rain-fed regions, as well as in quantitative and qualitative data on water resources. Because of this lack of information on the present situation, it is difficult to determine the trends of agricultural resources in terms of degradation, maintenance and enhancement.

3.114 Information about environmental conditions is also insufficient. The available information concerning elements such as humanity's impact on the current state of the planet's photosynthesis, the population carrying capacity of various lands, the effects of agricultural intensification on climate and changes in genetic diversity is inaccurate.

3.115 All these issues are essential in order to measure the state and evolution of natural-resource capital and to determine which factors are necessary to establish conditions for sustainable development (FAO/UNESCO/WMO, 1977; UNESCO, 1985a,1985b; World Commission on Environment and Development, 1987).

Insufficient studies on interactions

3.116 Studies on the links among the various factors influencing agricultural production are too often lacking. Some examples in which population phenomena are often involved are provided here.

- Urbanization is often cited as being favourable to productivity. Probably, through concentration of resources and economies of scale, urbanization allows for investments or production conditions that would not be possible otherwise. This type of interaction between population concentration and productivity in agriculture needs to be clarified.
- Information is limited as to the interrelations among demographic growth, the exploitation of the land and the productivity of agriculture in developing countries, including gender aspects such as changes in female-headed households and differentials in migration (Boserup, 1965, 1985; Jolly and Torrey Boyle, 1993).
- The potential for sustainable development depends especially on the time frame necessary for demographic transition, which itself results in part from development. But there is also a lack of information on the links among demographic growth, development and the state of natural resources that highlights the impact of time (the time to establish development infrastructures and education and training programmes, to found cooperatives, to set up credit systems and to adapt plant and animal varieties to local conditions, etc.).
- What needs emerge when an examination is made of the rate at which technical innovations occur in agriculture and are diffused?
- It is important to know how rapidly technological changes came about in the past, if the pace has slowed, stopped or accelerated in key areas, if their field of application has expanded or contracted or if limits will be found to the technical changes that are expected, for example, in genetic engineering. This research into the scope and pace of technological innovations is capital for the future of agricultural productivity.

POLITICAL IMPLICATIONS OF CHANGES IN ENERGY REQUIREMENTS AND FOOD SUPPLY

3.117 The purpose of this document is to describe broadly the trends in energy requirements and the food supply necessary to fulfil such needs. It is not intended to propose political or economic solutions to the resulting problems. Nonetheless, it is important to present some of the political implications of the trends identified.

3.118 Certain regions of the globe – and, hence, all of humanity – will face a real social and economic challenge because of the lag in the development of certain regions and the related delay in demographic transition.

3.119 Those who are being challenged are the weakest and least able to face the difficulties. They have barely (or not at all) begun their demographic transition and are suffering from food shortages and continuing high mortality rates. They are facing tremendous difficulties in breaking out of the high-poverty/high-fertility mortality cycle. For example, to escape poverty, the temptation to migrate often becomes irresistible. Besides the ethical issues involved, the success or failure of these populations will have regional and global impacts.

A challenge that could be met by world agricultural production

3.120 The decrease in agricultural production growth rates observed since the mid-1980s is exclusively the result of lower production by the main net exporters of cereals. This decrease did not boost world prices; in fact, those prices have declined. Therefore, it cannot be interpreted as a harbinger of food shortages or as some production limit reached as a result of environmental conditions regulating agricultural activities. The observed pace of production is able to meet growing effective demand. The decline in production can be explained mostly by the slowdown in production growth by certain large exporting countries in order to avoid lower prices that could result from insufficient sales and accumulated surpluses.

3.121 A major problem is thus the slow growth of effective demand, or, in other words, the issue of poverty. It can be observed, then, that trends in large exporting countries result in limitations on the growth of available food per inhabitant in a social context where over 800 million people should be able to consume more to meet their food energy requirements, but do not have the necessary income to purchase additional food. Poverty acts as a brake on demand and, therefore, on food production. The world's agricultural production facilities are fully capable of increasing the quantity produced, but, in order to do this, demand must increase. At the same time, it is also important to contain growth in food energy requirements through deceleration of population growth.

3.122 Development is, above all, growth in consumer demand. Economic development, at least in the initial stages, lies mainly in the growth of domestic consumer demand and especially in the growth of the production necessary to meet such demand. It depends only very marginally on the development of exports, especially where chronic malnutrition exists (East Asia, South Asia, sub-Saharan Africa, etc.).

3.123 The growth of internal consumption depends significantly on the continuing decline in real prices of food and, in order for this to occur, on the continuing support of sustainable agricultural development by governments and the international community. This effort requires sufficiently strong stimuli in the different factors of production (human resources, land, water) to generate significant gains in income and an increase in effective demand, plus policies to promote health, nutrition and education of the entire population. In the context of malnutrition, such investments in the factors of production could have high returns (Rosegrant, Agcaoili-Sombilla and Perez, 1995).

3.124 Agriculture remains the main activity in the developing world. The population active in agriculture has not been the majority of the world's economically active population since 1980-1984, but it does constitute the greater part of the active population of developing countries (over 55 percent) (FAO, 1993a). With demographic growth, the population of the developing world continues to increase. Since 1980, it has been over 1 billion people.

3.125 Furthermore, the great majority of the most impoverished live in rural areas and work the land (World Bank, 1990). The rural population of developing countries was estimated at 3.1 billion in 1995.

3.126 This means that, for most of the population of the developing world, agriculture brings in both food for the family and the revenues needed to purchase the essential goods people cannot produce themselves.

3.127 The growth of agricultural production is an essential means of fighting poverty. It is already known that individuals must meet the basic nutritional needs that allow them to maintain a minimum level of activity; this is a condition governing populations' abilities to control their destinies. It has also become obvious that as long as developing countries remain heavily dependent on agriculture, the struggle against poverty will depend on increasing food production and agricultural productivity and enabling women to produce food under better conditions. The struggle against poverty and efforts to increase food production cannot be separated at the level of development where agriculture plays the major role.

3.128 Further capacity for intensifying agricultural production is still accessible. Any attempted projections in this domain are uncertain because of the inadequacy of available forecasting methods in evaluating changes in technological innovations. In the past, this has often led to a systematic underestimating of yield increases.

3.129 Cereal production will probably increase by 40 percent by the year 2010 (FAO, 1995a). The average yields of the three main cereals (rice, wheat and maize) could be expected to increase significantly between 1988/89 and 2010 (by 36, 42 and 39 percent, respectively). An annual increase in cereal yields of over 1.5 percent can therefore be expected.

3.130 Several factors will have an important role.
- Research should be concerned with developing yields for crops that up to now have been somewhat neglected.
- Studies of improved varieties of millet and sorghum should include varieties that grow in unfavourable climates. Stabilization of yields is more important than increasing maximum yields in this case.
- Research should be done on roots, tubers and plantains (Griffon, 1995). These crops will remain important to the energy requirements of large populations, especially in sub-Saharan Africa and in certain countries of Latin America and the Caribbean, where undernourishment is most serious. The main problem in growing root and tuber crops is keeping the plants free from disease. There has been insufficient effort to develop improved cultivars of these plants.

- Average yields could increase if a greater proportion of farming land were devoted to irrigation, even without increasing yields in irrigated or rain-fed crops.
- The increase in yields worldwide will come essentially from increased yields in countries representing the average part of global production. Neither the countries with the best yields nor those with the lowest will carry much weight in this respect.
- The increased yields will stem for the most part from improved cultivars. Research is geared towards maximizing yields and reducing the gap between maximum yields and actual farm production. Modern crop varieties have played an increasingly important role: their proportion in total seeds increased from 30 to 74 percent for rice in developing countries and from 20 to 70 percent for wheat (excluding China) between 1970 and 1990 (FAO, 1995a). Protection from pests will also contribute in this area (FAO, 1993b). Such issues should be seen within the framework of WFS companion papers 6, *Lessons from the green revolution: towards a new green revolution,* and 9, *Role of research in global food security and agricultural development.* The adoption of modern production methods is essential.

3.131 The efficient use of fertilizers is another important factor for increasing yields (Treche, 1995). It is difficult to forecast the future development of this area. However, the study of such issues is essential in view of the size of the investments involved and related questions on production, transport costs, etc. In many developing countries, inadequate quantities of fertilizer are applied, which leads to land degradation. It should be kept in mind that rehabilitation is a very costly and long-term endeavour. One of the challenges remains the intensification of agriculture in a subsistence context.

3.132 These remarks should not lead to the conclusion that genetic improvements constitute a panacea. Also relevant are some of the essential characteristics of rural development in countries within Class 6 (cassava, yams, taro and plantain). These countries generally have important humid land reserves on which crops can be expanded. In this respect, it should be kept in mind that soil quality can constitute a serious problem. Some of these countries, such as the Congo, have very small populations. In these conditions, the expansion of the cultivation of roots and tubers can constitute a solution to their food situation (Lee *et al.,* 1988). It should be noted that the cultivation of cassava does not require a high level of technical ability, while the cultivation of yams, used in particular in Nigeria, requires greater technical abilities. Furthermore, the land reserves of countries such as Cameroon, Gabon, Côte d'Ivoire and Togo are limited and gains in yields are therefore necessary. Finally, Rwanda and Burundi face a different situation because of the strong pressure they exert on their natural resources. These two countries derive a large part of their energy requirements from roots or tubers but complement their diets effectively with pulses rich in protein. Therefore, these countries need to increase the productivity of each production factor (human resources, land and water).

3.133 A substantial proportion of exploitable rain-fed land is still available. Many developing countries still have an important quantity of unexploited land available that is well adapted to rain-fed crops. The available land is about equivalent to the surface area already being farmed (over 700 million hectares). These lands do not include areas inhabited by human beings, forests or protected areas. To inhabit them could require important population movements.

3.134 This land is available especially in sub-Saharan Africa, to a lesser degree in East Asia (except China) and Latin America (which has a large area of forest land in reserve) and to a minor degree in South Asia. However, it should also be taken into account that forests have a role that may be important in contributing to agricultural incomes. It would appear that these lands are not very fertile naturally and that the colonization programmes aimed at new lands over the last few years have never absorbed large excess rural population groups. Furthermore, part of such lands will be used for expanding population settlements. According to FAO, the increase in cultivated arable lands will probably not surpass 12 percent by the year 2010.

3.135 Future development is largely dependent on dissemination of technical expertise. The acceleration of rural development will depend greatly on the dissemination of farming techniques and low-cost distribution of improved cultivars. This will apply especially to countries that possess particularly arable land and where available land is more limited. Good infrastructure, market access and competition in labour costs all stimulate such dissemination.

The role of human resources

3.136 The factors that influence development – setting up agricultural infrastructure, input supply policies, methods of preservation, extension policies and training, farm market regulation, development of banking service infrastructure and political and credit infrastructure – are not addressed in this paper.

3.137 However, it is necessary to point out that once there are productivity gains as a result of enhanced inputs and improved cultivars, the continuing struggle for productivity depends increasingly on human resources. It is only by recognizing the value of human resource development that this quest for productivity can be successful. Professional training and integration of farming populations into the process of development must therefore be added to improved health conditions, improved nutritional conditions and increased literacy levels of populations.

Holistic responses to the challenges

3.138 This document considers populations as groups of individuals who have not only fertility, mortality or migration characteristics at certain ages, but also energy requirements and diets that change over time. From such a perspective it is sufficient to raise questions about development strategies, considering the magnitude of the direct demographic challenges, especially those caused by population growth, as well as the indirect demographic challenges of factors such as dietary patterns. It is certain that holistic rather than isolated sectoral strategies are necessary at all levels. The challenges can be met, but not if population or agricultural policies are implemented without regard for each other. A carefully planned synergy of these areas is urgently needed. In order to be more effective, population programmes need to take into account the food security and the biophysical, social, economic and institutional environments of rural populations which can influence their demographic behaviour. Agricultural strategies can be either assisted or endangered according to the demographic characteristics and trends of the populations they are meant to serve. This document has highlighted the enormousness of the challenges: to be effective, decision-makers need to implement solutions that are truly commensurate with the magnitudes identified. Finally, in view of the inertia of demographic factors and the various time frames required for human resource and agricultural development, time is an essential consideration. Finding and implementing solutions that address the combination of the magnitudes in relation to the problems of time is the crux of the matter.

4. Conclusions

4.1 The world will inherit a very diversified food situation at the end of the second millennium.

4.2 The positive aspects of the picture can be summarized as follows: coming from a very acute food deficit in 1962, Asia has continually improved its coverage rate of energy requirements by its food supplies and is catching up with the situation of Latin America, where, after a period of increase in coverage, a stabilization can now be observed.

4.3 On the negative side, Africa has not managed to improve its food situation. Furthermore, some countries – those that consume mainly cassava, yams or taro – have experienced an acute decline. Demographic transition in Africa would facilitate the process of achieving food security; the annual growth rate in available plant-derived energy would be 2.6 percent in the low variant, as opposed to 3.3 percent in the high variant of the United Nations population projections.

4.4 Energy requirements of developing countries will increase towards the year 2050 because of the growth of their population numbers and also, to a lesser degree, as a consequence of change in their population structure. The ageing of the population and the increase in its physical height as a consequence of better nutrition are factors increasing energy requirements, whereas declining fertility and increasing urbanization are factors reducing energy requirements. As a result, by the year 2050, energy requirements will be doubled in developing countries as a group (but more than trebled in sub-Saharan Africa).

4.5 Developing countries will have to complement their national diets in order to create the prerequisite conditions for eliminating chronic undernutrition. As a result of differences in food distribution inside countries, this process could require an increase in plant-derived food energy availability of 30 percent in Africa (but 40 percent for sub-Saharan populations), 15 percent in Asia and less than 10 percent in Latin America.

4.6 In order to achieve well-balanced diets (in terms of amino acids, vitamins and nutrients), diets will need to be diversified. As a result, Africa would have to improve its plant-derived energy by another 25 percent (46 percent for countries consuming mainly roots and tubers) and Asia by 21 percent.

4.7 All included, developing countries would have to increase their plant-derived energy by 174 percent. This means that while countries of Latin America and Asia would roughly have to double their plant-derived energy, African countries would have to multiply theirs by five (by seven for the root- and tuber-consuming countries).

4.8 While for Asia or Latin America such a perspective represents a lower rate of productivity growth than was seen in the last 15 years, Africa would have to accelerate the growth of its productivity drastically.

4.9 Climatic change could be a crucial factor for food production in the future. This complex issue will create new challenges to satisfy human food energy requirements and changes in diets and could modify plant, animal and human pathologies as well as the distribution and location of human settlements.

4.10 Where land becomes scarce, increases in yield will be achieved mostly by drawing more heavily on natural resources and through the development of human capacities. Because of the existing level of education in Asia, many Asian countries seem to be well prepared for the change in the nature of development. On the other hand, the current development level of economic infrastructure and human resources will constitute a serious handicap in Africa. Africa will thus be faced with the obstacle of improving its human and infrastructure resources while dealing with a very difficult food situation. In doing so, Africa would also be preparing the basis for solving its food security problem in the long term, after the year 2025.

4.11 In view of the importance of the interrelations between population trends and food, decision-makers and researchers face the continuing challenge of harmonizing agricultural and population policies and programmes in order to help develop an approach towards achieving universal food security for the benefit of humanity.

Bibliography

Boserup, E. 1965. *The conditions of agricultural growth: the economics of agrarian change under population pressure.* New York, NY, USA, Aldine Press.

Boserup, E. 1985. Economic and demographic inter-relationships in Sub-Saharan Africa. *Pop. Dev. Rev.,* 11(3): 383-397.

Cépède, M. & Lengellé, M. 1953. *Economie alimentaire du globe – Essai d'interprétation.* Paris, France, Librairie Médicis, Editions M.-Th. Génin.

Chesnais, J.-C. 1985. *La transition démographique – Trente ans de bouleversements 1965-1995.* Les dossiers du CEPED No. 34. Paris, France.

Collomb, P. 1988. Sécurité alimentaire et développement – Confrontations avec des incertitudes croissantes, Septième Congrès mondial de sociologie rurale, Bologna, Italy, 25-28 July 1988. *Population,* 1: 271-275.

Collomb, P. 1989. Transition démographique, transition alimentaire: I – La logique économique. *Population,* 3: 583-612; II – De la logique démographique à la logique alimentaire. *Population,* 4-5: 777-807.

Cosio-Zavala, M.-E. 1992. *Transitions démographiques et développement social dans les pays en développement.* Communication presented to the Réunion du groupe d'experts sur la croissance de la population et l'évolution des structures démographiques, Paris, 16-20 November 1992. New York, NY, USA, United Nations.

Erlich, P. & Erlich, A. 1991. *Healing the planet.* Reading, MA, USA, Addison-Wesley.

FAO. 1982. Potential population supporting capacities of lands in the developing world. *In* G.M. Higgins *et al.,* eds. *Technical report of project: land resources for populations of the future.* Rome, FAO, New York, NY, USA, United Nations Fund for Population Activities (UNFPA) and Rome, International Institute for Applied Systems Analysis.

FAO. 1987. *The Fifth World Food Survey.* Rome.

FAO. 1992. *World food supplies and the prevalence of chronic undernourishment in the developing regions: 1992 assessment.* Document ESS/MISC/1/92. Rome.

FAO. 1993a. *Production yearbook 1992.* Vol. 46. FAO Statistics Series No. 112. Rome.

FAO. 1993b. *Trends of plant nutrient management in developing countries,* by A.L. Angé. Rome.

FAO. 1995a. *World agriculture: towards 2010.* N. Alexandratos, ed. Rome, FAO and Chichester, UK, John Wiley.

FAO. 1995b. *Production yearbook 1994.* Vol 48. FAO Statistics Series No. 125. Rome.

FAO/WHO (World Health Organization). 1992. *Nutrition and development: a global assessment.* International Conference on Nutrition. Rome.

FAO/United Nations Educational, Scientific and Cultural Organization (UNESCO)/ World Meteorological Organization (WMO). 1977. *United Nations map of world desertification.* Nairobi, Kenya.

Griffon, D. 1995. Des orientations pour la recherche et le développement des racines et des tubercules tropicaux. In *Transformation alimentaire du manioc.* Paris, France, ORSTOM.

James, W.P.T. & Schofield, E.C. 1990. *Human energy requirements: a manual for planners and nuitritionists.* Oxford, UK, Oxford University Press.

Jolly, C.L. & Torrey Boyle, B. 1993. *Population and land use in developing countries: report of a workshop.* National Research Council, Committee on Population,

Commission on Behavioral and Social Sciences and Education, National Research Council. Washington, DC, USA, National Academy Press.

Lee, R.E., Arthur, W.B., Kenney, A.C., Rodgers, G. & Srinivasan, T.N. 1988. *Population, food and rural development.* Liège, France, International Union for the Scientific Study of Population (IUSSP).

Levy, M.L. 1985. *Horizon 2025.* Population et Société, No. 190. Paris, France.

Peng, Y. 1994. *Statement by Mme Peng Yu, Representative of China,* 27th Session of the United Nations Population Commission, Agenda Item 3(a): General debate on national experience in population matters, New York, 28 March 1994.

Peng, Y. 1995. *Statement by Mme Peng Yu, Representative of China,* 28th Session of the United Nations Population Commission, Agenda Item 3(a): General debate on national experience in population matters, New York, 21 February 1995.

Piazza, A. 1986. *Food consumption and nutritional status in the PRC.* Westview Special Studies on China. Boulder, CO, USA and London, UK, Westview Press.

Popkins, B.M. 1994. The nutrition transition in low-income countries: an emerging crisis. *Nutr. Rev.,* 52(9): 285-98.

Quesnel, A., Vimard, P. & Guillaume, A. 1991. *Modifications des coûts et bénéfices des enfants supportés par les parents: différentiation socio-économique et son impact sur la fécondité – Évolution de la fécondité et rôle des enfants en milieu rural ouest-africain.* Seminar on the Course of Fertility Transition in Sub-Saharan Africa, Harare, Zimbabwe, 19-22 November 1991. IUSSP Committee on Comparative Analysis of Fertility and University of Zimbabwe

Rosegrant, M.W., Agcaoili-Sombilla, M. & Perez, N.D. 1995. *Global food supply, demand and trade to 2050: projections and implications for policy and investment.* Paper prepared for the workshops A 2020 Vision for Food, Agriculture, and Nutrition: Issues Facing South Asia, 27-29 March 1995, Kathmandu, Nepal, and Long Term Projections for 2020, 11-12 April 1995, Washington, DC, USA. Washington, International Food Policy Research Institute (IFPRI).

SOLAGRAL. 1995. *Synthèse de l'enquête en vue du Sommet mondial de l'alimentation.* Paris, France, Ministère de la coopération.

Treche, S. 1995. Importance du manioc en alimentation humaine dans différentes régions du monde. In *Transformation alimentaire du manioc.* Paris, France, ORSTOM.

United Nations. 1991. *World population prospects 1990.* New York, NY, USA.

United Nations. 1992. *Long-range world population projections: two centuries of population growth, 1960-2150.* New York, NY, USA.

United Nations. 1995a. *World population prospects: the 1994 revision.* New York, NY, USA.

United Nations. 1995b. *World urbanization prospects: the 1994 revision.* Estimates and projections of urban and rural populations and of urban agglomerations. New York, NY, USA.

United Nations. 1995c. *Population and development.* Programme of Action adopted at the International Conference on Population and Development, Cairo, Egypt, 5-13 September 1994. Vol. 1. ST/ESA/SER.A/149. New York, NY, USA.

United Nations Educational, Scientific and Cultural Organization (UNESCO). 1985a. *Biosphere reserves* (map). Paris, France, Man and the Biosphere Programme Secretariat.

UNESCO. 1985b. *Action plan for biosphere reserves.* Paris, France, Man and the Biosphere Programme Secretariat.

United Nations Population Fund (UNFPA). 1991. *Population, resources and the environment: the critical challenges.* New York, NY, USA.

UNFPA. 1995. *National perspectives on population and development.* Synthesis of 168 national reports prepared for the International Conference on Population and Development, Cairo, Egypt, 5-13 September 1994. ST/ESA/SER.A/149. New York, NY, USA.

Uvin, P. 1995. The state of world hunger. *In* E. Messer & P. Uvin, eds. *Hunger report.* New York, NY, USA, Gordon & Breach.

Wang, Q. & Wang, H. 1995. Survey of quality of basic level family planning statistics of Hebei and Hubei Province by State Family Planning Commission. *Population Res.,* 19(3). (In Chinese, translated into English by M. Sun, at INED, Beijing)

World Bank. 1990. *World development report 1990: poverty.* World Development Indicators. Washington, DC, USA, World Bank.

World Bank. 1994. *World development report 1994: infrastructure for development.* World Development Indicators. Washington, DC, USA, World Bank.

World Commission on Environment and Development. 1987. *Our common future.* New York, NY, USA, Oxford University Press.

Zeng, Y. 1995. Has China's fertility in 1991 and 1992 been far below the replacement level? *Population Res.,* 19(3). (In Chinese, translated into English by M. Sun, INED, Beijing)

5
Food security and nutrition

Contents

Acknowledgements

The preparation of the World Food Summit technical background documents has mobilized, in addition to FAO's own staff contribution, a considerable amount of expertise in the international scientific community, drawn from partner international institutions and governmental or nongovernmental circles. The process has been monitored at FAO by an internal Reading Committee, composed of staff selected ad personam and established to ensure that the whole collection meets appropriate quality and consistency criteria.

The present document has been prepared by Dr Joachim von Braun of the University of Kiel, Germany, in collaboration with John Lupien, Jean-Pierre Cotier, Maarten Immink and Brian Thompson of FAO; Joanne Csete, Micheline Beaudry and David Alnwick of the United Nations Children's Fund (UNICEF); David Steeds, Hans Binswanger, Harold Alderman and Judith McGuire of the World Bank; and Mercedes de Onís and Chizurun Nishida of the World Health Organization (WHO). After initial review within FAO by all technical departments, invited colleagues and the Reading Committee, a first version was published and circulated for comments to governments, international governmental organizations (IGOs) and nongovernmental organizations (NGOs), as well as to peer reviewers. Much appreciated comments and advice have been received from Dr Gopalan of the Nutrition Foundation of India; Suzanne S. Harris of the Human Nutrition Institute, International Life Sciences Institute (ILSI); Dr R. Uauy Dagach of the Institute of Nutrition and Food Technology, University of Chile; Gérard Viatte of the Organisation for Economic Co-operation and Development (OECD); Prof. Chen Chunming of the Chinese Academy of Preventive Medicine, Beijing, China; Per Pinstrup-Andersen and Lawrence Haddad of the International Food Policy Research Institute (IFPRI); Gérard Ghersi of Université Laval, Canada; Patrick Webb of the World Food Programme (WFP); Marc Cohen of Bread for the World, United States; Clive Robinson of Christian Aid, United Kingdom; and Vicky Quinn of the United Nations Children's Fund (UNICEF), Ghana.

While grateful for the contributions received from all reviewers, the FAO Secretariat bears responsibility for the content of the document.

Executive summary

Improving nutrition is an issue of supreme importance to many millions of people throughout the world who are suffering from persistent hunger and malnutrition and to others who are at risk of doing so in the future. There is general consensus today that a complex set of factors determines hunger and malnutrition. Important causes are related not only to food and agriculture, but also to people's knowledge and behaviour. Policies have a strong influence on all causes. The aim of this paper is to examine the relationships among food security, agriculture and nutrition and to outline nutrition-improvement policies that offer the promise of bringing about rapid and sustained improvement.

Malnutrition may be viewed from three different perspectives: as the lack of a basic human right, as a symptom of broader poverty and underdevelopment problems or as a cause of these poverty and underdevelopment problems. There are powerful arguments for all three perspectives and, in terms of considering specific actions, the three are certainly complementary.

In order to design effective policies, it is necessary to gain a clear understanding of the linkages among food security, agriculture and nutrition as well as all determinants of nutritional well-being.

- Food and the security of its supply are preconditions for nutritional well-being. Poverty is a major determinant of food insecurity and poor health; the poor lack adequate means to obtain food in the quantities and qualities needed for a healthy life. In addition, food insecurity and hunger in a number of countries are caused primarily by armed conflicts or are actually used as instruments to conduct such conflicts.

- The significance of agriculture in improving nutrition is due, first, to its principal role, i.e. the production of food of the desired quality and quantity, and, second, to its direct and indirect role in providing employment and income to the poor throughout the economy, particularly in low-income countries.

- Health, sanitation and the care given to vulnerable members of society have a strong influence on nutrition. Malnutrition leads to substantial losses in productivity and the misallocation of scarce resources as a result of decreased work performance and diminished cognitive ability and school performance.

Exactly how many households and individuals are affected by malnutrition is unknown because of difficulties of definition and measurement and inadequate data. Any overview of best estimates of major nutritional problems must emphasize the following:

- An estimated 841 million people are hungry (food-energy deficient), i.e. 20 percent of the developing countries' total population. This figure does not include the hungry in industrialized countries and in economies in transition.

- Some 190 million children are underweight, 230 million children are stunted and 50 million children are wasted. The last figure may understate the actual magnitude of the problem because it captures only current acute problems which may worsen in certain seasons or circumstances.

Nutritional problems resulting in low body weight are also prevalent among adults and adolescents in developing countries.

- Vitamin A deficiency is a public-health problem in at least 60 countries; some 40 million children are suffering from this deficiency. About 29 percent of the world's population is at risk of iodine deficiency. Worldwide, about 2 billion people are affected by iron deficiency, a condition to which women and preschool children are particularly prone.
- The problem of undernutrition is paralleled by extensive and growing public-health problems with obesity, not only in the richest and the poorest countries, but also in low- and middle-income countries, and especially in urban areas.

It is necessary to fulfil a number of preconditions before it is possible to conduct sustained actions to improve nutrition, and the specific actions needed to tackle a given country's nutritional problems vary according to its situation. These often unfulfilled preconditions include:

- appropriate macroeconomic policies and development strategies (with related trade, storage and food-aid policies, where applicable), which are a precondition for a functioning economy capable of employment-intensive growth;
- policies and programmes for increasing agricultural production and raising productivity in low-income countries, which are a precondition for future security of adequate nutrition – a precondition in which effective national and international agricultural research systems play a key role of sustainable nutritional improvement.

The range of specific actions to be taken varies from one country to another and may include:

- programmes for reducing poverty (including employment and infrastructure-improvement programmes);
- sustainable food- and nutrition-related transfer programmes (such as food subsidies and food stamps), which address the immediate causes of malnutrition of the poor as much as possible;
- direct nutrition and health interventions (e.g. targeted feeding, micronutrient programmes, nutrition education, integrated nutrition programmes, sanitation and health actions and relief programmes), which address both the short- and long-term symptoms and causes of nutritional problems, including those of higher-income groups, by focusing on changing behaviour.

Building on past international commitments and ongoing initiatives for nutritional improvement, the paper concludes with a set of priority areas of attention and actions addressing:

- the malnutrition/mortality cycle, with clearly defined targets for measurably reducing malnutrition;
- human-resource development for nutrition, including attention to actions facilitating reduced population growth;
- the promotion of employment-intensive growth, especially through agricultural growth promotion and employment programmes for the poor;
- famine prevention, including mechanisms for preventing famines related to armed conflicts;
- the facilitation of community and household self-help through education and empowerment, especially for women.

Any consideration of the costs of nutritional improvement must also take into account the benefits that would be forfeited through non-action. Focusing on (fiscal) spending and ignoring the resultant benefits is misleading. The guiding principle in considering the cost aspects of improving nutrition must be to achieve the defined nutritional goals rapidly and sustainably through the use of a portfolio of the most cost-effective policy instruments.

Only if the urgency and significance of the food security and nutritional situation are readily apparent will appropriate action be taken and the international support for such action be sustained. The availability of organizational capacity is a prerequisite for monitoring changes in the nutritional situation and for evaluating the effects of nutrition policies and programmes.

It is imperative that the governmental organizations, particularly ministries, as well as non-governmental interests involved in nutrition improvement activities be well coordinated at the national level. Such coordination can be stimulated by international organizations, but it often lacks a well-established framework. It is necessary to develop national strategies involving all food and agricultural interests in order to ensure that actions aimed at food-security and nutritional improvement are sustained and consistent. Progress in implementing the strategy will be enhanced when all nutrition improvement efforts are coordinated by a problem-oriented, lean management structure that recognizes that improving and maintaining adequate nutrition for all at all times strongly depends upon the relevant actors in the non-governmental arena, especially food producers.

Past international initiatives regarding food security and nutrition have stimulated actions for improvement. Drawing on new insights, new global circumstances and new forms of cooperation, the World Food Summit offers an opportunity to build on past initiatives. The creation of a transparent and reliable international reporting system for measuring national progress in achieving nutritional well-being (e.g. reduction in the proportion and number of underweight children and other relevant indicators, presented in map and other forms) will be instrumental in creating the proper political understanding for implementing the needed actions. National food-for-all campaign committees will be one of the most appropriate instruments to monitor the food and nutrition situation at national and subnational levels and to promote actions that will alleviate problems of hunger and malnutrition. The follow-ups to previous international commitments, i.e. the World Summit for Children and the International Conference on Nutrition (ICN), have gone in the right direction, and this approach should be reinforced.

1. Introduction

1.1 In order to find effective and efficient solutions for improving nutritional well-being, it is necessary to consider a range of policies and actions aimed directly and indirectly at overcoming the diverse nutritional problems that may exist in widely varying circumstances. This paper focuses on nutrition-related policies, yet it does so from a broad perspective emphasizing the complementarity of indirect (for example, social and economic) agricultural and food security policies and direct nutrition policies and programmes such as nutritional considerations in agriculture, targeted programmes, integrated nutrition and health programmes.[1]

1.2 The paper conceptualizes and explores the linkages among food security, agriculture and nutrition; points out food-security and nutritional implications that are inherent within selected policies on food and agricultural development and nutrition; and makes recommendations for improving the nutritional benefits arising from social, economic and agricultural development, as well as from direct nutrition-oriented policies and programmes. The paper focuses mainly on the nutritional problems of the poor in low-income countries. To a limited extent, it also addresses the nutritional problems and scope for action in economies under transition and high-income countries.

COMPLEMENTARY PERSPECTIVES ON NUTRITION

1.3 To achieve food security and nutritional well-being for all, it is important that planners and policy-makers in every sector be aware of the impact that their decisions and actions are likely to have on nutrition. At the same time, the basic perspectives of the nutrition problems must be clear. Malnutrition may be viewed from three different perspectives: first, as an unfulfilled basic human right; second, as a symptom of broader poverty and development problems; and third, as a cause of these poverty and development problems.

Nutrition as a human right

1.4 Considering nutritional well-being to be a basic human right of every individual means that, in principle, no compromise is acceptable concerning the right to food. The *International covenant on economic, social and cultural rights* adopted by the United Nations General Assembly in 1966 defined and formalized the right to food as a basic human right, which had already been mentioned in the *Universal declaration of human rights of the United Nations* in 1948. By 1989, 85 States had signed the covenant. Although States continue to endorse the right to food, they have not translated this right into specific legal obligations, and there are no national or international mechanisms to supervise the implementation of this right.[2]

[1] This paper is to be seen within the context of other World Food Summit technical background documents, most notably documents 2, *Success stories in food security*; 3, *Socio-political and economic environment for food security*; 6, *Lessons from the green revolution: towards a new green revolution*; 8, *Food for consumers: marketing, processing and distribution*; 12, *Food and international trade*; 13, *Food security and food assistance*; and 14, *Assessment of feasible progress in food security*.

[2] The *Universal declaration on the eradication of hunger and malnutrition* adopted at the 1974 World Food Conference states "Every man, woman, and child has the inalienable right to be free from hunger and malnutrition..." (United Nations, 1975).

1.5 This does not imply that the stated human right is meaningless. The consensus and its codification provide a foundation for advocacy and political pressure in the countries that signed the covenant or related declarations.

Malnutrition as a symptom of poverty

1.6 Considering undernutrition to be a symptom of poverty and development problems (i.e. as an outcome) suggests that the availability of and access to food – which are mainly functions of structural conditions and changes in income, agriculture and trade – interact with the health and sanitation environment and human behaviour and knowledge in giving rise to nutritional outcomes. Policy is then called upon to rectify constraints in any of these domains.

1.7 While food availability may be a problem for many people when availability declines and prices rise, the problem assumes crisis proportions mostly for the poor. This is why food availability needs to be evaluated within the context of poverty when availability problems turn into access problems (e.g. when prices rise), whether at the national or household level.

1.8 Increasing the incomes of households that have malnourished members can improve their access to food. Increases in income are strongly related to non-staple food consumption, particularly of meat.[3]

Nutrition as a precondition for development

1.9 Taking the view that nutritional well-being is a precondition for development argues that lack of productivity (in a broad sense) is partly a result of malnutrition. The nutritional well-being of the poor is thus not merely an outcome of development, but a precondition for it. Nutrition and development have both direct, short-term linkages and indirect, long-term ones; the latter are also closely related to population growth.

1.10 Improved adult nutrition leads to higher physical productivity and higher productivity in the labour market.[4] Undernutrition results in substantial productivity losses, e.g. through high levels of morbidity and impaired cognitive development (Mason, Jonsson and Csete, 1995; Scrimshaw, 1994).[5]

1.11 In addition to their current income flow, poor households build their asset bases out of incremental income. This is one of the key links between short- and long-term food security and nutrition. Expanded asset bases reduce the vulnerability of households to short-term downturns in income flows; part of the asset base can be liquidated in times of adversity, an action that helps to maintain household-level food security.[6]

1.12 The efforts of food-insecure households to acquire food may also have important implications for the environment and the use of natural resources. Many poor and food-insecure households live in ecologically vulnerable areas

[3] Consequently, income has an extensive effect on the consumption of micronutrients that are found primarily in meats, such as iron, but a more limited effect on the consumption of micronutrients that come primarily from vegetables, such as vitamin A. An analysis of Philippine farm households showed that the income elasticity of iron was 0.44, whereas the income elasticities of vitamins A and C were not significantly different from zero (Bouis, 1991).
[4] Empirical studies find nutritional status and labour productivity, as measured by wages or own-farm output or both, to be positively related (Strauss, 1986; Sahn and Alderman, 1988). In environments where physical productivity matters, therefore, substantial lifetime losses may be expected among adults who are stunted as a result of poor health and nutrition during childhood.
[5] An innovative study in Guatemala tracked down, after 14 years, most of the schoolchildren who had received supplemental feeding in a study project and found that, although there had been no further feeding interventions, those children who had received the supplements maintained their height advantage and performed better in achievement tests (Martorell *et al.*, 1991). Iodine deficiency, protein-energy malnutrition (PEM) and iron deficiency have negative consequences for learning capacity and cognitive behaviour (Scrimshaw, 1994).
[6] For example, during a famine period in Ethiopia, households in the upper-income tercile in a survey population were able to obtain US$15 from asset sales, while households in the lower-income tercile were only able to obtain US$5, because the former owned larger herds and other assets (Webb and Reardon, 1992).

(Leonard, 1989), and inappropriate or desperate land-use practices can cause environmental degradation which can further undermine their livelihoods and those of future generations.

1.13 The search for nutritional well-being may also have important implications for a region's demographic situation, especially if it leads to short- or long-term migration to other areas in search of employment and income or, in the extreme, in search of emergency relief food. Such out-migration may result in an increased number of female-headed households, a higher dependency ratio in the sending area and changes in the dynamics of the labour market. The receiving areas, mostly urban slums, experience considerable food-security strains because of the influx of migrants.

1.14 Nutrition and population growth stand in a complex, long-term relationship. Only over the medium term is the relationship partly one of food availability competing with population growth. Over the long term, improved nutrition, as an element of human welfare, may contribute to slowing down population growth. Clearly, there are strong positive relationships between improved nutrition and economic development (Fogel, 1994) and between economic development and the demographic transition from a high birth rate and low life expectancy to longer life expectancy and, thereafter, lower birth rates. Thus, to the extent that improved nutrition fosters economic development, it is also a fundamental force for alleviating the mounting problem of population growth.

1.15 This paper accepts each of the three views (human right, symptom of poverty and precondition for development) as having equal validity rather than playing one off against the other. This approach may facilitate the formation of larger and more influential coalitions, both international and domestic, which can improve nutrition rapidly.

2. Current and future dimensions of the nutrition problem

2.1 The nutrition problem has a number of dimensions, and some of the problems overlap or are parts of larger nutrition- and food-related problem areas. This chapter addresses the following questions:
- How many people are malnourished?
- Where and who are these people?
- What are the future challenges and risks for nutrition arising from the pressure of population growth and other forces of change?

HOW MANY PEOPLE ARE HUNGRY AND/OR MALNOURISHED?

2.2 It is difficult to know how many people suffer from nutritional problems, including hunger and malnutrition, because of definition and measurement problems and the inadequacy of data. Related measurement difficulties result from regional, community-level, household and intrahousehold inequalities and from dynamics that are difficult to quantify. Many regions of the world have never been in the position to make the sizeable investment needed to put in place data systems capable of comprehensively assessing chronic malnutrition. Moreover, the nutritional well-being of a population may change rapidly, yet the monitoring of food insecurity and malnutrition in disaster zones and areas of armed conflict is limited, for obvious reasons. Nonetheless, the lack of precise figures should not stand in the way of efforts to devise and implement policies and programmes for improving nutrition and food security.

Measuring malnutrition

2.3 Instead of relying on general approximations, it is necessary to strive to approach as closely as possible some form of measurement of people's actual nutritional situation. Anthropometric measurements serve this purpose well (see Box 1). However, such proxies for nutritional status do not permit distinctions to be drawn between specific nutritional risks such as diet and nutrient deficiencies, so different information and approaches are required to trace the causes of undernutrition. Nevertheless, the prevalence of underweight is considered to be an important indicator of many nutrition-related problems at the individual and population level (Mason, Jonsson and Csete, 1995; FAO/WHO, 1992e).

Measuring food security

2.4 Food security in its most basic form is defined as the access of all people to the food needed for a healthy life at all times (FAO/WHO, 1992b). Food

---

Box 1
MEASURING NUTRITIONAL STATUS

The nutritional status of an individual can be assessed through the use of one or more anthropometric measurements to determine whether the individual is likely to be well-nourished, undernourished or overnourished. The method generates objective measurements of body dimensions and composition as a proxy indicator of nutritional status.

The most commonly used measurements for assessing nutritional status are based on growth and development in children and on body composition of adults. The assessment of child and adult nutritional status is presented in terms of ratios of weight and height (e.g. weight for height, and in the case of children, weight for age), and these indicators are presented in relation to age and gender-specific points of reference (cut-off points). In this approach, the ratio of height to age measures stunting, while weight to height indicates wasting, and weight adjusted for age may signify that a child is at risk of being weight deficient. For adults, body mass index (BMI), weight/height squared, is considered at present to be the most suitable anthropometric indicator of under- or overnutrition (see FAO, 1994a; WHO, 1995a).

---

insecurity is a prime cause of undernutrition. Given the multiple dimensions (chronic, transitory, short-term and long-term) of food insecurity, there can be no single indicator for its measurement (Maxwell and Frankenberger, 1992). Proposed indicators relate to household food security in different ways. The relation may be temporal (leading, concurrent or trailing indicators), conceptual (consumption, nutrition, coping strategies, resource-related and non-household measures) and/or definitional (access, adequacy, vulnerability and sustainability) (Csete and Maxwell, 1995).

- Food security at the national level (the ability to obtain sufficient food to meet the needs of all citizens) can, to some extent, be monitored in terms of needs and supply indicators; that is, the quantities of available food versus needs.
- Food security at the household level may be measured by direct surveys of dietary intake (in comparison with appropriate adequacy norms). Such data are costly because of the considerable time required for their collection and processing.[7]
- If properly analysed, the level of, and changes in, socio-economic and demographic variables such as real wage rates, employment, price ratios and migration can serve as proxies to indicate the status of, and changes in, food security.[8]

Best estimates of the state of nutrition

2.5 Any overview of major nutritional problems must emphasize the following.
- An estimated 841 million people are hungry (food-energy deficient), i.e. 20 percent of the developing countries' populations (Table 1). This figure does not include the hungry in the industrialized countries or in the countries with economies under transition.

[7] The development of a household food security index for the purpose of monitoring food security at the international level is an area of current research. As household food security is influenced by a multitude of factors, no single indicator can accurately reflect the situation. It has therefore been proposed that a composite index be used, composed of the per caput daily dietary energy supply (DES) as an indicator of aggregate food availability, per caput gross national product (GNP) in purchasing power parity (PPP) units as a measure of overall real purchasing power, and the coefficient of variation of income distribution as a proxy of equality or inequality of income distribution. It was noted that there is a need for further research concerning the data and design of the index (FAO, 1993).

[8] A study of the International Food Policy Research Institute (IFPRI) identified a set of relatively simple indicators of food and nutrition security (Haddad, Kennedy and Sullivan, 1994). The indicators analysed included the number of unique foods consumed, region, dependency ratio, household size, rooms per caput, incidence of illness, vaccination status, drinking-water facilities, health facilities, etc. These indicators were used as single proxies or in combinations. The study found that these simple indicators "perform well in locating the food- and nutrition-insecure". The ideal combination of indicators was observed to be dependent on local characteristics.

Table 1
ESTIMATES OF FOOD ENERGY DEFICIENCY IN DEVELOPING REGIONS

Region/economic group	Period	% of population	Number of persons (million)
Region			
Sub-Saharan Africa	1969-71	38	103
	1979-81	41	148
	1990-92	43	215
Near East and North Africa	1969-71	27	48
	1979-81	12	27
	1990-92	12	37
East Asia and Southeast Asia	1969-71	41	476
	1979-81	27	379
	1990-92	16	269
South Asia	1969-71	33	238
	1979-81	34	303
	1990-92	22	255
Latin America and the Caribbean	1969-71	19	53
	1979-81	14	48
	1990-92	15	64
Economic group			
Low-income	1969-71	39	752
	1979-81	33	783
	1990-92	23	696
Middle- to high-income	1969-71	25	166
	1979-81	14	123
	1990-92	13	144
Developing regions (Total)	1969-71	35	918
	1979-81	28	906
	1990-92	20	841

Source: FAO, 1996.

- Some 190 million children are underweight, 230 million children are stunted and 50 million children are wasted. The last figure may understate the actual magnitude of the problem because it captures only current acute problems that may worsen in certain seasons or circumstances (WHO, 1995c; de Onís *et al.*, 1993) (Table 2). Each year, about 20 million infants are born with low birth weights. Nutritional problems resulting in underweight are also prevalent among adults and adolescents in developing countries. For instance, 12.5 percent of adults in China and 48.6 percent in India have body mass index (BMI) figures below 18.5, which is the lower limit of normality (FAO, 1996).
- The nutritional problems of children (low weight for age) in developing countries are considered to be associated with more than half of all child deaths. Most such deaths are attributable to mild or moderate malnutrition, as opposed to severe malnutrition (Pelletier *et al.*, 1995).

2.6 Some 40 million children are suffering from vitamin A deficiency, which is a public-health problem in at least 60 countries (WHO/UNICEF, 1995); about 251 million children have severe or moderately subclinical deficiencies (UN ACC/SCN, 1989).[9] About 1.6 billion people (29 percent of the world's

[9] These estimates are made independent of recent widespread interventions. More than 70 countries now iodize over 75 percent of their salt, so the incidence of iodine deficiency disorders (IDD) is decreasing, but the decrease has not yet been quantified. Similarly, about 20 countries have large-scale vitamin supplementation programmes.

Table 2

ESTIMATES OF THE NUMBER OF WASTED, STUNTED AND UNDERWEIGHT CHILDREN UNDER FIVE YEARS OF AGE IN DEVELOPING COUNTRIES, 1990

Region/economic class	Wasted		Stunted		Underweight	
	(%)	*(million)*	*(%)*	*(million)*	*(%)*	*(million)*
Region						
Sub-Saharan Africa	7.0	6.1	38.8	33.7	30.2	26.2
Near East and North Africa	8.8	4.4	32.4	16.0	25.3	12.5
South Asia	17.1	26.6	59.5	92.7	58.3	90.7
East and Southeast Asia	5.2	9.4	33.3	59.8	23.6	42.5
Latin America	2.6	1.5	22.7	12.7	12.0	6.7
Economic class						
Low-income countries	10.3	40.0	45.2	174.4	38.2	147.6
Middle- to high-income countries	5.6	8.0	28.7	40.8	22.0	31.2
TOTAL	9.1	47.9	40.7	215.2	33.9	178.8

Source: WHO, 1995c, as presented in FAO, 1996.

population) are at risk of iodine deficiency (WHO/UNICEF/ICCIDD, 1993). Worldwide, about 2 billion people are affected by iron deficiency, a condition to which women and preschool children are particularly prone.

2.7 The problem of undernutrition is paralleled by increasing public health problems associated with the incidence of overweight and obesity, not only in rich countries, but also in low- and middle-income countries, and especially in urban areas.

2.8 Table 2 provides an overview of the prevalence of underweight among children under the age of five years in developing countries in 1990. Since then, that is in the first half of the 1990s, a number of African countries (e.g. Ethiopia, Kenya, Madagascar and Rwanda) have recorded a disturbing increase in malnutrition among preschool children. India, too, reported a slight increase from 1989 to 1992, while there have recently been reports of improvements in Bangladesh, China and Brazil (UN ACC/SCN, 1994).

2.9 In addition to the factors outlined above, nutritional status is also determined by food safety. The relevance of food safety for adequate nutrition is especially important in developing countries, but unsafe foods also pose problems (e.g. salmonellosis) in industrialized countries. Particularly in developing countries, access to good-quality and safe food is closely related to socio-economic factors. These range from storage and food processing conditions to sanitation, water quality and food-control infrastructure. The incidence of foodborne diseases remains largely uncertain as most cases either are not reported or are not being related to the factor of unsafe foods. It is estimated that up to 70 percent of the estimated 1.5 billion cases of diarrhoea occurring among children under five years of age, resulting in some 3 million deaths, are of foodborne origin (FAO/WHO, 1992c).

Prevalence of food insecurity

2.10 Severe food insecurity that degenerates into famine has been on the decline. Today, in contrast to the late 1960s and early 1970s or even the 1980s, the symptoms of famine are evident only in several African countries such as Ethiopia, Mozambique and the Sudan and are localized in war zones. The risk of famine continues to exist, however, because of political, economic and environmental shocks and inadequate preparedness, mainly at the national level (Drèze and Sen, 1989; Teklu, von Braun and Zaki, 1991; Webb and von Braun, 1994).

2.11 Although there has been a global increase in the availability of energy, protein and fat, the availability of the last two has not risen in the least-developed countries (Tables 3 to 5). This indicates some global improvement in the availability of food, but not necessarily in food consumption among the poor. At least the proportion of people with inadequate food-energy consumption has declined in all regions except sub-Saharan Africa (Table 1).

2.12 These estimates convey a rough idea of the prevalence of food deficiency among the poor, but not of food (in)security as defined above. They disregard fluctuations and risks in the availability of and access to food. Estimates of food deficiency for a given period, say a specific year, understate the prevalence of food insecurity,[10] but the degree of their inaccuracy is unknown.

Micronutrient deficiencies

2.13 Over the past decade, the combination of more sensitive and more widely available methods of measuring nutrient status, more and better-quality epidemiological studies and advances in sciences such as biochemistry and immunology have resulted in a heightened awareness of the crucial importance of micronutrients – that is, food ingredients other than protein, energy, fat and fibre. The importance of micronutrients such as vitamin A, iron, iodine, zinc, copper and selenium for a whole range of vital functions has now been realized, and the significance of marginal deficiencies is becoming clearer. This is of relevance not only for low-income countries.

2.14 Internationally, a good deal of attention has recently been focused on vitamin A. It is now recognized that adequate amounts of this vitamin are fundamental to all stages of body development and functioning (e.g. cellular differentiation, adequate functioning of the immune system, optimal functioning of the eye). Populations in developing countries obtain most of their vitamin A from carotenoids of plant origin, whose absorption and utilization depend on adequate dietary fat, protein, iron and zinc. The causes of vitamin A deficiency can be traced to a variety of factors: ecological factors, for example the lack of resources such as water to grow foods rich in vitamin A; feeding practices, for example use of foods containing insufficient vitamin A or inadequate intakes of the above-mentioned nutrients which constrain its utilization; and disease patterns, for example diarrhoeal and respiratory diseases which have been followed by observed increases in vitamin A deficiency (WHO/UNICEF, 1995).

[10] For example, a Philippine data set shows that of 323 households with average Calorie adequacy above 80 percent of requirements (that is, not food-deficient in a chronic sense), 197 dipped below 80 percent at least once during a 16-month period (Haddad, Sullivan and Kennedy, 1991).

Table 3
PER CAPUT DIETARY ENERGY SUPPLY (DES) BY REGION AND ECONOMIC GROUP

Region/economic group	DES (Calories/caput/day)		
	1969-71	1979-81	1990-92
Developed countries	3 190	3 280	3 350
Developing countries	2 140	2 330	2 520
Least-developed countries	2 060	2 040	2 040
Low-income countries	2 060	2 210	2 430
World	2 440	2 580	2 720

Table 4
PROTEIN SUPPLIES BY REGION AND ECONOMIC GROUP

Region/economic group	Total protein (g/caput/day)		
	1969-71	1979-81	1990-92
Developed countries	95	99	102
Developing countries	53	57	62
Least-developed countries	52	51	50
Low-income countries	51	53	59
World	65	68	71

Table 5
FAT AND OIL SUPPLIES BY REGION AND ECONOMIC GROUP

Region/economic group	Total fat and oil (g/caput/day)		
	1969-71	1979-81	1990-92
Developed countries	108	118	125
Developing countries	33	40	51
Least-developed countries	31	31	32
Low-income countries	28	34	45
World	55	61	69

Source: FAO, 1996.

2.15 Iodine deficiency disorders (IDD) are the single most important cause of preventable brain damage and mental retardation in the world. Iodine deficiency during pregnancy may lead to irreversible brain damage in the foetus. Other severe manifestations in children are impaired learning capacity and psychomotor retardation. Iodine deficiency among pregnant women, particularly in the first trimester, may lead to an increase in the incidence of stillbirths, spontaneous abortions and congenital abnormalities (WHO/UNICEF/ICCIDD, 1993; Sullivan *et al.*, 1995; Mannar and Dunn, 1995). The IDD problem is not limited to the developing world, but exists in many European countries as well. Crops grown in iodine-deficient regions are also low in iodine. The consumption of foods with sufficient iodine (in particular seafoods) or iodine-fortified salt may prevent IDD even in regions with iodine-depleted soils.

2.16 Iron deficiency is associated not only with low iron intake but also with a lack of factors in the diet that enhance the utilization of non-haem iron, for example vitamin C. Worldwide, over 2 billion people are affected by iron deficiency. Women and preschool children are particularly prone to this deficiency; in some areas, more than 50 percent of women and children are anaemic. In children and infants, anaemia is associated with the retardation of physical and cognitive development. It also leads to reduced resistance to infections. In adults, iron deficiency can be a cause of fatigue and of reduced work capacity, and it may severely impair reproductive functions. Anaemia causes about 20 percent of maternal deaths as it predisposes the body to haemorrhage and infections before, during or after childbirth. Anaemia during pregnancy may result in retardation of foetal growth, low birth weights and increased rates of perinatal mortality (FAO/WHO, 1992f).

2.17 There is increasing evidence of widespread zinc deficiency in developing countries and further evidence that this deficiency is an important contributor to poor growth, poor resistance to infectious illness, increased incidence of stillbirths and possibly impaired cognitive development. Providing young children with zinc supplements has shown clear benefits in several countries. Zinc deficiency is associated with low consumption of animal products, which are the richest source of bio-available zinc. Better food-processing techniques may improve the bio-availability of zinc in cereals and legumes. This nutrient has been somewhat neglected because there have been no good methods of assessing the zinc status of populations (D. Alnwick, personal communication).

WHERE AND WHO ARE THE FOOD-INSECURE AND MALNOURISHED?
In particular regions and in rural settings

2.18 Essentially, all estimates concur that South Asia, and particularly India and Bangladesh, contains the largest proportion of the developing world's underweight children, followed by sub-Saharan Africa (Table 2). The incidence of food deficiency, as expressed in estimated food-energy deficiency, is highest in Africa and South Asia and considerably lower in East Asia and Latin America and the Caribbean. While the percentage of energy-deficient persons in the populations of South Asia has decreased, their absolute number in South Asia and sub-Saharan Africa has increased (Table 1).

2.19 Regarding the location of the food-energy-deficient population by agro-ecological zone (AEZ), it is found that deficiency tends to be least prevalent in wet zones and most prevalent in arid zones (Broca and Oram, 1991). Most of the poor in sub-Saharan Africa were located in the arid zone. In most instances, the distribution of the poor mirrors the population distribution in the AEZ (Garcia *et al.*, 1995).

2.20 Food-insecure households in different areas may belong to different socio-economic and demographic groups, depending on factors such as agro-ecological characteristics, access to land, diversity of income sources and the state of development of the economy. Food-deficient households tend to be larger and to have a higher number of dependants and a younger age composition (von Braun and Pandya-Lorch, 1991).[11] The prevalence of food insecurity tends to be higher among landless or quasi-landless households, which are much more dependent on less reliable sources of income than farm income and on the diversification of the rural economy.[12]

In urban areas

2.21 In urban areas, household food security is primarily a function of the real wage rate (i.e. the rate relative to food prices) and the level of employment. The prevalence of food deficiency and malnutrition tends to be lower in urban areas than in rural areas. However, the miserable sanitation environment in poor urban locations and certain aspects of urban lifestyles sometimes make the urban nutritional situation qualitatively different from the rural situation. Urban food insecurity and malnutrition will become an increasingly important problem in the future as rates of urbanization increase while problems with urban sanitation, diet quality and food safety grow (von Braun *et al.*, 1992; UNICEF, 1994b). For instance, by the year 2025, 57 percent of Africa's population may be urban, as opposed to only 34 percent in 1990. In South Asia, the figure may be 52 percent. In Latin America, the urban population had already reached 72 percent in 1990 (United Nations, 1991).

Among refugees and the displaced

2.22 Unable to secure a living or adequate food, often as a consequence of armed conflicts and discrimination, vast numbers of the poor migrate to more peaceful areas in their own country or into neighbouring countries. There are now an estimated 20 million refugees, plus some 30 million internally displaced people, making a total of 50 million (WFP, 1995). Another 35 million people live outside their own country in search of employment (Chen, 1992; Russell, Jacobsen and Stanley, 1990). Such movements are accompanied by problems of increased food insecurity and specific nutritional problems among the refugees and displaced poor (UN ACC/SCN, 1994).

In transitional economies

2.23 Because of malfunctioning markets, lack of safety nets and underemployment, the early 1990s have seen a substantial increase in the food-insecure population groups of some economies in transition. Particularly in central Asian countries and in parts of the Russian Federation, absolute poverty has increased and the symptoms of nutritional deficiencies are widespread. In the Russian Federation, preliminary estimates report that 3.6 percent of children under two years of age were underweight in 1993, and 21

[11] For example, food-insecure households in the Sahelian zone of Burkina Faso had an average household size of 11 and a dependency ratio of 0.51, compared with a size of 8 and a dependency ratio of 0.40 for food-secure households (Reardon, 1991).
[12] During the drought year of 1982/83, for example, 73 percent of the landless households in North Arcot, India, were food deficient, as compared with 61 percent of farm households (Yohannes, 1991).

percent were stunted. In the same year, considerable obesity was found among Russian adults (20 percent of those between the ages of 30 and 59) (Mroz and Popkin, 1995). The significance of access to land for household food security has increased. In the Russian Federation, for instance, 25 million households derive much of their staple foods from garden plots. The income earned in cash and kind from the household plots is about 26 percent in the western part of the Russian Federation, and the contribution to household food energy is large. Contrary to what might be expected, the poorest 25 percent of households derive not only absolutely but also relatively less food and income from their household plots (8 percent of income) than the richest 25 percent (32 percent of income) (von Braun *et al.*, 1996).

In industrialized countries

2.24 In high-income countries and among the high-income groups of low- and middle-income countries, the prime causes of unhealthy diets include behaviourial and lifestyle choices, social stratification and lack of knowledge (FAO/WHO, 1992d). Particularly in the industrialized countries, there has been increasing recognition over the past 40 years that certain chronic, non-communicable diseases are closely related to diet and aspects of lifestyle, such as emotional stress, reduced physical activity and tobacco use. These factors have been found to be particularly important in relation to obesity, cardiovascular diseases, hypertension, stroke, diabetes mellitus (non-insulin-dependent), various forms of cancer, liver diseases and gastro-intestinal diseases. These diseases are responsible for more than 70 percent of all deaths in developed countries (FAO/WHO, 1992f). The dietary problems and related effects on health entail substantial costs for society; for example, the costs have been estimated at about US$50 billion per year for Germany (Kohlmeier *et al.*, 1993). In the course of the 1980s and 1990s, as the distribution of income in the industrialized countries of North America and Europe has become more uneven and as social-welfare spending has been cut back in the face of rising unemployment, the need for food assistance among low-income groups has grown (Feichtinger, 1995). Homeless people are especially vulnerable to food insecurity.

FUTURE CHALLENGES POSED BY POPULATION PRESSURE AND ECONOMIC CHANGE

2.25 Realistic projections of malnutrition indicate that the goals of the World Children's Summit and the International Conference on Nutrition (ICN), i.e. to bring about a "substantial reduction in undernutrition among children by the year 2000" (FAO/WHO, 1992a), cannot be achieved with the current approaches and levels of commitment. According to an optimistic scenario, there will still be 100 million undernourished preschool children in the year 2020. A pessimistic scenario sees this figure rising to about 200 million children by the year 2000 and remaining at that level until the year 2020 (Garcia, 1994). According to the optimistic scenario, the absolute numbers of underweight preschool children will fall in every developing region with the exception of sub-Saharan Africa. Mainly because of population growth, the number of malnourished children in that region will rise to about 34 million by the year 2020, even at unchanging prevalence. Improvement is projected for China and Southeast Asia, where the number of underweight children is expected to fall from 44 million in 1990 to 6 million in 2020 (Garcia, 1994). Thus for these regions and a few others the set goals may well be achieved.

2.26 In a world increasingly integrated through trade and political and economic ties among nations, the availability of sufficient food throughout the world is of increasing importance for household food security and nutrition. Thus far, world production has kept pace with population growth (FAO, 1996). However, global food availability cannot be taken for granted over the long term in view of continuing population growth, increasing land scarcity and mounting difficulties in achieving sustainable increases in food-crop yields (Pinstrup-Andersen, 1994). By the year 2025, the world is expected to have a population of 8.47 billion, of whom 61 percent will live in large cities (Bongaarts, 1995), with many in rural areas settled on marginal lands of low productivity.

2.27 Projections indicate that population growth will account for about 90 percent of the rate of increase in global food (cereal) demand until the year 2010 (FAO, 1995c). However, changing dietary habits will have an important role in increasing food demand in many developing countries, as discussed in other WFS background papers.[13] Rising incomes, increasing urbanization, improvements in marketing efficiencies, competitive prices and increasing availability of a wide range of foods will lead to diversification of the diet away from dependence on a few food items to an increased variety of foods. For these developing countries the expected increase in per caput consumption is estimated to be between 2.2 and 2.4 percent annually for the period 1990 to 2010. This would amount to an annual per caput cereal consumption of 250 to 255 kg, as compared with 237 kg for the years 1989 to 1991. It is expected that this increase will result mainly from indirect demand, i.e. consumption as animal feed. Human consumption of cereals, on the other hand, is predicted to remain relatively stable.

2.28 Projections by FAO for food supplies by region suggest that future food problems will be concentrated in sub-Saharan Africa and South Asia. Availabilities in all other regions are projected to be adequate by the year 2010, as agricultural production growth is expected to keep pace with growing food requirements. The FAO projections, shown in Table 6, estimate an average daily per caput food-energy supply of 2 730 Calories in developing countries in the year 2010 (FAO, 1995c). In these countries, chronic undernutrition is expected to affect 11 percent of the population, or 637 million people. These global figures conceal important regional differences. In three regions (the Near East and North Africa, East Asia and Latin America and the Caribbean) food-energy supply is projected at about 3 000 Calories per day. The prevalence of chronic undernutrition is expected to be between 4 and 6 percent of the population. South Asia (2 450 Calories/caput/day) and especially sub-Saharan Africa (2 170 Calories/caput/day) are expected to be the regions with the lowest per caput food-energy supplies by the year 2010.

[13] See WFS companion paper 4, *Food requirements and population growth.*

Table 6
FAO PROJECTIONS OF PER CAPUT FOOD SUPPLIES FOR DIRECT HUMAN CONSUMPTION AND POSSIBLE EVOLUTION OF THE INCIDENCE OF CHRONIC UNDERNUTRITION, BY REGION

Region	Per caput food supplies (Calories/day)		Chronic undernutrition			
			% of population		Number of persons (million)	
	1988-90	2010	1988-90	2010	1988-90	2010
World	2 700	2 860				
Developed countries	3 400	3 470				
Developing countries	2 470	2 730	20	11	781	637
Sub-Saharan Africa	2 100	2 170	37	32	175	296
Near East and North Africa	3 010	3 120	8	6	24	29
East Asia	2 600	3 040	16	4	258	77
South Asia	2 220	2 450	24	12	265	195
Latin America and the Caribbean	2 690	2 950	13	6	59	40

Table 7
PER CAPUT FOOD AVAILABILITY: 1990 AND 2020, VARIOUS SCENARIOS

Country/region	1990	2020			
		Baseline	Low population	Low investment	High investment
		(Calories/day)			
World	2 773	2 888	3 038	2 752	3 026
Developed	3 353	3 537	3 630	3 497	3 604
Developing	2 500	2 814	2 966	2 656	2 972
Latin America and the Caribbean	2 722	3 054	3 166	2 900	3 216
Sub-Saharan Africa	2 053	2 136	2 301	2 018	2 229
Near East and North Africa	2 988	3 301	3 485	3 079	3 474
Asia	2 500	2 999	3 155	2 825	3 183

Table 8
PERCENTAGE OF MALNOURISHED CHILDREN IN DEVELOPING COUNTRIES: 1990 AND 2020, VARIOUS SCENARIOS

Country/region	1990	2020			
		Baseline	Low population	Low investment	High investment
Developing	34.3	25.4	23.8	33.2	19.0
Latin America and the Caribbean	20.4	14.0	13.0	22.9	5.4
Sub-Saharan Africa	28.4	25.3	24.7	31.2	20.0
West Asia/North Africa	13.4	9.7	8.8	17.0	2.9

Source: Rosegrant, Agcaoili-Sombilla and Perez, 1995.
Notes: The scenarios are described as follows: low population reflects the low population growth rate projections of the United Nations. Slow growth, low investment simulates the combined effect of a 25 percent reduction in the growth rates of non-agricultural income and cuts in investment in public agricultural research and social services. Rapid growth, high investment simulates a 25 percent increase in the growth of non-agricultural income and higher investment in agricultural research and social services.

2.29 The future food and nutrition situation is by no means an immutable fate, but a function of the actions taken in the meantime. This becomes readily apparent when food availability consequences are derived from alternative scenarios involving different population and investment policies. Results of such scenarios prepared by the International Food Policy Research Institute (IFPRI) regarding projected food availability and malnutrition among preschool children are shown in Tables 7 and 8. According to a baseline scenario, food availability will increase in all developing regions except sub-Saharan Africa. Greater food availability may result in a declining proportion of underweight children. This highlights the critical importance of investment in sustainable agricultural productivity, an issue addressed further below. Also, a positive effect in the form of a reduction in population growth would become apparent within a 25-year horizon (Rosegrant, Agcaoili-Sombilla and Perez, 1995).

3. Basing policy action on an understanding of the causes of malnutrition

CAUSES AND LINKAGES

3.1 This section outlines a broad framework of the causes of malnutrition before turning to a more specific examination of the linkages among agriculture, food security and nutrition. Poverty, including the associated vulnerability to natural or human-made shocks, is one of the root causes of hunger and malnutrition. Yet poverty and its dynamics may be seen as an endogenous outcome of limited human and natural resources and flawed policies, as discussed above. If the root causes of malnutrition such as policy failures, poverty and population growth remain unaddressed, both public programmes and private actions (e.g. household strategies) will have limited effectiveness in sustainably improving nutrition.

3.2 In the Figure, the top row represents basic causal factors: economic strategies and policy interacting with social discrimination and conflict; resource endowments and their relationship to climate and disasters influencing levels of poverty and food availability; and population growth. These factors directly affect the success of any policy and programme interventions (such as subsidies and asset distribution). The Figure is intended to highlight the primary importance of addressing the basic causes of nutritional problems because of the predominance of the downstream links. Otherwise, for instance, public actions in the areas listed in the second row of the Figure (services, transfers, etc.) can be only partial remedies.

3.3 Policies (such as wage policy) and project interventions (such as employment programmes for poverty reduction) interact at the level of capital, labour and product markets. These relationships determine the prices and terms of trade faced by the poor, and hence their real purchasing power.

3.4 Nutritional well-being is linked to labour markets and production (via productivity effects) and to population (via mortality, fertility and migration) and can be influenced by direct intervention (health, social, educational and other services, transfers and subsidies). These linkages and their development policy implications are discussed briefly below. Actual nutritional well-being is then determined by a number of interrelated factors at the micro level, as depicted at the bottom of the Figure:

- availability of food through market and other channels, which is a function of production, stockholding and trade opportunities;
- access to food, i.e. the ability of households to acquire whatever food is available, which is a function of household income (including the resource base for subsistence farming);

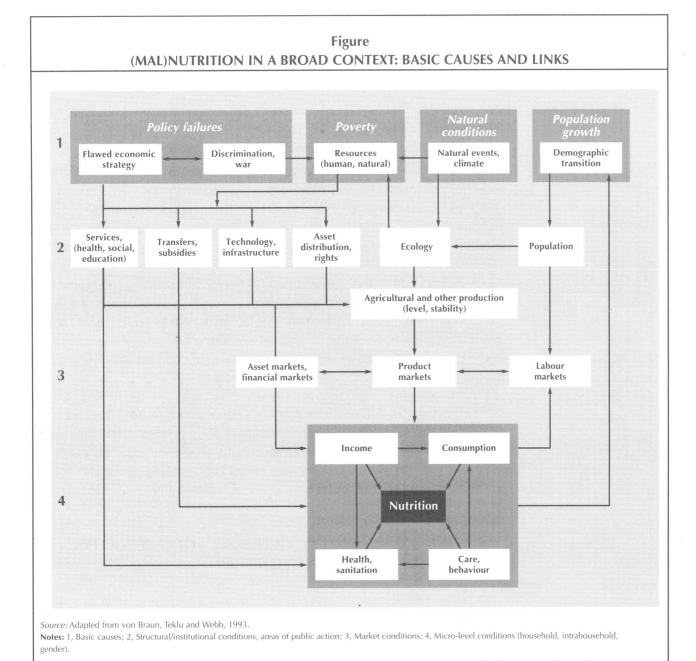

Figure
(MAL)NUTRITION IN A BROAD CONTEXT: BASIC CAUSES AND LINKS

Source: Adapted from von Braun, Teklu and Webb, 1993.
Notes: 1, Basic causes; 2, Structural/institutional conditions, areas of public action; 3, Market conditions; 4, Micro-level conditions (household, intrahousehold, gender).

- behaviour and knowledge, which under certain conditions of availability and access predispose people to buy specific foods or to grow them for home consumption, influence the preparation and distribution of food among household members (including the meeting of special feeding needs, for example of young children) and affect breast-feeding and general aspects of care;
- health status of individuals, which is governed by factors such as the health and sanitary environment at the household and community levels, behaviour and care-taking, as well as (in a circular link) by nutritional status itself (e.g. mother-child links/low birth weights).

3.5 Of the more directly food-linked factors of nutritional well-being, emphasis should be placed on the quantity and quality of the diet, its variety and composition including the availability of animal products and other micronutrient-rich and energy-dense foods, the mode of processing and preparing food, the frequency of feeding and, for infants, the extent of breast-feeding. The less directly food-linked factors include, for example, the allocation of women's time and knowledge, which may have significant nutritional effects through changes in breast-feeding, child care and health and sanitation factors.

3.6 While improving access to food, increases in household income do not always directly contribute to improving the nutritional well-being of all household members. Intrahousehold decision-making plays a role (Alderman *et al.*, 1995), as do knowledge and care. Even if patterns of household spending and consumption seem rational to the head of the household, they may not necessarily be optimal from a nutritional perspective. Nutrition is only one of a series of considerations that are taken into account in decisions regarding household spending and consumption. A lack of knowledge regarding the nutritional needs of household members may lead to the withholding of needed food, even when it is available. This problem may be aggravated by incorrect information from outside the household and the promotion of inappropriate foods. Moreover, the health and nutritional status of children are substantially affected by the quality of care (UNICEF, 1995b).

3.7 Although women have key roles as guardians of household food security and of children's nutrition and fulfil many food-related, economic and reproductive responsibilities in the household, they frequently do not have commensurate control over resources or decision-making authority. This is one of the causes of poor women's increased vulnerability to nutritional risks.

LINKAGES AMONG AGRICULTURE, FOOD SECURITY AND NUTRITION

3.8 The most obvious link between agriculture and nutrition is that agriculture (with aquaculture) provides virtually all the food consumed by humankind. A healthy diet requires diversified local production of perishable products (e.g. fresh vegetables from markets or home gardens) and regional or international availability of traded food products. Thus dietary needs are to be considered in production, technology policy and trade promotion. The focus in technology promotion must be not only on the volume of staples but also, for example, on the diverse dietary needs of the poor (e.g. the availability of pulses in regions where they are an important part of the diet). The focus here is on the less obvious linkages between agriculture and nutrition related to the nature of technology utilization in agriculture. These linkages are to be examined under two distinctly different conditions: if new agricultural technology is available, and if it is not available. The first condition focuses on water control, seed and plant nutrition and protection technology, while the second focuses on agricultural expansion in marginal areas.

3.9 In the first instance, if new agricultural technology is available, the expansion of agriculture through the utilization of appropriate technology is usually accompanied by increases in income and in spending on goods and services, also in non-agricultural sectors. The beneficial effects of agricultural growth are thus spread through the economy. It is necessary to re-emphasize these favourable consumption effects for producers and consumers in low-income countries. Creating and disseminating nutrition-enhancing agricultural technology continues to be a challenge. Actions to meet the consumption needs of today and the future are discussed in Chapter 4.

3.10 Apart from the consumption effects, however, knowledge of the nutrition and health linkages of agricultural technology is incomplete. Nutritional concerns include indirect income and employment effects on consumption (for example, when the poor are bypassed by agricultural technology) and effects of technology on health. Water-borne diseases and pesticides are predominant among the health concerns associated with the technology package that combines water control, seeds, plant nutrition and plant protection (see Table 9).

3.11 In the second instance, agricultural growth without technical improvement is possible for a limited time only through resource mining and area expansion (where excess land and labour exist). Such growth does not raise incomes and is not sustainable. It leads typically to resource degradation. Yet food-insecure households do not deliberately degrade their resource base; on the contrary, they are usually fully aware that their food security is threatened if their environment is threatened (Davies, Leach and David, 1991). Much environmental destruction such as deforestation and soil erosion can be ascribed to the struggle of the poor to feed themselves (Vosti and Scherr, 1994). It is estimated that half of Africa's poor farmers live in environments with a highly vulnerable natural-resource base. In Latin America, the figure is closer to 80 percent (Leonard, 1989). In marginal areas appropriate agricultural technology can go a long way towards stabilizing food availability and facilitating food

Table 9 **ENVIRONMENTAL AND NUTRITION AND HEALTH RISKS RELATED TO AGRICULTURAL TECHNOLOGY**		
Technology	Potential environmental degradation	Disease and nutrition risks
Irrigation	Water quality/quantity Mosquito increase Aquatic snail increase Blackfly increase	Diarrhoea, cholera, typhoid, etc. Malaria Schistosomiasis (bilharzia) Onchocercosis
Crop protection through pesticides	Contamination of soil, plants, air	Acute or chronic poisoning
Fertilizer	Leakage of excessive nitrates in drainage water	Diseases of the circulatory system in infants
Secondary effects Crowding, inadequate sanitation, diet change, vector control (following inappropriate pesticide use)		Communicable diseases, nutritional deficiencies, increased physical vulnerability, poisoning

Source: Adapted from von Braun, 1991.

Table 10 ENVIRONMENTAL, HOUSEHOLD-LEVEL AND NUTRITIONAL AND HEALTH EFFECTS OF AGRICULTURAL CHANGE			
Agricultural change/ practices	Environmental effects		Household-level effects and nutritional and health effects
	Primary	Secondary	
Excessive expansion of land-use area	Desertification	Drought	Impoverishment/productivity decline
	Deforestation	Floods	Migration-related health stress
	Watershed degradation	Climate change	Vector-borne disease (when moving into disease-prone areas)
Resource mining (e.g. soil mining, overgrazing)	Soil erosion		Communicable diseases (when sanitation breaks down)
	Soil fertility decline		Chronic food insecurity
	Loss of pasture		Seasonal malnutrition
			Famines

Source: Adapted from von Braun, 1991.

access for the poor. When agriculture expands into marginal areas or when resource mining occurs, primary and secondary environmental degradation effects may result (see Table 10).

3.12 Extensive areas in the arid zone are threatened by desertification. Traditionally, drought-prone areas on desert fringes are used mainly by pastoralists, but there are a great variety of land-use systems and system-specific environmental risks. In recent decades pastoralists have increasingly found themselves being squeezed between more extensive crop farming on the one hand and desert encroachment on the other. The nutritional vulnerability of pastoralists has increased in the process (Webb and Reardon, 1992).

3.13 Many hillside regions in low-income countries have high person/land ratios and are subsistence oriented because of limited infrastructure, lack of markets and food-security risks. Despite this, hillsides make a major contribution to tropical agriculture. Local-level linkages are closely related to the productivity of human time allocated to the production of home goods that are relevant to health and nutrition, and especially to water and fuel acquisition. A reduction in the availability of fuel or of time for cooking could result in consumption of more uncooked or reheated foods, increasing nutritional risks.

3.14 Agriculture expands into the tropical rain forest zone in a variety of ways: in the form of pasture, tree-crop cultivation, shifting cultivation or land rotation by settled farmers. Whatever the form, the expansion of agriculture into the rain forest zone can affect the health and nutrition both of the people moving in and of the (indigenous) people already living there. Malnutrition in rain forest communities is very strongly related to infectious and vector-borne diseases. Settlers who move to the Amazon, for instance, suffer disproportionately from malaria, lacking the long-term residents' immunity to the disease (Vosti and Loker, 1990).

3.15 To sum up, different types of nutritional risks affect different groups of households and their members in different ways (Table 11). The most severe nutritional problems arise when vulnerable household members are hit by negative outcomes of two or more risks simultaneously. The possible combinations are numerous. In order to improve nutrition, it is necessary to identify the specific risks involved and to develop effective means of reducing them.

Table 11
SOURCES OF PROBLEMS RELATED TO FOOD SECURITY AND NUTRITION, AND EXAMPLES OF AFFECTED POPULATIONS

Risks	Households and people at risk of food insecurity and malnutrition
Political and policy-failure risks	Households in war zones and areas of civil unrest Households in low-potential areas that are not connected to growth centres via infrastructure
Lack of employment	Wage-earning households and informal-sector employees (in urban areas and, when there is a sudden crop production failure, in rural areas)
Agricultural trade risks (disruption of exports or imports)	Smallholders who are highly specialized in an export crop Small-scale pastoralists Poor households that are highly dependent on imported food Urban poor
Food-price fluctuations (substantial, sudden price rises)	Poor, net food-purchasing households
Crop production risks (pests, drought and others)	Smallholders with little income diversification and limited access to improved technology such as improved seeds, fertilizer, irrigation and pest control Landless farm labourers
Health and sanitation problems (infectious diseases, including AIDS)	Entire communities, but especially households that cannot afford preventive or curative care and vulnerable members of these households, especially women, children and elderly people
Problems of care and social insecurity	Women, especially when they have no access to education Female-headed households Children at weaning age Elderly people

Source: Adapted from von Braun *et al.*, 1992.

4. Policies and actions needed to improve nutrition

PAST INTERNATIONAL INITIATIVES

4.1 It is the present unsatisfactory state of nutrition and the risks of the future that have prompted the call for the World Food Summit in 1996. It thus seems fair to ask how food security and nutritional well-being have been addressed in past international initiatives, and what lessons can be learned from them. This approach will make it possible to build new initiatives on past knowledge, take advantage of institutional capital for nutritional improvement and assert that past commitments regarding nutrition are being respected and renewed.

4.2 Several conferences and initiatives have emphasized the importance of eliminating hunger and malnutrition and improving food security for all people. Over the past 50 years, international initiatives have evolved into a plausible set of proposed actions. The Annex provides a brief review of the principal nutrition-related goals of various important conferences and initiatives.

4.3 While many of the earlier initiatives were concerned with hunger and malnutrition, not all of them translate the concern for improving nutritional well-being into action. Moreover, all of these initiatives attracted considerable attention when they occurred, but too often there was little connection between the stated commitments for nutritional improvement and the mechanisms for effective follow-up. Some explicit monitoring of past plans of action related to nutritional goals resulted from the World Summit for Children and the ICN. While these mechanisms can be strengthened further, it is noteworthy that there is generally a positive tendency among the concerned international organizations, notably UNICEF (1994a), FAO (1995a) and WHO (1995b), as well as among non-governmental organizations (NGOs) to adopt more concrete follow-up processes for international initiatives regarding nutrition.

4.4 Over the past five decades there have also been a number of scientific and action-oriented conferences and fora that are not listed here but that have certainly influenced the philosophy and technical focus of the main events described above. Also relevant to the poverty and nutrition issue are the international initiatives on social aspects (Social Summit, Copenhagen, Denmark, 1995) and women's rights (International Conference on Women, Beijing, China, 1995) as well as Agenda 21 of the United Nations Conference on Environment and Development (UNCED, Rio de Janeiro, Brazil, 1992).

4.5 Clearly, knowledge concerning appropriate actions for ending hunger and malnutrition has markedly increased over the past five decades. The focus has also shifted to the nutritional well-being of future generations, the food needs of a growing world population and environmentally sustainable solutions to the food problem. The importance of an appropriate policy framework and the key role of human resources and human rights in nutritional improvement are now better understood but have yet to find their way into global agendas. However, while the complexity of nutrition problems is generally acknowledged, there is need for a renewed commitment to undertake the actions on the scale required.

POLICIES AND PROGRAMMES AND THEIR IMPACT

4.6 There is not only one general set of policies that is clearly optimal for achieving the nutritional well-being of all; rather, there is a wide range of policy options from which to choose, after a set of preconditions has been fulfilled. The policies and programmes proposed below are structured along the lines of the major factors causing malnutrition, as outlined above.

4.7 In making policy choices, the following characteristics of the nutrition problem need to be considered: its prevalence and severity, its duration (short- or long-term), whether it is related to a specific deficiency or to general malnutrition, its distribution (whether it is related to a specific population group or is more widespread) and the relative importance of the various determining factors. Such information is necessary to guide policy-makers and to evaluate actions taken for which routine food and nutrition surveillance systems need to be developed. Also to be taken into account are the institutional capabilities of the countries involved and the economic, political and fiscal costs of the various policy choices.

4.8 Participants at the ICN discussed these issues under the themes "Incorporating nutrition objectives, considerations and components into development policies and programmes", "Assessing, analysing and monitoring nutrition interventions" and "Improving household food security" as part of the strategies and actions commonly agreed upon for improving nutrition. The actions discussed range from macroeconomic policies (i.e. the correction of bad policies), through various agricultural and income policies to specific nutrition-programme actions. Some of these, i.e. the appropriate macroeconomic policy framework and, in low-income countries, suitable consideration of the role of agriculture, are actually not options but preconditions for poverty-reducing development.

The key role of strategy and macroeconomic and trade policy

4.9 Long-term effects of alternative development strategies for growth and poverty reduction have shown the striking relevance of the choice of strategy. Similarly, the short-term effects on the poor of structural maladjustments in low-income countries in the 1980s have emphasized the relevance of macroeconomic policies for nutrition (Pinstrup-Andersen, 1990). Consequently, the effects of food and agricultural policies as well as non-agricultural and economy-wide policies on nutrition need to be considered.

4.10 Much can be done to reduce malnutrition through national public action, even when the national per caput income is low, as is demonstrated by the experiences of China, Sri Lanka, Costa Rica and the state of Kerala in India (Drèze and Sen, 1989), for example. The sustainability of public action depends, however, upon a growth-facilitating macroeconomic and trade environment. While public funding is warranted, it is not always necessary for nutrition-related goods and services to be provided by public agencies. There needs to be an appropriate division of responsibilities and functions among different levels of government, NGOs and the market (Streeten, 1994) as well as complementarity between market forces and national planning interventions. Cooperation between the public and private sectors should also be pursued. In order to achieve nutritional goals, these strategic considerations should be taken into account.

4.11 The regional, national or local availability of food is determined primarily by food production, stockholding and trade at any of these levels. Fluctuations in any of these parameters can contribute to food insecurity. For example, increased fluctuation in cereal production at the regional and national levels has been shown to place significant stress on food consumption. Policy can mitigate such fluctuations, but the capacity for such mitigation is a function of the concerned countries' state of development (Sahn and von Braun, 1989). At least in the short term, the current (1995/96) increases in world food prices have adverse effects on the poor in low-income food-deficit countries (LIFDCs). Storage and food-trade policies require renewed attention, given the conditions of rapidly changing international and regional trade environments. Policy-makers often feel strongly that some storage under public control is essential for food security. Production fluctuations, infrastructure, location and sectoral diversification are important determinants of a country's need for storage in order to achieve the desired stabilization of food availability and prices. Stabilization efforts need to be attuned to a country's specific production risks (for example, agricultural areas prone to droughts or floods) and trade risks (for example, a country's landlocked position) (Sarris, 1985). It is necessary to take into account the administrative and opportunity costs of the resources tied up in stabilization.[14] Benefits are expressed in terms of a more stable investment climate and reduced short-term adjustment stress on households.[15] There is, however, also evidence that supports the argument for a minimalist approach to price stabilization (Knudsen and Nash, 1990).

4.12 Fluctuations in a country's capacity to import food (which is a function of export earnings, world prices and debt service obligations, among other variables) also contribute to food insecurity. For many food-deficit and foreign-exchange-deficit countries, recourse to the international market is limited, and food aid represents an important form of access to food. Seasonal variations in production and seasonally high food prices can lead to nutritional deterioration (Sahn, 1989). This is a matter for national policy.

4.13 Global supply of and demand for food aid and its allocation among countries is driven by complex factors – not just market forces and charity, but also political factors. Although food aid has played a critical role for some countries in times of emergency, it is not a reliable source of food for LIFDCs; it has been observed that when world market prices rise, the supply of food aid from donors generally diminishes. This correlation was observed again in the

[14] For country experiences and policy proposals see, for example, the work of Ravallion (1987) on Bangladesh.

[15] The prevention of drastic price shocks is of the greatest importance. When the real prices of cereals more than tripled and cereal-livestock terms of trade increased eightfold in the Sudan in 1985, the prevalence of malnutrition among children (the proportion of children with weight for height below 80 percent of standard) rose from 5 to 20 percent in the region of Kordofan (Teklu, von Braun and Zaki, 1991).

mid-1990s, when policies in industrialized countries changed simultaneously with rising demand (e.g. in East Asia) and reduced supply (e.g. in Eastern Europe); cereal prices on international markets increased by 30 to 40 percent, and by 1995 food-aid supplies were cut to about half of their record high levels of 1992/93 (FAO, 1995b).[16]

Policies and programmes to augment agricultural production and marketing

4.14 Policies and programmes that aim to increase food and non-food agricultural production and productivity have favourable effects on nutrition if they directly or indirectly increase or stabilize the real incomes and food consumption of the people facing food insecurity. The impact of these policies and programmes is mediated through changes in food prices and incomes and is influenced by trade policies, discussed in other WFS technical background documents.[17] Boosting agricultural production stimulates overall economic growth and development, particularly in those countries that have a high economic dependence on agriculture. In such countries, agricultural and rural development acts as an engine for sustainable economic development and poverty alleviation. This does not necessarily mean that higher food self-sufficiency should be the goal; however, it is recognized that growth in food supplies has a dual effect on food security by reducing food prices, which benefits food-purchasing households in rural and urban areas, and by promoting employment.

4.15 Appropriate technological innovations in agriculture reduce the unit costs of production and marketing and induce economic gains by stimulating agricultural growth, improving employment opportunities and expanding food supplies, all of which involve and benefit poor producers and consumers and help to reduce food insecurity. The green revolution, i.e. the irrigation, seed, fertilizer and pest-control package for rice and wheat, in particular, has expanded farm and non-farm output, employment and wages, thus contributing to food security (Hazell and Ramasamy, 1991).[18] National and international agricultural organizations and research systems are the main forces driving the technological innovation required to achieve the sustainable agricultural growth that will make the needed food available to the world's growing population. Renewed actions are needed to accelerate technological innovation in many smallholder-dominated regions of the world in order to meet nutritional goals directly and indirectly.[19]

4.16 Nutritional considerations in production policies and programmes can avoid the adverse effects noted earlier and can foster nutritional well-being. Plant-breeding research can have favourable effects on diet quality, for instance when scarce micronutrients can be bred into staple crops (Bouis, 1995) or when crop storage is improved. International agricultural research also plays a key role in this respect, and sufficient funding for such research is a central priority for achieving food security and nutritional improvement. Developing and testing appropriate technologies for the diverse agro-ecologies will remain a major task for decades to come. The health and nutrition risks of technological

[16] A detailed treatment of issues related to food-aid policy may be found in WFS companion paper 13, *Food security and food assistance.*
[17] See in particular documents 7, *Food production: the critical role of water,* and 10, *Investment in agriculture: evolution and prospects.*
[18] See also WFS companion paper 6, *Lessons from the green revolution: towards a new green revolution.*
[19] In three case-studies from the Gambia, Guatemala and Rwanda, a 10 percent increase in income from a level of US$100 per caput resulted in a 3.5 to 4.9 percent increase in household food-energy consumption and a 1.1 to 2.5 percent increase in the weight-for-age ratio of children (von Braun and Kennedy, 1994). Macro-level data from a number of developing countries suggest that a doubling of per caput income from US$300 to $600 would be accompanied by an approximate 40 percent reduction in the proportion of children with substandard weight for age (von Braun and Pandya-Lorch, 1991).

change must be mitigated through appropriate technology design. There is substantial scope for agricultural, public-health and nutrition workers and researchers to collaborate on improving the design of agricultural programmes.

4.17 Marketing of agricultural crops frequently contributes to improving food security through increased income and employment generation. Gains in real income from marketing typically translate into gains in food consumption and nutritional welfare. Those affected can acquire more food; reduce their workloads and thus improve child care; and enhance their household sanitation and housing environment, thereby reducing their exposure to infectious diseases, improving water availability in terms of both quantity and quality and strengthening the effective demand for both preventive and curative health care. Furthermore, when household resources are less constrained, the household members are in a better position to utilize existing or new knowledge regarding nutritional improvement. Typically, raising incomes has a positive and significant effect on nutrition.[20]

4.18 Smallholders often strive to maintain subsistence food production along with new commercial production, despite higher returns to land and labour from cash crops. The poor are forced to adopt this strategy more than anyone else. Given their risky economic circumstances and the lack of insurance markets, maintaining their own food supplies may be a sound economic strategy. Agricultural policy can effectively support this strategy by promoting technological improvements in the production and handling of subsistence foods, for example improved processing to preserve foods, particularly those that are only seasonally available. Such policy also provides further latitude for specialization at the farm level and thereby permits smallholders to derive further gains from market integration.

4.19 The development of financial and insurance markets would be complementary and pay-offs would be ensured in terms of gains from commercialization. Research and extension policies and input supplies such as seed and fertilizer for subsistence crops are critical for a feasible commercialization strategy that meets smallholders' demands. Extension services in commercialization schemes with new crops or livestock can assist farmers in avoiding management mistakes. An explicit focus to include women would be needed, as women farmers typically participate less frequently in commercialization schemes unless special attention is given to this issue.

4.20 In some instances, however, the poor have failed to reap the benefits or have even lost from technological change or commercialization. Where these adverse effects have occurred, they are usually attributable to bad policies such as the eviction of tenants,[21] coerced production or forced procurement. Rectifying such policy failures remains important in general, but this is not an issue specifically related to the commercialization of agriculture.

4.21 While landowning households often benefit most from the direct income effects of agricultural growth, landless and small food-deficit farmers often benefit most from the indirect effects such as the generation of off-farm employment. Indirect employment effects that help the poorest households

[20] A 10 percent increase in income from a uniform income of US$100 per caput (i.e. from $100 to $110) in settings where commercialization of agriculture occurred had the effect of improving children's nutrition by between 1 and 4.9 percent (von Braun and Kennedy, 1994).
[21] For example, in an area of the Philippines where contracts for growing sugar cane were given only to landowners and not to tenants, it was observed that landlessness increased and the status of tenants around the sugar mill deteriorated (von Braun and Kennedy, 1994).

are further facilitated by infrastructural development (Ahmed and Hossain, 1990). Rural infrastructure development is a priority also from a food security and nutrition perspective, as such development is a precondition for effective rural services. Attention should also be devoted to reducing high marketing costs by improving infrastructure (as in most of sub-Saharan Africa).

Income- and employment-generation programmes for nutritional improvement

4.22 Malnutrition can be reduced not only by policies and programmes oriented towards improving the quantity and quality of agricultural production, but also by programmes for generating and diversifying employment and income and for alleviating poverty. While these programmes stimulate or stabilize the demand for food, they may not directly expand the food supply. Two such actions are highlighted here: employment programmes for food security, and credit to the poor for consumption stabilization and self-employment. Other income-generation programmes such as home gardening and the promotion of backyard livestock production may also be important.

4.23 Employment programmes for food security can simultaneously address three central problems facing many low-income countries today: food insecurity, growing unemployment and poor infrastructure (von Braun, 1995). Priority should be given to public investment that promotes development through employment programmes and thus to the creation of productive assets such as roads and improved land and water systems. Employment programmes can be a viable instrument for famine prevention, as demonstrated by the Employment Guarantee Scheme (EGS) of Maharashtra, India.[22] The employment guarantee feature of the scheme also triggers relief works at the local level when needed; that is, relief works are already in place and can be activated quickly so they do not have to be created from scratch in a crisis situation. This feature also makes it possible to address local crises that otherwise might seem too minor to trigger government action (an important lesson for dealing with the problem of localized famines in Africa). The group targeted by employment programmes, i.e. the food-insecure, is successfully reached through a variety of mechanisms and design features that include wage-rate policy, regional targeting and the specific selection of households (for example, displaced households) and of household members (for example, women). The frequent extensive participation of women in public-works programmes measurably improves nutrition. International attention should be drawn to the potential of this type of programme and the chances of sharing the experiences gained in many countries in the 1980s and 1990s.

4.24 Credit for consumption stabilization and self-employment is a mechanism of growing importance for improving nutrition in the diversifying rural economies of many low- and middle-income countries. The programmes that have been found to be most successful in generating self-employment for the poor and stabilizing their consumption are those that combine small-scale credit with group motivation, technical advice and assistance in institution-building, such as Bangladesh's Grameen Bank.[23] Experience with comparable

[22] The scheme provides an unlimited guarantee of employment to all adults in rural Maharashtra who are willing and able to work at the given wage (for a comprehensive review, see Dev, 1995).

[23] The Grameen Bank operates in 34 000 villages and currently lends to 1.7 million borrowers, 94 percent of whom are women. Accumulation of capital by the poor has increased significantly. New employment, particularly for poor women, has been generated. The rate of repayment is more than 98 percent (Yunus, 1994).

programmes in a number of countries has shown that facilitating the access of the poor to financial services can substantially contribute to the stabilization of food consumption (seasonally and over years) and thereby improve nutrition. It also improves nutrition by enhancing the access of the poor to other nutritionally relevant inputs such as health services and medication in times of need (Zeller, 1995). However, more work is needed to develop safety-net mechanisms for credit repayment, especially for poorer farmers, because crop failures caused by drought or erratic rainfall are not uncommon in some parts of Africa and as a result poorer farmers may be unable to pay back their loans and may find their food security situation even worse than before. Initiatives by the World Bank and others for internationally strengthening credit systems for the poor are worthy of international attention (Binswanger and Landell-Mills, 1995).

Food subsidies, rationing and food stamps

4.25 Food-related income transfers are a widely used means of improving nutrition. Two types of programme are considered here: food-price subsidies and rationing, and food stamps.

- Generalized food price subsidies are much more costly in terms of fiscal and economic costs than limited-access subsidies and are also more regressive in their distribution of economic benefits. Generally, programmes that provide fixed-quantity rations have been successful in reaching the population groups that they targeted. However, the experiences of Egypt, the Philippines and Sri Lanka illustrate the difficulty of achieving both universal household food security through the rationed distribution of food and targeted income-transfer goals within a single programme in a cost-effective manner (Pinstrup-Andersen, 1988; Garcia, 1988). Over time, the initial objectives have frequently been diluted as powerful interest groups, primarily the urban middle classes, have bought into the subsidy programmes for their own benefit.

- A combination of targeting methods can be used. Means tests can be used in limited-access programmes. Self-targeting can be achieved to some extent by using commodities that are considered inferior in terms of consumer preference and thus are more abundant in the expenditure patterns of the poorer populations. Geographical targeting can be employed by directing systems at food-deficit areas with poor populations (including urban neighbourhoods). While costs are lower than for generalized price-subsidy schemes, limited-access programmes often develop problems with leakage and corruption which require close supervision and management.

- Food stamp programmes are increasingly being used as a vehicle for providing income to poor households. Food stamp programmes are expected to retain the higher food-consumption effects of food-based income transfers and to reduce the administrative burden and costs imposed by food handling and transport. Experience with food stamp programmes is mixed; they have not been easy to administer. Providing the needed infrastructure for them has proved feasible when government considers the usual market incentives for traders. Still, even the largest experience with food stamps in a high-income country, the programme of the United States, still misses a large proportion of eligible households (Davis and Senauer, 1986). In order to be cost effective, food stamp programmes should be directed to those in need. While a general call for targeted food stamps for the very poor would not seem appropriate, attention should be drawn to the potential of these programmes under well-defined conditions.

4.26 An economically appropriate assessment of public food-distribution systems cannot just be performed on the basis of costs and benefits as observed in normal years. In countries and regions that are frequently subject to serious food shortages, a public distribution system in place helps to move emergency supplies into regions and to households in need in order to improve the food security of the poorest groups. The availability of such food-distribution programmes is credited with maintaining food security and nutrition levels for the very poorest during droughts in India (Drèze, 1988). A system of this kind cannot easily be remobilized once it has been dismantled. A cost-effective but organizationally more demanding alternative is a system of employment programmes and direct nutrition actions as discussed below.

Direct nutrition actions

4.27 Direct nutrition actions aimed at addressing immediate nutrition problems work best when they actively involve those who are directly affected. Such actions are directed at redressing problems associated with access to food (e.g. through supplementary or targeted feeding programmes), at combating specific nutrient deficiencies (e.g. micronutrient programmes), at providing knowledge about nutrition and behaviour, at overcoming detrimental nutrition-health linkages (e.g. health and sanitation programmes) or combinations of these (e.g. integrated nutrition programmes). Considerable progress has been achieved in the effectiveness of direct nutrition actions in the past decade. The scope for further strengthening the best practices of such programmes and their potential for achieving rapid nutritional improvement should be underlined.

Targeted supplementary feeding programmes

4.28 Targeted supplementary feeding programmes are generally aimed at those especially vulnerable to malnutrition, usually children and women of child-bearing age at low income levels. The targeting of feeding and food-distribution programmes is achieved in a variety of ways. Means tests and vulnerability tests are also used.[24] Politically and socially, feeding programmes are often more acceptable than other targeted income-transfer programmes. The experience of such programmes with regard to nutritional improvement, however, is mixed.

4.29 School feeding programmes target schooling (participation) as well as nutrition problems of school-age children. Many countries operate such programmes effectively and combine them with nutrition education and school gardening. In low-income countries where school enrolment does not include the entire population of school-age children, school feeding may miss the most needy.

[24] A means test is usually difficult to administer and often relies on community-level identification of recipients. Vulnerability tests are based on health or nutrition indicators and have been used to educate parents about the benefits of improving the dietary intakes of children and women.

The Food for Education Programme in Bangladesh has shown that such programmes can be highly effective in terms of increasing school enrolment, promoting school attendance and reducing dropout rates, thus contributing to long-term nutritional effects through education, and can at the same time be a very cost-effective mechanism for food-based, targeted transfers (Ahmed and Billah, 1994).

Micronutrient programmes

4.30 Considerable and successful actions have been taken in the past decade in the area of overcoming micronutrient deficiencies. Coordinated international action has made a difference in this field. Still, increased efforts are necessary to overcome micronutrient deficiencies and their detrimental effects. A combination of actions need to be adopted concerning the availability of micronutrient-rich foods, the promotion of adequate food processing and preservation techniques, education related to food and nutrition, dietary diversification through production and consumption of micronutrient-rich foods, legislation and implementation of food fortification and supplementation and appropriate public-health measures (FAO/WHO, 1992a). While it may appear convincing that for vitamin A deficiency, for instance, the short-term intervention is fortification and the long-term intervention is dietary improvement, the actual choices and their timing are very much dependent on population circumstances and organizational capacities as well as on the characteristics of the food economy. A widespread, successful global initiative has been implemented for reduction of iodine deficiency through salt iodization.

4.31 In the area of micronutrients, specific targets have been set by a variety of fora. In order to achieve these goals, the focus should be on the following issues. First, policy advocacy, social marketing and commercial advertising should be implemented to increase the consumer demand for micronutrient-rich and fortified foods. In the area of fortification of foods, more incentives should be given to private industry to maximize compliance. Building relevant regulatory enforcement institutions is part of the measure. The effectiveness and coverage of pharmaceutical delivery systems should be improved in cooperation with industry. Finally, it is necessary to design and manage decentralized, sustainable programmes while enhancing institutional capacity and human resources. These efforts should be monitored on the basis of management information (World Bank, 1994).

Promoting healthy diets and lifestyles through education

4.32 Promoting better eating habits and positive health behaviour is one of the most challenging tasks in overall efforts to improve nutrition. In addition to access to a variety of safe and affordable foods, people need accurate information as to what constitutes a healthy diet and how to meet their nutritional needs. Besides education, strategies to promote healthy diets must include providing motivation and creating opportunities for people to change their behaviour while recognizing individual preferences, lifestyles and time constraints (FAO/WHO, 1992d).

4.33 Dietary guidelines have been issued by governments and private organizations in some countries. In addition, scientific bodies have established recommended dietary allowances for the population. Traditionally, recommended dietary allowances have been designed to help educate populations about good dietary practices and have focused on safe and adequate intakes to avoid deficiencies and to cover the needs of nearly all individuals in the population. These allowances have been used widely in planning and procuring food supplies for population subgroups, in establishing standards for feeding programmes and as the basis for nutrition labelling. More recently, governments and private organizations have issued dietary guidelines reflecting growing concern about prevention of diet-related non-communicable diseases. Dietary guidelines for the public provide advice, appropriate to the country's population, about how to select a balanced diet and encourage related lifestyle behaviours to promote health, including breast-feeding. Dietary guidelines are most useful if they serve as the basis of and provide the guiding principles for all widely disseminated nutrition education messages given to the public.

4.34 Food and nutrition labelling can assist the public in selecting a healthy diet. Nutrient content information provided on food labels supports the implementation of dietary guidelines. The FAO/WHO Codex Alimentarius Commission has developed, for consideration by governments, guidelines on nutrition labelling which apply to all pre-packaged foods and foods for catering purposes. The role of the food industry in promoting healthy diets lies mainly in the development and marketing of a variety of safe and good-quality foods that can contribute to a healthy diet (FAO/WHO, 1992f).

4.35 The promotion of breast-feeding and improved weaning practices are of primary importance. Food and nutrition education is among the actions needed to achieve this. Food and nutrition education is not just about imparting information but also about changing behaviour (Berg, 1987). In some settings households seem adequately nourished but individuals are not. In such settings, malnutrition may be caused by the misallocation of food in the household, inappropriate breast-feeding practices, inappropriate foods for children, insufficient feeding frequencies, diarrhoea or other health-related causes and child-care practices, many of which can be changed through behavioural change. The ICN's Plan of Action for Nutrition (FAO/WHO, 1992a) called for implementation of community-based nutrition education programmes. Such actions have since been shown to have potentially extensive impact and to be cost effective.[25] FAO activities for nutrition education at all levels include using the mass media, primary and secondary schools, community participation programmes and higher-level education and training. The initiative *Get the best from your food* (FAO, 1994b) is part of that effort. The limitations of nutrition education must remain in perspective as well, however. Many desirable behavioural changes require resources (including time) from households for appropriate response. Nutrition education may thus be most effective in combination with other poverty-reducing and nutrition-enhancing

[25] A World Bank-assisted project to improve breast-feeding practices in Indonesia and related efforts to encourage mothers to add green leaves to a common rice-based porridge led to a significant improvement in the nutritional status of 40 percent of the children in the project by the time they were two years old. The annual cost per participant was about US$4 in the start-up phase and was estimated at US$2 for subsequent expansion (Berg, 1993).

actions. Increased attention to the nutrition of young children is also an element of the WHO/UNICEF Baby-Friendly Hospital Initiative, involving over 4 000 hospitals worldwide.

Protecting consumers through improved food quality and safety

4.36 A safe food and water supply of adequate quality is essential for proper nutrition. The food supply must have an appropriate nutrient content and it must be available in sufficient variety and quantity. It must not endanger consumer health through chemical, biological and other contaminants and it must be presented honestly. Food safety and quality control measures ensure that the desirable characteristics of food are retained throughout the production, handling, processing, packaging, distribution and preparation stages. These measures promote healthy diets, reduce food losses and encourage domestic and international food trade. Food quality encompasses the basic composition of foods and aspects concerning food safety. Consumers have the right to a good-quality and safe food supply, and government and food industry actions are needed to ensure this. Effective food quality and safety control programmes are essential and may comprise a variety of measures such as laws, regulations and standards, together with systems for effective inspection and compliance monitoring including laboratory analysis.

Nutritional health and integrated nutrition programmes

4.37 Since nutrition is a multifaceted problem, it seems logical to design policies and programmes in a similarly multifaceted way in order to achieve effective nutritional improvement. One of the most effective methods of identifying and targeting nutrition and health interventions is to monitor children's growth. The ICN in 1992 called on governments to develop and strengthen growth monitoring and promotion and nutrition surveillance within primary health care systems. While such monitoring alone does not necessarily change nutritional status, it does provide important information to be used in actions such as food supplementation, nutrition education and medical referral, when needed (UNICEF, 1994a; Miller Del Rosso, 1992). The Tamil Nadu Integrated Nutrition Project, for instance, couples universal growth monitoring of young children and nutrition counselling for their mothers with targeted interventions (on-site feeding, health checks and services) for children found to be nutritionally at risk.[26]

4.38 In the 1980s, Thailand managed to reduce the incidence of malnutrition dramatically (from 15 percent to less than 1 percent for moderate to severe malnutrition) through application of an integrated approach to meeting minimum basic needs (Tontisirin, 1994). Essential among the factors that produced this success were political commitment, health personnel development and concrete steps taken towards creating intersectoral collaboration and planning: nutrition was integrated into social and health development efforts, and programmes were designed to improve people's lives by involving community members as agents of change, not simply receivers of government services. Certainly, the success in Thailand was also facilitated

[26] The Tamil Nadu project trains and supervises community nutrition workers, who are local mothers with healthy children and are thus credible among their peers, and includes systematic monitoring and evaluation. By 1992 this project had reached 2 million women and children from the age of 6 to 36 months in 20 000 villages and managed to reduce the incidence of severe malnutrition by 55 percent at a cost of about US$11 per child (Miller Del Rosso, 1992).

by a favourable economic environment, but eliminating the nutrition problem was also seen as a prerequisite for development. The lessons learned from this and other successful integrated approaches to nutritional improvement suggest that narrow sectoral approaches that focus exclusively on health, agriculture or education cannot tackle the nutrition problem effectively. Other lessons include emphasis on working with local governments, which can best assess and adapt to local priorities; and integrated planning and staff training, with sectoral implementation.

Emergency prevention and relief

4.39 National and international resources for the above-mentioned actions for sustainable food security and nutritional improvement are increasingly squeezed by emergencies. Food emergencies are often an indication of a lack of preparedness and political commitment. The basic concept of preparedness entails public commitment to intervene effectively and on time; to build institutional capacity at international, national, regional and local levels; to detect and diagnose early indicators of distress; to prepare programmes and projects on a continuous basis; and to execute development and relief undertakings in times of need. The current operation of effective international early warning systems, such as those being used by FAO, the Permanent Interstate Committee for Drought Control in the Sahel (CILSS) and the United States Agency for International Development (USAID), represents a significant advance over the situation that existed in the 1970s.

4.40 Emergency preparedness at the national level applies mainly to natural and economic emergencies, while for armed conflicts prevention needs to occur at the international level. The stockholding, trade-policy actions and food-aid utilization (including relief employment programmes) discussed above are an integral part of preparedness and response to emergencies. For effective response, emergency relief requires food, capital and institutional capacity. NGOs often play a key role in overcoming institutional deficiencies, be it by setting up parallel structures of emergency operations in the context of governmental failures, or as an integral part of existing public organizations.

4.41 Successful relief management entails the establishment by the government of a system equipped with executive powers to take appropriate action in food handling and distribution (including emergency food aid from donors) with a network extending to the regional, provincial and local levels. Also important is well-structured relief legislation that incorporates the basic policies to which central and local governments are committed. All activities with short-term household food security effects, such as targeted feeding programmes, national food distribution, expanded food imports through trade and food aid, expanded employment programmes and household access to credit, may be elements of the relief action. Narrow targeting of relief has proved difficult in emergency situations (Buchanan-Smith, 1990). If ineffectively addressed, food emergencies typically result in health emergencies and nutritional deterioration (Drèze and Sen, 1989; Webb and von Braun, 1994).

COST CONSIDERATIONS

4.42 Malnutrition cannot be overcome without substantial national fiscal costs. Failure to overcome these problems, however, represents economic costs of much greater magnitude. In economic terms, the malnutrition problem is clearly the largest worldwide waste of potential economic resources – the lives of millions of potentially productive people, a loss now and over the coming decades – and is probably the biggest failure of market functioning yet to be resolved. Any consideration of the costs must therefore also take into account the benefits that would be forfeited through non-action. Focusing on (fiscal) spending and ignoring the resultant benefits yields a misleading picture.

4.43 A guiding principle in considering the cost aspects of improving nutrition is to achieve set nutritional goals fast, yet in a sustained way, with a portfolio of the least costly policy instruments. Following such cost-effective principles should lead to the use of optimal combinations of measures, rather than to the perfection of a single policy instrument and overreliance on short-term interventions. Integrated approaches have proved particularly cost effective in the context of a conducive growth-oriented macroeconomic framework. The success of such an approach depends to a great extent on public investment in capacity for research and organization related to food and nutrition policy and programmes.

PRIORITIES AND APPROACHES FOR NUTRITION POLICY ACTIONS

4.44 The complex task of setting priorities is not merely a matter of deciding what is of greater importance, but also of determining how to pursue goals under existing constraints. The constraints themselves and the means of overcoming or circumventing them are, of course, issues for coordinated international and national action as well. In resolving the question of "how", high priority must be given to the strengthening of operational and organizational capacities in government and of participation by and in communities.

Setting targets and planning follow-up

4.45 Practical understanding of the causes of food security risks and nutritional problems among the poor and of instruments for dealing with them is now good enough to make it possible to set ambitious and specific targets for improving household food security and nutrition in the 1990s and beyond. It may be appropriate to revisit, to review or perhaps even to re-adopt goals set by relevant previous international fora. These include especially the goals for the year 2000 set by the World Summit for Children in 1990 and by the ICN in 1992.

4.46 Underwriting ambitious targets requires political commitments and resources at national and international levels. Sustained improvement in food security and nutrition cannot be achieved with a few inexpensive interventions. A comprehensive, credible (i.e. independent) follow-up process to the World Food Summit may be a factor in enhancing the realization of the commitments made. In this context, it is necessary to consider continuing the ongoing monitoring of follow-up activities to meet the goals set in the plans of action of those initiatives mentioned in Paragraph 4.45.

4.47 The dimensions, causes and consequences of malnutrition differ from country to country, and even within the same country. In every country concerned, strengthening the capacities for diagnosis of the food security and nutrition problem is not only part of the solution, but actually a precondition for effective action. In the case of small countries, it may be advantageous to enter into regional cooperation to secure these capacities.

Combining short- and long-term nutrition actions

4.48 The typical problem of chronic and transitory food security combined with nutrition problems in poor households requires a well-designed portfolio of food security and nutrition policy actions. Such a portfolio should be based on problem assessments (i.e. assessments of the nature of nutrition problems and future risks) and on the instruments available, which are influenced by institutional capacities. In designing new programmes, it is advisable to build on the past experiences of other countries. To achieve optimal impact, it is usually necessary to pay attention to complementary actions in conjunction with nutrition policies and programmes. Such complementary actions include the development of an adequate market infrastructure and policies that do not impede trade. Often, however, the policy reforms needed involve changes in organization and privatization and new legal procedures, all of which take time. The time dimensions of optional actions vary, however.

4.49 As described earlier, food security risks and nutritional risks can originate from different sources, and the effectiveness of actions in dealing with these risks over the short and long term may vary. For example, a programme that raises yields of food crops may not have much effect on household food security over the short term, whereas a short-term feeding scheme, considered by itself, may not have much effect over the long term. Table 12 links food security and nutritional risks with policies and programmes as discussed in the preceding sections and highlights how much time is required for the latter to have an impact.

Priority areas for attention

4.50 From the outset, efforts to improve nutrition must take into account the reinforcing, detrimental linkages among food insecurity, disease, poor sanitation, inadequate education, lack of care and undernutrition. Otherwise, progress made with specific agricultural or health measures alone will have only a limited effect on nutritional improvement. The following are priority areas for attention.

Breaking the malnutrition-mortality cycle

4.51 The major problem of hunger in a broad sense, that is poor people's dietary deficiencies of both macro- and micronutrients in rural and urban areas, requires the undivided attention of national policy-makers and the global community. Addressing the large-scale, moderate nutrition problem is important in this context because it has a strong bearing on infant and child mortality (Pelletier *et al.*, 1995). Participatory monitoring of nutrition problems at the community level is a precondition for targeted action to achieve this goal. The successes of well-practised and administered nutrition programmes can be replicated more rapidly. Policies and programmes need to be selected in accordance with the circumstances of the countries involved and the specific nature of the problem. For example, consideration should be given to targeted subsidies, feeding programmes (including programmes in schools) and micronutrient actions (diet improvement, fortification and supplementation) (Table 12).

Human-resource development and population

4.52 Protection and promotion of human resources (education, especially for women, and including literacy and health education) are intrinsic to

---

Table 12
FOOD SECURITY AND NUTRITIONAL RISKS AND POLICIES WITH SHORT- AND LONG-TERM IMPACT

Policies and actions	Crop production risks	Availability and price risks	Employment and income risks	Health and sanitation risks
Macro-level policies		ss, III	s, III	II
Trade, stocks and food-aid policies		sss, I	ss, II	s
Agricultural production policies				
Technological change	III	III	III	I
Commercialization, diversification	II	III	III	
Other income- and employment-generation policies				
Employment programmes	I	ss, I	sss, III	
Credit and savings systems		ss, III	ss, II	ss, II
Promotion of behavioural change; nutrition education				s, III
Health and sanitation policies				ss, III
Subsidies and transfer policies				
Feeding programmes		sss	sss	sss, II
Food stamps, including transfers		ss	sss	s, I
Food price subsidies; rationing		sss	ss	s, I

Source: Adapted from von Braun *et al.*, 1992.
Note: The extent of positive effects is represented as follows: I, II, III = some, moderate, high long-term impact; s, ss, sss = some, moderate, high short-term impact.

nutritional improvement. In this context, reducing population growth to achieve a rapid transition to a stabilized population through appropriate social, health and education policies must figure prominently as a long-term priority. Nutritional improvement can contribute to this objective and is not merely dependent on a solution to the population-growth problem. An improvement in nutrition brought about through public action today will yield long-term benefits as the poor are relieved of the pressure to achieve food security privately through large families with replacement and insurance births.

Employment-intensive growth for food security through agriculture and works programmes

4.53 Renewed acceleration of employment-intensive and widely shared growth remains a prerequisite for household food security. High rates of population growth, increasingly limited land resources and the dependence of a large proportion of the rural food-insecure on agricultural employment and income require agricultural technology and undistorted incentives for agriculture as cornerstones for this response. In addition, however, large-scale employment programmes attracting the poor can be suggested for many rural areas of low- and middle-income countries.

Promotion of nutrition-friendly agriculture and food technology

4.54 Effective national and international agricultural research systems are a precondition for taking nutritional considerations into account in research and can also be seen as a global insurance mechanism for a food-secure future. Research, extension and information for appropriate food technology (e.g. in processing or in manufacture of weaning foods) require new forms of cooperation between public and private actors, as the opportunities provided by biotechnology are growing in the private sector. Governments can facilitate such cooperation.

Facilitation of community and household self-help for nutritional well-being

4.55 Households, and women and mothers in particular, in all usual instances, have the desire and often also the knowledge to improve the nutrition of vulnerable household members. Success is impeded by the lack of resources, including the lack of a voice in relevant community decisions. Empowerment of the vulnerable and their most likely agents is therefore needed in nutrition actions. Such empowerment can be fostered directly and indirectly through the assignment of resources and leadership tasks to women in community-based nutrition programmes, or through guidance and assistance in group formation, combined with the targeted transfer of knowledge to groups.

4.56 Public action involves not only governmental initiatives for delivering resources to target populations, but active participation by the public, both as individuals and through NGOs. Public participation can have positive and powerful roles in both collaborative and adversarial activities influencing government policies. Collaboration is essential in public-health campaigns, such as nutrition education, and in the participatory assessment of nutrition problems at the community level which require cooperative efforts to ensure success (Pinstrup-Andersen, Pelletier and Alderman, 1995). On the other hand, it is often the adversarial role of the public that brings problems to the government's attention and demands their resolution. The demand for action through political activism, journalistic pressure and informed criticism can help to identify the risk of persistent hunger. It is not merely a coincidence that the countries that have been successful in preventing famine are those with more pluralistic politics and open channels of communication and criticism (Drèze and Sen, 1989). The absence of political opposition and free speech have contributed greatly to malnutrition in Africa and elsewhere.

4.57 Among resource control aspects, access to even small amounts of land (e.g. garden plots for women) has remained an important component of household food security in many low- and middle-income countries and increasingly also in several transitional economies in Eastern Europe and Central Asia. It is necessary to give renewed consideration to land-reform issues and their relation to household food security. Advocacy of widespread access to garden plots (also in peri-urban areas) and appropriate agricultural services for this subsector can be suggested at least over the medium term for many countries facing problems of employment and credit-market development.

Famine prevention

4.58 The acute problem of famine prevention in the remaining famine-prone countries, where famine is typically caused or accelerated by armed conflict, needs to be addressed at the international level, as efforts at the country level continue to fail. Famines resulting from armed conflict are a matter to be considered at the highest political level and should also be made a subject of continuous diplomatic efforts. Moreover, there should be general acknowledgement of the successes achieved in famine prevention in many countries since the 1960s and 1970s, such as in the Sahel, parts of southern Africa (e.g. Botswana, Zimbabwe) and India, and their sustained support should be emphasized. Mechanisms with decision authority for international action to prevent famines caused by armed conflict and famines as instruments of war merit consideration. The consequences of events in Somalia, Rwanda, Sierra Leone and the Sudan in the 1990s are yet to be grasped.

Building organizational capacity

4.59 Only if the urgency and significance of the food-security and nutrition situation is readily apparent will appropriate action be taken and the international support for such action sustained. The availability of organizational capacity is a prerequisite for monitoring changes in the nutrition situation, for evaluating the effects of nutrition policies and programmes and for adjusting such policies and programmes to suit changing circumstances. The "learning by doing" approach, so effectively employed in some countries, is to be considered a viable alternative to complete planning prior to action.

4.60 It is imperative that governmental organizations, particularly ministries, as well as all non-governmental interests involved in nutritional improvement activities be well coordinated at the national level. Such coordination can be stimulated by international organizations, but it often lacks a well-established framework. It is necessary to develop national strategies involving all food and agricultural interests in order to ensure that actions aimed at food security and nutritional improvement are sustained and consistent. Progress in implementing the strategy will be enhanced when all nutrition improvement efforts are coordinated by a problem-oriented, lean management structure that recognizes that improving and maintaining adequate nutrition for all people at all times strongly depends upon the relevant actors in the non-governmental arena, and especially upon food producers.

4.61 Organizational capacity is important for facilitating the effective implementation of nutrition policies and programmes. Many programmes fail at this critical step because of faulty operational design, lack of capacity or lack of supervision. Attracting effective management to the tasks of improving nutrition is of prime importance.

Building alliances and changing attitudes

4.62 The problem of malnutrition may be viewed as an issue of human rights, an issue of humanitarian necessity or an issue of overcoming the main obstacle to development. There is now ample evidence that progress towards improving nutrition is good economic and social policy. The pay-offs are short-term and long-term, even intergenerational, as nutritional well-being leads to a sustainable increase in the productivity of societies. By stressing these basic facts, the World Food Summit offers opportunities to broaden and strengthen societal alliances (governmental and non-governmental) for food security and nutritional improvement within countries and internationally.[27]

4.63 Appeals to political will have very limited impact. Changing attitudes to the nutrition problem at a higher level of decision-making, so that it will no longer be considered a sad welfare issue but one of rights and of a precondition to human and economic development, may be more relevant than short-lived resource commitments to specific programmes. This requires instruments: a transparent and respected global nutrition monitoring system for measuring national progress in achieving nutritional well-being (e.g. reduction in the proportion and number of the undernourished and other relevant indicators) would be instrumental in creating the proper political incentives for implementing the actions outlined above. An increasingly well-informed national public and international support would respond to such information and make national approval and international support increasingly contingent upon progress towards achieving nutritional well-being. The follow-up to previous international initiatives, the World Summit for Children and the ICN, has gone in the right direction, and this approach should be reinforced.

[27] Fruitful attempts towards achieving this objective have included non-governmental initiatives such as the Overcoming Hunger in the 1990s initiative with its Bellagio Declaration of 1989 and associated follow-up.

Bibliography

Ahmed, A.U. & Billah, K. 1994. *Food for education program in Bangladesh: an early assessment.* Washington, DC, USA, International Food Policy Research Institute (IFPRI) and Dhaka, Bangladesh, Bangladesh Food Policy Project.

Ahmed, R. & Hossain, M. 1990. *Developmental impact of rural infrastructure in Bangladesh.* Research Report No. 83. Washington, DC, USA, International Food Policy Research Institute (IFPRI).

Alderman, H., Chiappori, P.-A., Haddad, L., Hoddinott, J. & Kanbur, R. 1995. Unitary versus collective models of the household: is it time to shift the burden of proof? *World Bank Res. Observ.,* 10(1): 1-19.

Berg, A. 1987. *Malnutrition: what can be done? Lessons from World Bank experience.* Baltimore, MD, USA, and London, UK, Johns Hopkins University Press, for the World Bank.

Berg, A. 1993. More resources for nutrition education: strengthening the case. *J. Nutr. Ed.,* 25(5): 278-282.

Binswanger, H.P. & Landell-Mills, P. 1995. *The World Bank's strategy for reducing poverty and hunger.* Environmentally Sustainable Development Studies and Monographs Series No. 4. Washington, DC, USA, World Bank.

Bongaarts, J. 1995. Global and regional population projections to 2025. *In* N. Islam, ed. *Population and food in the early twenty-first century: meeting future food demand of an increasing population,* p. 7-16. Washington, DC, USA, IFPRI. (Mimeograph)

Bouis, H.E. 1991. *The determinants of household-level demand for micronutrients: an analysis for Philippine farm households.* Washington, DC, USA, IFPRI.

Bouis, H.E. 1995. Breeding for nutrition. *Fed. Am. Sci. Public Interest Rep.,* 48(4): 1-16.

Broca, S. & Oram, P. 1991. *Study on the location of the poor.* Washington, DC, USA, IFPRI. (Mimeograph)

Buchanan-Smith, M. 1990. *Food security planning in the wake of an emergency relief operation: the case of Darfur, Western Sudan.* Institute of Development Studies Discussion Paper No. 278. Brighton, UK, University of Sussex.

Chen, R.S. 1992. Hunger among refugees and other people displaced across borders. In *Hunger 1993: uprooted people.* Washington, DC, USA, Bread for the World Institute on Hunger and Development.

Csete, J. & Maxwell, D. 1995. *Household food security: the challenge to UNICEF programmes.* New York, NY, USA, United Nations Children's Fund (UNICEF). (Mimeograph)

Davies, S., Leach, M. & David, R. 1991. *Food security and the environment: conflict or complementarity?* Institute of Development Studies Discussion Paper No. 285. Brighton, UK, University of Sussex.

Davis, C.G. & Senauer, B. 1986. Needed directions in domestic food assistance policies and programs. *Am. J. Agric. Econ.,* 68(5): 1253-1257.

de Onís, M., Monteiro, C., Akré, J. & Clugston, G. 1993. The worldwide magnitude of protein-energy malnutrition: an overview from the WHO Global Database on Child Growth. *WHO Bull.,* 71(6): 703-712.

Dev, S.M. 1995. India's (Maharashtra) Employment Guarantee Scheme: lessons from long experience. *In* J. von Braun, ed. *Employment for poverty reduction and food security,* p. 108-143. Washington, DC, USA, IFPRI.

Drèze, J. 1988. *Famine prevention in India.* Development Economics Research Programme Paper No. 3. London, UK, London School of Economics.

Drèze, J. & Sen, A. 1989. *Hunger and public action.* Oxford, UK, Clarendon Press.

FAO. 1993. *Progress report on the development of a household food security index.* Committee on World Food Security (CFS), 18th session, 29 March - 1 April 1993. CFS 93/2 Sup. 2. Rome.

FAO. 1994a. *Body mass index: a measure of chronic energy deficiency in adults.* Rome.

FAO. 1994b. *Get the best from your food.* Rome.

FAO. 1995a. *Report of 108th session of the Council of FAO,* June 1995. Rome.

FAO. 1995b. *Food outlook.* September 1995. Rome.

FAO. 1995c. *World agriculture: towards 2010.* N. Alexandratos, ed. Rome, FAO, and Chichester, UK, John Wiley and Sons.

FAO. 1996. *The sixth world food survey.* Rome.

FAO/World Health Organization (WHO). 1992a. *World Declaration and Plan of Action for Nutrition,* International Conference on Nutrition. Rome.

FAO/WHO. 1992b. Improving household food security. Theme Paper No. 1. In *Major issues for nutrition strategies,* International Conference on Nutrition. Rome.

FAO/WHO. 1992c. Protecting consumers through improved food quality and safety. Theme Paper No. 2. In *Major issues for nutrition strategies,* International Conference on Nutrition. Rome.

FAO/WHO. 1992d. Promoting appropriate diets and healthy lifestyles. Theme Paper No. 5. In *Major issues for nutrition strategies,* International Conference on Nutrition. Rome.

FAO/WHO. 1992e. Assessing, analysing and monitoring nutrition situations. Theme Paper No. 7. In *Major issues for nutrition strategies,* International Conference on Nutrition. Rome.

FAO/WHO. 1992f. *Nutrition and development – a global assessment,* International Conference on Nutrition. Rome.

Feichtinger, E. 1995. Armut, Gesundheit, Ernährung: eine Bestandsaufnahme. *Ernähr. Umsch.,* 42(5): 162-169.

Fogel, R.W. 1994. Economic growth, population theory, and physiology: the bearing of long-term processes on the making of economic policy. *Am. Econ. Rev.,* 84(3): 369-395.

Garcia, M. 1988. Food subsidies in the Philippines: preliminary results. *In* P. Pinstrup-Andersen, ed. *Food subsidies in developing countries: costs, benefits and policy options,* p. 206-218. Baltimore, MD, USA and London, UK, Johns Hopkins University Press, for IFPRI.

Garcia, M. 1994. *Malnutrition and food insecurity projections, 2020.* 2020 Brief No. 6. Washington, DC, USA, IFPRI.

Garcia, M., Sharma, M., Qureshi, A. & Brown, L. 1995. *Overcoming malnutrition: is there an ecoregional dimension?* Draft discussion paper. Washington, DC, USA, IFPRI. (Mimeograph)

Haddad, L.J., Kennedy, E. & Sullivan, J. 1994. Choice of indicators for food security and nutrition monitoring in Africa. *Food Policy,* 19(3): 329-343.

Haddad, L.J., Sullivan, J. & Kennedy, E. 1991. *Identification and evaluation of alternative indicators of food and nutrition security: some conceptual issues and an analysis of extant data.* Washington, DC, USA, IFPRI. (Mimeograph)

Hazell, P.B.R. & Ramasamy, C. 1991. *The green revolution reconsidered. The impact of high-yielding rice varieties in South India.* Baltimore, MD, USA and London, UK, Johns Hopkins University Press, for IFPRI.

International Food Policy Research Institute (IFPRI). 1995. *A 2020 vision for food, agriculture and the environment.* Washington, DC, USA.

Knudsen, O. & Nash, J. 1990. Domestic price stabilization schemes in developing countries. *Econ. Dev. Cult. Change,* 38(3): 539-558.

Kohlmeier, L.A.K., Plötzsch, J., Kohlmeier, M. & Martin, K. 1993. *Ernährungsabhängige Krankheiten und ihre Kosten.* Schriftenreihe des Bundesministeriums für Gesundheit No. 27. Baden-Baden, Germany, Nomos-Verlagsgesellschaft.

Leonard, H.J., ed. 1989. *Environment and the poor: development strategies for a common agenda.* US-Third World Policy Perspectives 11. New Brunswick, NJ, USA, Transaction Books.

Mannar, M.G.V. & Dunn, J.T. 1995. *Salt iodization for the elimination of iodine deficiency.* International Council for Control of Iodine Deficiency Disorders (ICCIDD), Micronutrient Initiative (MI), United Nations Children's Fund (UNICEF) and World Health Organization (WHO).

Martorell, R., Rivera, J., Kaplowitz, H. & Pollitt, E. 1991. *Long-term consequences of growth retardation during early childhood.* Paper presented at the 6th International Congress of Auxology, Madrid, Spain, 15-19 September.

Mason, J., Jonsson, U. & Csete, J. 1995. *Is malnutrition being overcome?* Paper prepared for the World Bank Hunger Programme meeting Overcoming Hunger in the 1990s, Salaya, Thailand, 6-11 November 1994.

Maxwell, S. & Frankenberger, T. 1992. *Household food security: concepts, indicators, measurements – a technical review.* New York, NY, USA, United Nations Children's Fund (UNICEF) and Rome, International Fund for Agricultural Development (IFAD).

Miller Del Rosso, J. 1992. *Investing in nutrition with World Bank assistance.* Washington, DC, USA, World Bank.

Mroz, T.A. & Popkin, B.M. 1995. Poverty and the economic transition in the Russian Federation. *Econ. Dev. Cult. Change,* 44(1): 1-31.

Pelletier, D.L., Frongillo, E.A., Schroeder, D.G. & Habicht, J.-P. 1995. The effects of malnutrition on child mortality in developing countries. *WHO Bull.,* 73(4): 443-448.

Pinstrup-Andersen, P. 1988. The social and economic effects of consumer-oriented food subsidies: a summary of current evidence. *In* P. Pinstrup-Andersen, ed. *Food subsidies in developing countries: costs, benefits and policy options,* p. 3-18. Baltimore, MD, USA and London, UK, Johns Hopkins University Press, for the International Food Policy Research Institute (IFPRI).

Pinstrup-Andersen, P., ed. 1990. *Macroeconomic policy reforms, poverty, and nutrition: analytical methodologies.* Cornell Food and Nutrition Policy Program Monograph No. 3. Ithaca, NY, USA, Cornell Food and Nutrition Policy Program.

Pinstrup-Andersen, P. 1994. *World food trends and future food security.* Food Policy Report. Washington, DC, USA, IFPRI.

Pinstrup-Andersen, P., Pelletier, D. & Alderman, H., eds. 1995. *Child growth and nutrition in developing countries. Priorities for action.* Ithaca, NY, USA and London, UK, Cornell University Press.

Ravallion, M. 1987. *Markets and famines.* Oxford, UK, Clarendon Press.

Reardon, T. 1991. Income sources of the malnourished rural poor in a drought year in Burkina Faso. *In* J. von Braun & R. Pandya-Lorch, eds. *Income sources of malnourished people in rural areas: microlevel information and policy implications,* p. 95-104. Working Papers on Commercialization of Agriculture and Nutrition No. 5. Washington, DC, USA, IFPRI.

Rosegrant, M.W., Agcaoili-Sombilla, M. & Perez, N.D. 1995. *Global food projections to 2020: implications for investment.* Food, Agriculture and the Environment Discussion Paper No. 5. Washington, DC, USA, IFPRI.

Russell, S.S., Jacobsen, K. & Stanley, W.D. 1990. *International migration and development in sub-Saharan Africa,* Vol. 2, *Country analyses.* Discussion Paper No. 102. Washington, DC, USA, World Bank.

Sahn, D.E., ed. 1989. *Seasonal variability in Third World agriculture: the consequences for food security.* Baltimore, MD, USA and London, UK, Johns Hopkins University Press, for IFPRI.

Sahn, D.E. & Alderman, H. 1988. The effects of human capital on wages and the determinants of labor supply in a developing country. *J. Dev. Econ.,* 29(2): 157-184.

Sahn, D.E. & von Braun, J. 1989. The implications of variability in food production for national and household food security. *In* J.R. Anderson & P.B.R. Hazell, eds. *Variability in grain yields,* p. 320-338. Baltimore, MD, USA and London, UK, Johns Hopkins University Press, for IFPRI.

Sarris, A.H. 1985. Degree of reliance on national food stocks and imports. In *World food security: selected themes and issues.* FAO Economic and Social Development Paper No. 53, p. 52-63. Rome, FAO.

Scrimshaw, N.S. 1994. Effects of iron deficiency and protein-calorie malnutrition on cognitive behavior and neurological function. *In* J.B. Stanbury, ed. *The damaged brain of iodine deficiency,* p. 59-65. New York, NY, USA, Sydney, Australia and Tokyo, Japan, Cognizant Communication Corporation.

Serageldin, I. 1994. Closing remarks. *In* I. Serageldin & P. Landell-Mills, eds. *Overcoming global hunger. Proceedings of a conference on actions to reduce hunger worldwide,* p. 116-123. Environmentally Sustainable Development Proceedings Series No. 3. Washington, DC, USA, World Bank.

Strauss, J. 1986. Does better nutrition raise farm productivity? *J. Polit. Econ.,* 94(2): 297-320.

Streeten, P. 1994. *Strategies for human development. Global poverty and unemployment.* Copenhagen, Denmark, Handelshojskolens Ferlag.

Sullivan, K.M., Houston, R., Gorstein, J. & Cervinskas, J., eds. 1995. *Monitoring universal salt iodization programmes.* United Nations Children's Fund (UNICEF), Programme Against Micronutrient Malnutrition (PAMM), International Council for Control of Iodine Deficiency Disorders (ICCIDD) and World Health Organization (WHO).

Teklu, T., von Braun, J. & Zaki, E. 1991. *Drought and famine relationships in Sudan: policy implications.* Research Report No. 88. Washington, DC, USA, IFPRI.

Tontisirin, K. 1994. *Sensitizing a nation on nutrition: one decade of nutrition planning and implementation in Thailand.* Paper prepared for the symposium Ending Malnutrition: Lessons from Successful Nutrition Policies and Programs in Developing Countries, 29-31 March 1994. Washington, DC, USA, IFPRI. (Mimeograph)

United Nations (UN). 1943. *Final act of the United Nations Conference on Food and Agriculture,* Hot Springs, VA, USA, 18 May - 3 June 1943. New York, NY, USA.

UN. 1975. *Report of the World Food Conference,* Rome, 5-16 November 1974. New York, NY, USA.

UN. 1991. *World population prospects 1990.* New York, NY, USA.

UN Administrative Committee on Coordination/Subcommittee on Nutrition (ACC/SCN). 1989. *Update on the nutrition situation: recent trends in nutrition in 33 countries.* Geneva.

UN ACC/SCN. 1994. *Update on the nutrition situation, 1994.* Geneva.

United Nations Children's Fund (UNICEF). 1990. *First call for children,* New York, NY, USA.

UNICEF. 1994a. *The progress of nations.* New York, NY, USA.

UNICEF. 1994b. *The urban poor and household food security.* Urban Examples Vol. 19. New York, NY, USA.

UNICEF. 1995a. *The progress of nations.* New York, NY, USA.

UNICEF. 1995b. *Care for life. Guidelines for assessment, analysis and action to improve care for nutrition.* New York, NY, USA. (Draft mimeograph)

von Braun, J. 1991. The links between agricultural growth, environmental degradation and nutrition. *In* S. Vosti, T. Reardon & W. von Urff, eds. *Agricultural sustainability, growth and poverty alleviation: issues and policies.* Feldafing, Germany, German Foundation for International Development.

von Braun, J., ed. 1995. *Employment for poverty reduction and food security.* Washington, DC, USA, International Food Policy Research Institute (IFPRI).

von Braun, J., Bouis, H., Kumar, S. & Pandya-Lorch, R. 1992. *Improving food security of the poor: concept, policy and programs.* Washington, DC, USA, IFPRI.

von Braun, J. & Kennedy, E., eds. 1994. *Agricultural commercialization, economic development and nutrition.* Baltimore, MD, USA and London, UK, Johns Hopkins University Press.

von Braun, J. & Pandya-Lorch, R., eds. 1991. *Income sources of malnourished people in rural areas: microlevel information and policy implications.* Working Papers on Commercialization of Agriculture and Nutrition No. 5. Washington, DC, USA, IFPRI.

von Braun, J., Serova, E., Seeth, H.T. & Melyukhina, O. 1996. *Russia's food economy in transition: current policy issues and long-term consumption and production perspectives.* Discussion paper. Washington, DC, USA, IFPRI.

von Braun, J., Teklu, T. & Webb, P. 1993. Famine as the outcome of political, production and market failure. *IDS Bull.,* 24(4): 73-79.

Vosti, S.A. & Loker, W.M. 1990. Some environmental and health aspects of agricultural settlement in the western Amazon basin. In *Environmental aspects of agricultural development.* Policy Brief No. 6, p. 11-12. Washington, DC, USA, IFPRI.

Vosti, S. & Scherr, S. 1994. *Conservation and enhancement of natural resources.* 2020 Brief No. 8. Washington, DC, USA, IFPRI.

Webb, P. & Reardon, T. 1992. Drought impact and household response in East and West Africa. *Q. J. Int. Agric.,* 31(3): 221-259.

Webb, P. & von Braun, J. 1994. *Famine and food security in Ethiopia: lessons for Africa.* Chichester, UK and New York, NY, USA, John Wiley and Sons.

World Bank. 1994. *Enriching lives: overcoming vitamin and mineral malnutrition in developing countries.* Washington, DC, USA.

World Food Programme (WFP). 1995. *Investing in the poor to prevent emergencies.* Background Paper No. 4, prepared for the European Conference on Hunger and Poverty, Brussels, Belgium, 21-22 November.

WFP. 1996. *Tackling hunger in a world full of food: tasks ahead for food aid.* Rome.

World Health Organization (WHO). 1995a. *Physical status: the use and interpretation of anthropometry.* Report of a WHO Expert Committee. WHO Technical Report Series No. 854. Geneva.

WHO. 1995b. *Nutrition. Highlights of recent activities in the context of the World Declaration and Plan of Action for Nutrition.* Geneva.

WHO. 1995c. *Global database on child growth.* Geneva.

WHO/United Nations Children's Fund (UNICEF). 1995. *Global prevalence of vitamin-A deficiency.* Micronutrient Deficiency Information System Working Paper No. 2. Geneva.

WHO/UNICEF/International Council for Control of Iodine Deficiency Disorders (ICCIDD). 1993. *Global prevalence of iodine deficiency disorders.* Micronutrient Deficiency Information System Working Paper No. 1. Geneva.

Yohannes, Y. 1991. Patterns and fluctuations of income of the malnourished rural poor in North Arcot District, India. *In* J. von Braun and R. Pandya-Lorch, eds. *Income sources of malnourished people in rural areas: microlevel information and policy implications*, p. 162-170. Working Papers on Commercialization of Agriculture and Nutrition No. 5. Washington, DC, USA, IFPRI.

Yunus, M. 1994. Lessons of experience. *In* I. Serageldin & P. Landell-Mills, eds. *Overcoming global hunger. Proceedings of a conference on actions to reduce hunger worldwide*, p. 65-68. Environmentally Sustainable Development Proceedings Series No. 3. Washington, DC, USA, World Bank.

Zeller, M. 1995. The demand for financial services by rural households – theory and empirical findings. *Q. J. Int. Agric.*, 34(2): 149-170.

Annex: Nutritional considerations in past global initiatives

INTERNATIONAL CONFERENCE ON NUTRITION (1992)

The World Declaration on Nutrition which was endorsed at the FAO/WHO International Conference on Nutrition declared a "...determination to eliminate hunger and to reduce all forms of malnutrition". Inequitable access to food was regarded as a primary problem. The declaration recognized poverty and lack of education as main causes of hunger and undernutrition. The high incidence of malnourished children below the age of five years and micronutrient deficiencies were regarded as particularly worrying. The declaration considered nutritional well-being to be a prerequisite for development. It stressed that nutritional programmes should be people-focused and participatory and underscored the importance of gender issues.

The declaration called for the following principal objectives to be reached by the year 2000:

- elimination of famine and famine-related deaths,
- elimination of starvation and nutritional deficiency diseases in communities affected by natural and human-made disasters,
- elimination of iodine and vitamin A deficiencies.

The declaration also envisaged a substantial reduction in the following areas:

- starvation and chronic hunger,
- undernutrition, with emphasis on children, women and the elderly,
- other micronutrient deficiencies, e.g. iron,
- impediments to breast-feeding,
- inadequate sanitation and hygiene.

Follow-up monitoring at national and international levels was called for.

WORLD SUMMIT FOR CHILDREN (1990)

The World Summit for Children, organized by UNICEF, gave a specific commitment to improving the nutrition of children. The declaration included the commitment to "work for optimal growth and development in childhood, through measures to eradicate hunger, malnutrition and famine, and thus relieve millions of children of tragic sufferings in a world that has the means to feed all its citizens". Adequate household food security, a healthy environment, control of infections and adequate maternal and child care were viewed as principal requirements for nutritional improvement. The World Summit for Children's Plan of Action included a specific set of quantified goals. It called for the achievement of the following goals by the year 2000:

- reduction of severe and moderate malnutrition among children below the age of five years to one-half the 1990 levels,
- reduction of the percentage of children with low birth weight (i.e. less than 2.5 kg) to less than 10 percent,

- virtual elimination of iodine and vitamin A deficiencies,
- promotion of breast-feeding practices,
- institutionalization of the promotion and monitoring of growth,
- reduction of iron-deficiency anaemia among women to one-third the 1990 levels.

The commitments made at the World Summit for Children are monitored globally, and reports on progress or the lack thereof are issued on a regular basis (e.g. UNICEF, 1994a, 1995a).

UNITED NATIONS WORLD FOOD CONFERENCE (1974)

The World Food Conference noted the existence of major problems related to nutrition and recommended the formulation and integration of "concerted food and nutrition plans" at national and international levels. It highlighted actions in the area of food intervention programmes, nutrition education, basic health, increased participation of women, fortification of staple foods, consumer education services and food legislation. The World Food Conference advocated the establishment of a global nutrition-surveillance system by FAO, WHO and UNICEF and stressed the need to intensify nutrition-related research in the areas of food production, processing, preservation, storage, distribution and utilization. The conference defined no quantitative goals for nutritional improvement within a fixed time frame, nor did it provide for any comprehensive, long-term follow-up or monitoring of the goals that were set.

UNITED NATIONS CONFERENCE ON FOOD AND AGRICULTURE (1943)

The United Nations Conference on Food and Agriculture, held in Virginia, USA, in the midst of the Second World War had as its main objective the "freedom from want of food, suitable and adequate for the health and strength of all peoples". The need for the expansion of the entire world economy and markets in order to increase purchasing power and thereby make possible "an adequate diet for all" was emphasized. The conference considered poverty to be the primary cause of malnutrition and hunger, and adequate food was seen as the most fundamental of primary necessities. Economic development as a means of improving nutrition was emphasized, and nutritional adequacy was noted as the most fundamental need. These are positions upon which the international community appears to be converging again more than 50 years later.